An Illustrated Encyclopaedia

WONDERS *of* ANIMAL LIFE

also available by the same editor

An Illustrated World Gazetteer

Peoples of all Nations

Their Life Today and Story of Their Past

In 14 Volumes

Volume One
Abyssinia **to** Azerbaijan
Volume Two
Belgium **to** British Empire in America
Volume Three
British Empire in Asia **to** Canada
Volume Four
Ceylon **to** Dahomey
Volume Five
Danzig **to** England
Volume Six
Esthonia **to** France
Volume Seven
Georgia **to** Iceland
Volume Eight
India **to** Italy
Volume Nine
Japan **to** Mexico
Volume Ten
Monaco **to** Oman
Volume Eleven
Palestine **to** Rumania
Volume Twelve
Russia **to** Sin-kiang
Volume Thirteen
South Africa **to** The Ukraine
Volume Fourteen
The United States **to** Wales
with General Index

About the Editor

Sir John Alexander Hammerton (1871-1949) was an English statesman and author, best-known for his editorship of popular encyclopaedias published in the first half of the 20th century, such as the 10-volume New Book of Knowledge.

From 1914 to 1919, Hammerton was joint editor with HW Wilson of the periodical "The Great War: The Standard History of the All-Europe Conflict", published by the Amalgamated Press. It was lavishly illustrated with photographs and with realistic drawings which were sometimes hardly distinguishable from photographs.

He was also a contemporary and friend of Arthur Mee, about whom he wrote a biography.

An Illustrated Encyclopaedia

WONDERS *of* ANIMAL LIFE

by Famous Writers on Natural History

Volume Three

Edited by

J.A. Hammerton

Over Three Thousand Illustrations from Photographs and Thirty-three Colour Plates

LOGOS PRESS, NEW DELHI

ISBN -13: 978-81-7268-175-3 (Set)
ISBN -10: 81-7268-175-5 (Set)

ISBN -13: 978-81-7268-176-0 (Vol. I)
ISBN -13: 978-81-7268-177-7 (Vol. II)
ISBN -13: 978-81-7268-178-4 (Vol. III)
ISBN -13: 978-81-7268-179-1 (Vol. IV)
ISBN -13: 978-81-7268-180-7 (Vol. V)
ISBN -13: 978-81-7268-181-4 (Vol. VI)
ISBN -13: 978-81-7268-182-1 (Vol. VII)
ISBN -13: 978-81-7268-183-8 (Vol. VIII)

ISBN -10: 81-7268-176-3 (Vol. I)
ISBN -10: 81-7268-177-1 (Vol. II)
ISBN -10: 81-7268-178-X (Vol. III)
ISBN -10: 81-7268-179-8 (Vol. IV)
ISBN -10: 81-7268-180-1 (Vol. V)
ISBN -10: 81-7268-181-X (Vol. VI)
ISBN -10: 81-7268-182-8 (Vol. VII)
ISBN -10: 81-7268-183-6 (Vol. VIII)

Edition : 2008

Printed & Published by

LOGOS PRESS

Building No. 4788-90, Street No. 23, Ansari Road, Darya Ganj, New Delhi-110 002 (India)
Phone : 23272187

Foreword

Here is not a 'natural history' in the accepted meaning of that description. There exist many and excellent natural histories and more than fifteen years ago the present editor was associated with the publication of one which, in its authoritative letter-press and profuse illustration, had wide acceptance. But it is undeniable that the general reader finds large and exhaustive treatises on animal life, encumbered with Latin names, somewhat hard reading, however fine their illustrations, if they are arranged on the approved scientific divisions—order, family, genus, species—into which naturalists split up animated nature. A proper natural history, however, must follow this method of treatment if it is to form the basis of a scientific knowledge of the subject.

Does the ordinary reader desire such knowledge? Does he require it?

The answer to both questions is a negative: emphatic in the first and modified in the second case. No matter how slightly youth is drawn to the conventional study of zoology, not even the forbidding scientific approach to natural history can rob it of its inherent fascination.

A boundless curiosity about the infinite diversity of creatures that share the life of the globe with him is a deep and abiding and a most natural trait in man. The stories of a Adam naming the beasts, and of the animals, two by two, going into the ark are ancient evidence of man's interest in his fellow-creatures of the so-called lower orders. A study of the life-histories of many animals and birds, fishes and reptiles, or of the astounding social systems of certain insects, is calculated to limit man's pride in himself as the incarnation of the highest intelligence or the finest physical product of the animal world. Especially is it likely to extend his sympathy to all lowly things that are living out their little days with him upon this planet. It lies at the root of humanitarianism. Interest in animal life is never an idle curiosity, and it may prove more absorbing than any other interest that could be named.

Not, then, to add a new natural history to a list already adequate, but to meet this universal and most healthy interest in the astonishing realities and the mysterious ways of the animal kingdom is the purpose of WONDERS OF ANIMAL LIFE. Its title adequately suggests its scope: to enquire into and to illustrate all that is of uncommon interest in the life of the animal kingdom.

While the reader will find in our pages a constantly changing panorama of animal life, with no more apparent order than the naturalist finds in the Brazilian jungle, he can hardly fail to be interested and he is certain to be instructed, for though the only method that is observed throughout our chapters is a rough alternation of interest, now in mammals, next in reptiles, then in birds, fishes, insects, each chapter of this work is written either by one of the leading specialists on his subject or—where expert knowledge is less needed than vividness of descriptive style—by a popular author.

A glance at the list of contributors, their scientific and literary credentials, and the subjects allotted to them in our scheme, will indicate to the reader that though WONDERS OF ANIMAL LIFE is designedly popular in its appeal, it is not the less authoritative in being more entertaining than the conventional sort of natural history.

Never before has there been brought together so representative and so varied a collection of photographic documents covering the whole range of animated nature. In the last decade, and particularly within the latter part of it, naturalists have acquired an immense amount of new knowledge, and marked progress has been made in recording the wild life of the world by means of direct photography.

The exploits of the camera experts employed by the organizers of some of the great 'nature and adventure' films—'Simba' is a fine example—that have fascinated millions throughout the world in these years have produced so rich a body of material for illustrating such a work as this that editorially we are in a more favoured position than any of our predecessors in the same field and we hope the reader will agree with us in thinking that we have taken advantage of that fortunate circumstance for his entertainment and instruction.

J.A. HAMMERTON

Publisher's Note

We are happy to present the illustrated encyclopaedia—Wonders of Animal Life—to the learned readers. As its title suggests, it attempts to enquire into the astonishing realities and the mysterious ways of life of the animal kingdom—mammals, reptiles, birds, fishes and insects.

Presented in eight volumes, each chapter of this work is written either by one of the leading specialists on the subject or—where expert knowledge is less needed than vividness of descriptive style—by a popular author. The text is enriched with a representative and varied collection of photographic documents covering the whole range of animated nature. Our other notable illustrated encyclopaedias include *The Living Animals of the World* (4 volumes), *The Wonders of the World* (4 volumes), *Peoples of All Nations* (14 volumes), and *The Earth and Its Inhabitants* (8 volumes).

TABLE OF CONTENTS

Volume One

List of Colour Plates

Volume Two

List of Colour Plates

Volume Three

List of Colour Plates

Volume Four

List of Colour Plates

Volume Five

List of Colour Plates

Volume Six

List of Colour Plates

Volume Seven

List of Colour Plates

Volume Eight

List of Colour Plates

Chapter XLIV

Sacred Animals

By Lewis Spence

Author of "A Dictionary of Mythology"

The worship of animals among the ancient Egyptians, which so greatly amused the Greeks and tickled the risible faculty even of the grave Herodotus, is merely a phase of religious experience through which practically all peoples have passed. That the inhabitants of Britain were no exception to the general rule is clear enough from the statements of Julius Caesar, who, as his own war correspondent, noticed most things during his brief and stormy stay among our ancestors, for he assures us that they refused to eat the hare, the hen and the goose. This abstention from the flesh of certain animals is perhaps the surest sign that they are, or once were, the objects of adoration, or exercised a mysterious guardianship over the tribes who regarded them as unfit for food.

This forbearance from the flesh of certain beasts and birds is associated with the extremely involved system of social taboos and tribal economy which has come to be known to students of savage life as "totemism," a scheme or "way" of life developed throughout long ages of savage experience, regarding the basic principles of which authorities are by no means in agreement. In all probability early man regarded the lower animals as being much on the same plane with himself. He spoke, as do some living savages, of "the Beaver People," or "the Bear People," and in some cases believed that animals distinguished for sagacity or courage were the ancestors of his own tribe or clan. Many legends of such kinship exist, and this supposed actual or spiritual relationship rendered the whole species of the ancestor beast sacred to him. There was a powerful taboo against its slaughter save at certain periods, when it was ceremonially eaten to inspire an access of its qualities.

W. S Berridge

SACRED KINGFISHER OF THE MAORIS

All kingfishers do not live by the waterside. Here is one which is often seen flitting over the burial grounds of the Maoris of New Zealand. This fine race has for ages held the bird sacred in view of its supposed connexion with the dead and their mystery.

This theory, however, does not account for all the circumstances of animal-worship. At a later stage of totemic belief the beast-form of the guardian or patron animal shaded off into a semi-human form, the body of a man with the head of a bird or beast. But in other cases certain animals were thought of as possessing the symbolic attributes of gods, their wisdom, courage or cunning, and came to be adored as their earthly representatives. It is often extremely difficult to ascertain whether a god originated in the animal form, or whether the animal form merely symbolized the god, and it is only by a careful comparative study of the early forms of the deity as expressed in paintings or sculptures that this can be ascertained. Even so, many cases remain where scanty proof makes it impossible to arrive at any definite conclusion.

It is reasonably clear, for example, that the bull which represented the Egyptian god Osiris was regarded rather as symbolical of his attribute of fertility than as the survival of a totem form, and that the rat which invariably accompanies the Indian elephant-headed god Ganesha, is typical of his sagacity. It seems probable, too, that the owl, represented along with Pallas Athena or Minerva, was characteristic of the wisdom of that goddess rather than reminiscent of any more primitive form of her, even though Homer does allude to her as "the owl-eyed Athena."

Ancient Egypt was perhaps more rich in sacred animals than any other country of antiquity — the bull, the serpent, the cat, crocodile, ape, hippopotamus, ibis and dog, scorpion and frog all figured in her animal pantheon. The sanctity with which these animals were regarded may, in some instances, have been a legacy from totemic forms of worship, but,

W. S. Berridge

IBIS, THE BIRD ROUND WHICH THE EGYPTIANS MADE A CULT

One of the most important religious cults in ancient Egypt was the cult of the ibis, which is a bird of the crane species. It was associated with the deity Thoth and with the moon, and was supposed to meet and kill certain terrible winged snakes which were said to invade the land each year from Arabia. Indeed, Herodotus, the great Greek historian, who has preserved so much of the myths current in his time, says that there was believed to be a gorge at the mouth of which the ibis mounted guard, there to slay the snakes as they flew past.

Be that as it may, they were adored in one or other of the provinces of the Nile country either as local patrons, or personifications of the gods. When they died they were mourned for as if they had been human, and were embalmed in the same manner as the dead Egyptian.

The cult of the Apis bull in Egypt is traceable to early dynastic times. Careful search was made for him as a calf, for he must bear the prescribed marks of sanctity. He must be jet black, with a square, white blaze on the forehead, the figure of an eagle on the back, double hairs in the tail and the outline of a beetle on the tongue. When found, he was placed on board a barge in a gilded cabin and transported by water to Memphis, where he was installed in a gorgeous shrine, given rich beds to lie on, fed with the most delicate food, and supplied with water from a sacred well. As a general rule, he was kept in strict seclusion, but on certain festal occasions he appeared in public, surrounded by priests and chanting choristers. His birthday rejoicings alone lasted for seven days every year. As an oracle the sacred animal enjoyed the most extraordinary celebrity, and distinguished strangers in Egypt seldom neglected to visit his temple. When the Apis bull refused to eat from the hand of Germanicus that conqueror's speedy death was prophesied, and the conquest of the Nile land by Augustus was supposed to have been foretold by his bellowings. On his death the Apis bull was embalmed and buried in the Serapeum at Memphis, and the most elaborate funerary rites were observed, a sarcophagus nearly sixty tons in weight being provided for his last resting-place. When defunct he was supposed to become one with Osiris, and took the form of Osiris-Apis, or Serapis, as it was known to the Greeks, a deity whose cult found its way to Rome, and ultimately to Britain, where he had a temple on the site of the present York Minster. At Heliopolis another sacred bull, Mnevis, was worshipped with equally elaborate ceremonial.

At Mendes, Hermopolis and Lycopolis the sacred ram associated with Osiris and Ra was worshipped, and this animal also bore specific symbols of deity. The crocodile was regarded as the incarnation of the god Sebek, and its propitiation was secured during the dry season by permitting it to wander at will

E.N.A.

MONKEYS UNDISTURBED IN THE HOLY PRECINCTS OF A TEMPLE IN BENARES

Benares, the great Indian city on the Ganges, is one of the most holy places of the Hindus, and thousands of pilgrims go there every year. This is one of the many temples and with the worshippers crowds of monkeys mingle, secure of food and safety within the sacred precincts. Animals have always played an important part in the drama of the Hindu pantheon, not as symbols of the gods, but because certain beasts are regarded as having acted, at one time or another, as the bodily regenerations of the gods.

E.N.A

SACRED MONKEYS BEING FED ON THE ROOF OF A HILL TEMPLE IN INDIA

This temple stands in the Galata Pass, and is built at the foot of a rocky hill. The monkeys come down from the heights above to receive a regular ration of food, which generations of this practice has led them to expect. We see one of the guardians of the place feeding the little creatures on the roof in the blazing sunshine. They are considered as being under the protection of the being worshipped at this shrine, and are safe from men. But there is a good deal more of habit than of religious fervour in all this, for animal worship, as such, has greatly deteriorated in India from the tremendously powerful and extremely widespread institution that it once was.

W. S. Berridge

EGYPTIAN CAT SAID TO BE THE INCARNATION OF THE SUN GODDESS

At about the time of the Twenty-Second Dynasty, nearly a thousand years before Christ, the cult of Bast, goddess of the sun, seems to have arisen in Egypt. The animal associated with her and regarded as her incarnation was the cat and so this animal was held to be particularly sacred. Death was the only punishment that fitted the crime of killing a cat, and there is a record of later years when a foreigner, a Roman, was unfortunate enough to kill one, and was lynched by the crowd. This particular animal is the Egyptian or fettered cat.

over the cultivated lands, devouring any living thing which chanced to come in its way. It was believed to be the tutelary god of the dead, who restored to them the functions enjoyed in life. On the banks of Lake Moeris the crocodile was regarded with special sanctity, people bedecked the tame saurians in these waters with jewels and fed them on the choicest foods. After death they were buried in a subterranean labyrinth, and Strabo, who visited Egypt during the reign of Emperor Augustus, provides us with an interesting account of the manner in which the tame reptilian representatives of the god were pampered by the priests of the cult, who fed them with cakes, honey and wine.

At Leontopolis in the Delta, lions were worshipped as the presiding animal guardians, and were fed upon live calves, which were thrust into their dens so that they might have the savage joy of killing them, and thus be kept in a propitious mood. These beasts were identified with the guardian god Aker, who was supposed to keep watch over the gates of dawn, and his sacred lions, Sef and Dua, "Yesterday" and "To-day," were thought of as guarding the portals of the past and the present.

But no animal received a greater meed of popular adoration than the harmless necessary cat, which was regarded as an incarnation of Bast, the goddess of the sun. Her cult appears to have arisen somewhere about the period of the Twenty-second Dynasty (954 B.C.), and for her sake all cats in Egypt received particular veneration and protection. Death was the penalty among the Egyptians for killing a cat, even by accident, and a Roman who had done so was lynched by the infuriated populace. When dead, cats were carefully mummified, and, says Herodotus, buried in the city of Bubastis, the town of their patron goddess.

The hippopotamus was the animal representative of the goddess Ta-urt, who, though protective and benevolent, still retained her original traits of ferocious destructiveness. The dog-headed ape, or cynocephalus, was also greatly revered by the Egyptians, and apes were kept in many temples, especially in those of lunar deities, as that of Khensu, at Thebes, and that they were in some manner associated with the moon there can be no doubt. The jackal was sacred to Anubis, the guide of the souls of the dead through the Underworld, a connection which probably arose through the haunting of burial-places by that animal, but the serpent was perhaps more feared than venerated. The frog seems to have been worshipped as the symbol of fecundity, and his was certainly one of the oldest cults in Egypt. The goddess Heqt, identified with the cow-headed goddess of the sky Hathor, the Great Mother, was depicted with the head of a frog.

A cult of great importance was that of the ibis, a bird of the crane species, associated with Thoth

E.N.A.

CROCODILES OF KARACHI CRAWL ACROSS THE MUD TO BE FED

This is the famous " mugger " pit at Karachi. It consists of a muddy pool about three hundred yards round, and out of the water grow tufts of dank grass making little islands on which the great, repulsive saurians lie basking. In the photograph we see the ugly crew coming out of this tepid swamp across the warm ooze to where one of the keepers waits with food for these well tended monsters. In olden days the crocodile was also regarded as sacred in Egypt and sacrifices were made to it.

and the moon, and the nucleus of this worship centred at Hermopolis. The ibis was chiefly venerated as the destroyer of serpents, and was believed to meet and slay the mythical winged snakes which were supposed to invade Egypt from Arabia Herodotus tells a weird story of how the ibis in the spring season takes its stand at the mouth of a gorge through which the winged snakes fly, barring their entrance and killing them.

THE bennu, a bird also not unlike the crane, was identified by the Egyptians with the mythical phoenix, which was believed to seek out a funeral pyre once in five hundred years, from which it arose in the plenitude of vigour, to live for another five centuries. It was, of course, a symbol of the deathless nature of the sun, re-arising from the fires of dawn. The falcon was also sacred to Ra and Osiris, the bird of the sun and of the regenerated human soul.

The worship of animals continued unabated during the Hellenic period. It is even probable that this phase of the Egyptian religion had become more pronounced under Greek rule, for Strabo, writing in the time of Augustus, asserts that statues of sacred animals had practically displaced those of the gods. The sacred ram (Khnemu) of Mendes was worshipped both by conquered and conquerors, as was the Apis bull and the sacred crocodile, and it would seem that the temple revenues were at times increased by displaying these animals to the curious gaze of strangers. The European Greeks, however, retained their contempt for the Egyptian custom.

I have alluded to Caesar's mention of British sacred animals. Many such must have been worshipped. Several of the British clans were called after animals, such as the Bibroci of South-Eastern Britain, who seem to have been a beaver-worshipping tribe, or the Clan Chattan of Scotland, " the People of the Cat." The Keltic goddess Epona seems to have been developed from an equine form, and the Irish hero-god Cuchullin from a bull, just as the Indian god Indra is developed from that animal, as was Dionysus or Bacchus in Greece. But the question of animal worship in Britain is much too obscure to permit of dogmatic statement, and it is plain that at the period when the native religion of the Britons was first brought under Roman observation it had long surpassed the first primitive stage

J. W. Read

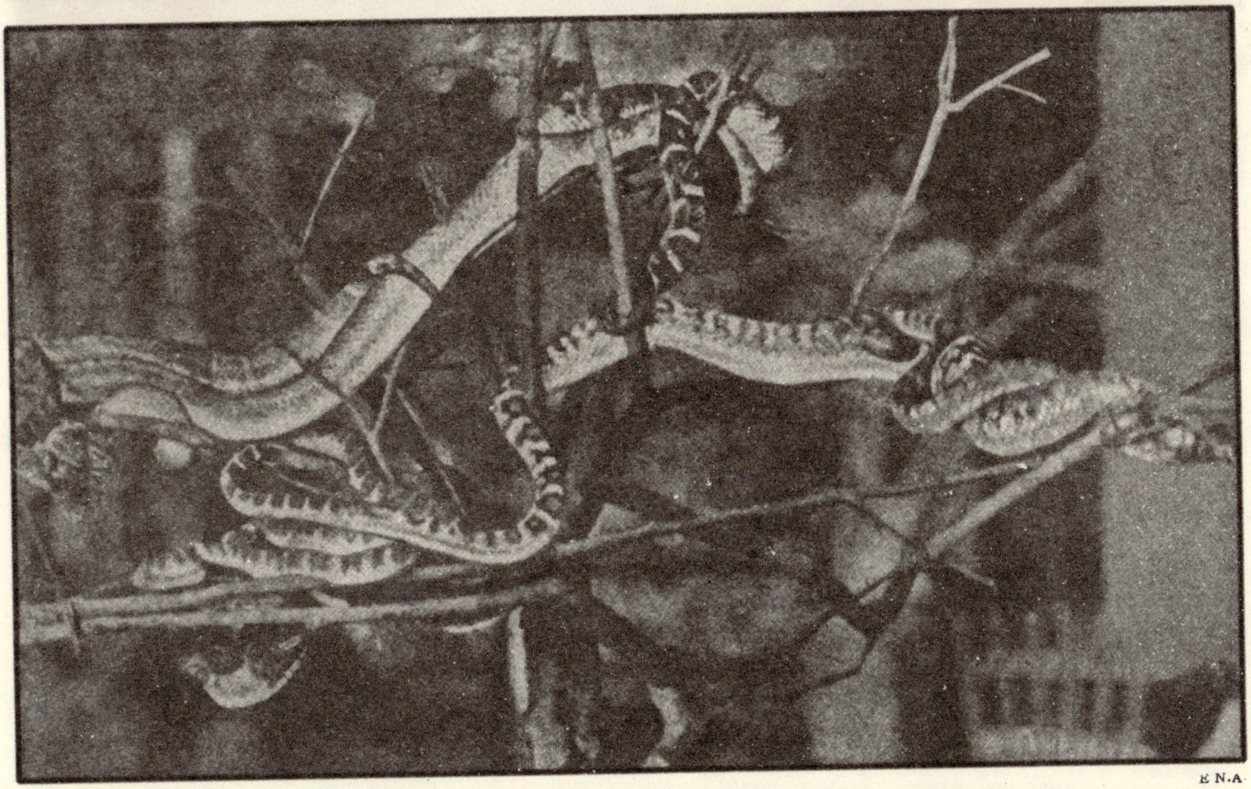

E.N.A.

SNAKES WORSHIPPED IN A TEMPLE OF PENANG AND A WHITE COBRA

In the temple of the snake god of a village near Georgetown, Penang (bottom), there are branches stuck into pots before the shrine and among these branches many snakes cling drowsily, or writhe and glide amongst each other's coils. These snakes are fed upon eggs delivered to them in baskets, nor do they ever harm their attendants or the worshippers in this temple which they never leave. The upper photograph shows one of the rare white cobras of India, which are held to be sacred.

SACRED ELEPHANT WITH ITS ATTENDANT OUTSIDE A TEMPLE OF MANDALAY

Here is a young elephant which is kept in the grounds of a temple in Mandalay, Burma. In this country certain light-coloured elephants known as " white " elephants are often called sacred simply because they are used for state purposes, automatically becoming royal property as soon as they are born. Being kept apart for processions and occasions of pomp only they have become associated with the purpose of such pageantry when it was in use for religion's sake. These elephants' prestige was also added to by their being royal.

E N.A.

CATTLE ENJOYING THE RIGHTS OF SANCTITY IN CALCUTTA STREETS

Hindu feelings are very strong on the question of the sacred humped cattle. At whatever cost to human inconvenience these creatures are allowed to wander at will through the bazaars and streets, the police being bound to support the custom. Hence we find, in a great city like Calcutta, such sights as this, where a pavement built after the western fashion is encumbered by a number of cattle placidly chewing their cud as though the street belonged to them. Pedestrians have to step into the roadway to pass them.

E.N.A

WORSHIP FOR A COW IN THE STREET

Such a scene as this is not uncommon in the holy city of Benares. A Hindu woman has stopped to put up a prayer beside the indifferent looking cow which, to her, is a symbol of divine things. In Benares devotions come before traffic convenience.

of totemism, and had preserved only a few reminiscences of the direct adoration of animals.

The sacred animals of India are revered not as in Egypt, as symbols of the gods, so much as the possible reincarnations of human beings whose souls have entered their bodies in the process of transmigration. To the Buddhist all animals are inviolate, and the life of even the smallest insect may not be taken without offence. But in the Hindu pantheon certain animals are regarded as having at one time or another acted as the avatars or bodily regenerations of the gods, and have thus an especial sanctity. All cows possess a certain degree of sacredness because of their former association with Krishna, the divine cowherd, the elephant because of its symbolical connection with Ganesha, the god of knowledge, and the serpent, whose affinities are with the cloud-gods, is also venerated, or rather feared. But animal worship in India has greatly deteriorated since early times and seems steadily to decline under the later dispensations of Hinduism.

Some of the aboriginal tribes of America are still in the totemic stage of religious belief, and there is abundant evidence that certain of them anciently worshipped animals, directly or symbolically. Many of the North American and some of the South American tribes believed and still believe, that the various species of animals, deer, birds, fish, and so forth, are governed by a divine Great Deer, a Great Turkey, a Great Fish, who send their subjects as food to man, but who must be placated before or after these are killed. For example, among the Zuñi of New Mexico the deer god must have his lips smeared with the blood of the slain deer immediately after it is shot. This notion throws considerable light on the origins of animal deities as a whole, and it may be that the idea of animal gods as great food-senders or producers accounts for the creation of certain classes of such deities in the savage mind, though it certainly cannot account for those which were not of a food-giving character.

Specific animals were also venerated in Old America because of the fear they inspired. The Creek Indians worshipped the alligator, and never destroyed one. The jaguar was adored by the Moxis of Bolivia, who appointed as priests those who had escaped from its claws, and by the Maya and Quiche of Central America, who on meeting a jaguar in the forest calmly knelt down and awaited their fate, considering it blasphemous to attempt to slaughter the beast. The mysterious anti-Christian cult of Nagualism, which still lingers in the remoter parts of Mexico and Central America, is based on the belief that each individual has a beast as a patron or personal guide and familiar.

The ancient Mexicans and Maya also worshipped Camazotz, the bat, as a god of the Underworld, affixing his head to a human body in precisely the same way as did the Egyptians with the jackal or the ram. The caves in which bats lurked were regarded as places of the utmost sanctity, and their inmates were never disturbed. The civilized Incan Peruvians, on conquering the barbarous province of Huanca, in pre-Spanish times, were disgusted to find temples raised to the worship of the dog as the highest form of deity. To this canine Jupiter the priests offered up fatted representatives of his own species, and afterwards devoured them. Many of the wild tribes of the Pacific Coast united in the adoration of the coyote, of whose doings and adventures the most extraordinary tales are recounted in the myths and legends current among those people.

Besides these, the owl, the frog, the tortoise and many other animals were worshipped in Old America, and among the coastal Peruvians even the shark was regarded as divine, these creatures being thought to possess special attributes of wisdom, fertility or courage.

Some animals commonly referred to as "sacred" are so described merely because they are employed for especial or state purposes. For example, the royal white elephants of Burmah were frequently alluded to as "sacred elephants," but were used exclusively for processions and galas, and for that reason were kept apart, and this, in all probability, is the reason why they were regarded as partaking of the divine. The doves of Venus, held in such sanctity by the Romans, among whom to kill one was regarded as a dreadful misdemeanour, are an example of another class of "sacred" animals devoted to a god or goddess because of some fancied resemblance in temperament. Such, too, were the mice of Apollo, the leopards of Bacchus, the eagle of Jove and the ravens of Odin. In Britain, too, we find examples of this sort of thing. A Briton, says the old chronicler, will never kill a crow, for it is believed by our ancestors that the great King Arthur on his death took the form of one of these birds—pretty sure evidence that they were in some manner associated with his cult as a British deity.

Chapter XLV

British Reptiles and Amphibians

By Gerald Leighton, M.D., D.Sc.

Author of "British Serpents"

These two groups of vertebrates, for some reason not easy to understand, are frequently associated together in the popular mind. As a matter of fact, they have not very much in common, except that a large number of people have a considerable repugnance to both. From the point of view of the zoologist the reptiles are more closely related to the birds than to the amphibians, while the amphibians are nearer to the fish.

One important characteristic, however, is common to amphibians, reptiles and fish, and that is that all three groups are cold-blooded. The temperature of their blood is that of their immediate environment, whether that be water or air, varying with it. This dependence upon the environment for warmth is closely associated with the varying seasonal habits of the species concerned. Thus, the condition of hibernation, which is referred to later, is obviously an attempt on the part of the cold-blooded animal to withstand the rigours of the winter in cold or temperate climates. As far as the British Isles are concerned the species are few, small and, with the exception of the adder or viper, absolutely harmless.

The reptiles have certain characteristics common to all of them. Besides being cold-blooded they have an external covering which differs entirely from that of either mammals, birds, or amphibians. All reptiles are covered with scales of a hard or horny nature, as in the snakes and lizards, or in the form of plates such as are seen in the turtles. Associated with the cold condition of the blood is a very simple breathing apparatus as compared with birds or mammals, and in all reptiles the breathing takes place through lungs throughout the whole life.

As regards reproduction, in all reptiles fertilisation is internal and in most cases results in the deposit of eggs. Some reptiles, however, carry the young until they are fully developed, when they rupture the egg-membrane and escape alive. In this case the reptile is termed ovo-viviparous or viviparous, as opposed to oviparous or egg-laying species.

There are many other anatomical details characteristic of reptiles, recognized only by the expert anatomist, of which we may mention the blood corpuscles. In reptiles the red cells of the blood have a nucleus, they are oval in shape and biconvex, characters which separate them sharply from the blood of mammals. The skin covering differentiates them from birds, as does the structure of the heart. From the amphibians they differ in never having gills in early life, and also in many characteristics in the bony skeleton.

The grass snake or ring snake (*Tropidonotus natrix*) is by far the most numerous of English snakes, but is practically absent from Scotland and unknown in Ireland. It is abundant in Wiltshire, Gloucestershire, some Welsh counties, and many parts of the South, the Cumbrian mountains marking its northern limit somewhat abruptly.

It is by far our largest reptile. The average adult length is from thirty to thirty-six inches, but much larger specimens are not rare. Any snake over thirty inches long in this country may safely be diagnosed as a grass snake. It is thinner and more attenuated than the adder, the tail tapering off gradually, whereas that of the adder is short.

Grass snakes are fond of water and are usually found in its neighbourhood. This is associated with their favourite food, namely frogs. The frog is seized by one hind leg, which is gradually swallowed, and then the snake slowly gets the body of the frog into its distended jaw, at which stage the other three legs and head of the frog project forward in a very curious picture. Birds, mice and eggs are also eaten. The snake is an expert swimmer.

The young are produced from eggs which are deposited in some warm spot, often in manure heaps or garden rubbish. They are deposited in bundles which adhere together, each bundle containing on the average nearly thirty eggs.

This snake is often called the ring snake from the yellow collar on the neck by which it is readily distinguished. The general body colour is olive green, darker above, shading off into a greenish yellow on the sides, the belly being dark bluish black. There are two rows of irregularly-shaped black patches, one on either side of the long body. The young are dark at first but soon develop the colours, and in a few weeks the yellow collar is quite brilliant in appearance.

The grass snake is an interesting pet, being docile and perfectly harmless.

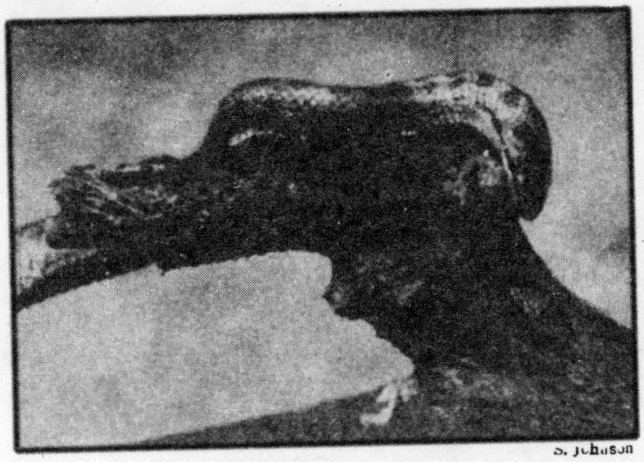

S. Johnson

RARE SMOOTH SNAKE

In Dorset and the neighbouring counties the handsome smooth snake or coronella is occasionally found. A careless observer might mistake it for an adder and this mistake often causes the destruction of this already rare and quite harmless creature

S Crook

Neville Kingston

ADDERS, THE ONLY VENOMOUS SNAKES OF BRITAIN

Britain's single poisonous snake is the adder or viper and it may be told by the " V "-shaped mark upon its head, which is shown up by the light bordered portion of the skin just behind it. Down the back runs a zig-zag dark line. Adders prefer warm sandy places and are harmless enough if unmolested. Bites, which are seldom fatal except in persons in poor health, are usually the result of inadvertant disturbance of the snake caused by not noticing its presence. Warm places where it can bask in the sun are the adder's favourite haunts.

S. Crook

GRASS SNAKE AND THE SLOW-WORM THAT IS REALLY A LIZARD

To most people the slow-worm (top) looks like a snake and often this entirely harmless and quite useful lizard gets killed in case it might after all be poisonous. For the slow-worm is a lizard, not a snake or a worm. The limbs are rudimentary and do not appear outside the skin but the surest way of seeing that it really is a lizard is by noting the fact that it has eyelids, which no snakes have. The grass-snake (bottom) is the largest and most numerous of British snakes. It grows to a length of from three to four feet and is very fond of the water.

S. Johnson

MALE AND FEMALE OF COMMON BRITISH AMPHIBIANS: SMOOTH AND CRESTED NEWTS

Of newts the most often seen is the smooth or common newt (lower photographs) which occurs all over Britain and also in Ireland. The back and sides may be either brown or green while the under parts are yellow and spotted with black. The ordinary length is about three and a half inches. In the male (bottom left) the under side of the flattened tail is in red with blue markings while in the female (bottom right) it is a plain yellow. The great water newt or crested newt is the largest British newt, the female (top right) being rather bigger than the male (top left). The back of this newt is dark brown or black, while the toes are yellow and ringed with black.

S. Crook

IN THE BREEDING SEASON: NEWTS AMONG THE RUSHES

All the British newts live on land except during the breeding season when they take to the water in which they were born. During this time the males develop a crest. The spawn is deposited among water-weeds in the spring or early summer and the tadpoles hatch out in about a month. The forelegs are the first to develop and the young newt at first breathes by means of gills which protrude from the neck. After about six months the gills have gradually dwindled away and the newt leaves the water for a life ashore.

The adder or viper (*Vipera berus*), the sole venomous reptile in Great Britain, occurs in greater or less frequency in every county. It is the only indigenous snake in Scotland, where it is very plentiful in some northern districts. Like the other snakes, it is absent from Ireland. In Wales it is very common in certain parts, rarer in others. It is common on the islands of Mull and Jura.

VERY exaggerated stories are often told regarding the size of adders. Hasty estimates of snake measurements are not to be relied upon, and it is easy to stretch the body of a snake an inch or two.

It is important to remember that the average size of adult adders is from 20 to 25 inches. Specimens of 26 inches are rare, and none have been authenticated of 30 inches despite the stories one bears. The largest ever measured by the writer, out of several hundreds, was 28½ inches. The female is rather larger than the male.

In appearance the adder is well defined and ought not to be mistaken for the harmless grass snake, though it bears a close resemblance to the very rare smooth snake. At the back of the head are two dark bands converging to form the characteristic V-shaped mark. These are always present, but in great variety of detailed shape. Immediately behind them is a lighter part, which shows them up. Then running along the middle of the back is the well-known zig-zag black or dark line, continued to the tip of the short tail. There is a row of dark patches along each side of the body.

The lip scales, usually eight or nine, are yellow. The belly varies with age and sex from grey to slate-blue or darker. The sexes can be easily distinguished by the tail, which in the females is an obvious appendage, while in the male it is not sharply defined.

Adders like heat, and the warmest spot in the locality is their favourite haunt. As a rule, they avoid water but are capable swimmers if necessity arises. Their favourite food is the field mouse, but they also take lizards, especially slow-worms, eggs, small birds, and insects. The writer has also found the smooth newt, water voles, and young rats to form part of the food.

The poison apparatus consists of fangs, a gland to secrete venom, a duct from the gland to the fang, and special muscular arrangements to enable the adder to strike its victim. When about to strike, the

S. Crook

S Johns on

John T. Roberts

PALMATED NEWT AND ITS SKIN

The palmated newt is the smallest of British newts and is only three inches long (top and centre). The lower photograph shows a complete skin found in the water after it had been shed by a growing newt. All newts are harmless to man, and carnivorous.

lower jaw is opened and turned back, while the upper jaw moves so as to bring the fang into position; this is then erected, and the whole head is brought swiftly down with the motion of a hammer. The fangs, which are very delicate and easily broken, are readily replaced by a series of new ones. The venom itself, a chemical poison, is very dangerous if injected in large doses, and the effect of an adder's bite depends primarily upon the dose received. Fatal cases in this country have occurred but are fortunately very rare.

THERE is a small red viper, thought by some to be a separate variety. It measures from 12 to 15 inches in length, and is of a coppery red colour in both sexes. Its distribution is limited.

Male and female adders are often found pairing in April or May. Development takes about four months and the young adders are born alive usually early in September. The average number of the family, in the writer's experience, is thirteen. The fewest found was seven, the most twenty. They are from four to six or more inches long at birth, and at once show the vicious temperament of the species. All adders are untamable and refuse food in captivity.

There is a common belief in many places that the mother adder will swallow or take into her gullet the whole family in case of danger threatening them. It need only be said that this phenomenon has never been proved to the satisfaction of any naturalist.

The smooth snake (*Coronella austriaca*), though common abroad, is rare in Great Britain. It is probably restricted to Dorset, Hants, Surrey, and Berks, and is scarce even there. Adults are about two feet long, brownish in colour, having two series of irregular dark spots on the back. The favourite food consists of lizards and mice. It is quite harmless, but rather fierce in disposition. In general size and appearance the smooth snake somewhat resembles the adder, and has been killed in mistake for that reptile, but the characteristic adder markings are entirely absent.

All British lizards have one anatomical character which differentiates them from the snakes, namely, the two halves of the lower jaw are firmly united by a bony joint which does not allow of distension. Most have two pairs of limbs built on the typical vertebrate style, but some show no external limbs at all, giving them a snake-like appearance such as that seen in the British slow-worm. Most have movable eyelids, whilst snakes have none.

A curious property of some lizards is the readiness with which a portion of the tail breaks off, and the capacity for very imperfectly reproducing the lost portion. Like snakes, they cast their sloughs periodically, sometimes whole, more often in pieces. The majority reproduce their young from deposited eggs, while some carry the embryos till just on full time, when the eggs are laid. Still others bring forth the young alive.

Only three species of lizards are found on the mainland of Great Britain, but if we include the

Channel Islands as a British area, two others must be included. The mainland species are the common lizard, the sand lizard, and the slow-worm (or blind-worm); the extra two in the Channel Islands are the green lizard and the wall lizard. We may note some special features of each of these.

The common lizard (*Lacerta vivipara*), also known as the viviparous lizard and sometimes as the scale lizard, has a wide European distribution and is chiefly found in high lands and mountainous districts rather than in very low-lying parts. In this it differs from the sand lizard. We find the common lizard in England, Scotland, Ireland and Wales, unlike the slow-worm, which is altogether absent from Ireland.

The frequent statement that there are no reptiles in Ireland is, therefore, inaccurate; but there are no snakes. To account for the fact that the common lizard is the only Irish reptile, it is thought by some that this species preceded the other reptilian species in their spread from the continent, and arrived at a time when the mainland was continuous from the Continent to Ireland. Ireland then became cut off from Great Britain, but in the latter country the common lizard had been followed by the slow-worm and the sand lizard, as well as by three snakes, before the separation occurred.

THE general colour of the common lizard is brownish above with small spots, often with a black streak along the back and a dark streak along the sides. The belly in the male is orange red with black spots, and paler in the female.

In England the common lizard is found in flat districts as well as hilly ones, especially, in my experience, in dry and sandy spots. Moors and commons and heaths, as well as sandy places near the sea, are equally favoured. Deep valleys and dark woods seem to be avoided.

Many reptiles are slow and sluggish, but the common lizard is a very active little creature, and very difficult to catch once it is in motion. This lizard has a greater objection to being handled than either the slow-worm or the sand lizard, but nevertheless it does become accustomed to it in captivity, as may be seen in the illustration in page 476 of two (male and female) basking in the writer's hand. These were captured on a sunny bank on the coast of the Isle of Man.

Insects constitute the main food supply. Flies of various kinds, as well as ground insects, are taken. Worms, too, are welcomed.

The scientific name of the common lizard indicates that the young are born alive or carried to full time. The family varies in number from six to twelve, and is born from July onwards, according to the earliness of the local summer. No nest of any kind is made; the young burst the egg membrane and are left to their own devices. They are perfectly developed at birth and quite able to look for insects and otherwise to fend for themselves without assistance being rendered by their parents.

M. H. Crawford

HOW THE TOAD HIDES

Here is a toad which was found in front of a stone (bottom). Upon alarm it retreated backwards (centre) in typical toad fashion, throwing up the soil in front of it as it went, until finally it had made good its retreat (top) under the stone's protection.

S. Johnson

COMMON AND EDIBLE FROG AND THE RARELY SEEN NATTERJACK TOAD

The common frog (bottom photographs) is found almost everywhere in Great Britain and it lives largely upon insects which it catches with its specialised tongue. The usual length is about three inches and the hind legs are more than half as long again. The colouring is brown and the skin is often spotted. Most of its life the frog spends on land. The edible frog (top right) is usually larger in size and is found chiefly in the eastern counties. It may be distinguished by the fold in the skin on either side of the back. On the Continent this species is highly thought of as a dish the thighs resembling young chicken. The natterjack (top left) is rather rare and less clumsy-looking than the common toad. The general colour is green.

The sand lizard (*Lacerta agilis*) is a dweller of the plains rather than the mountains, and is widely distributed in Europe but sparsely in Great Britain, where it is practically restricted to Dorset, Hants, Surrey and the neighbourhood of Southport. It is sometimes reported in error for the common lizard.

It is larger than the common lizard, the females reaching eight inches long, or a little more. The colour varies much. Brown predominates in the females and green in the males. Rows of dark and light spots occur in both sexes. The male tail is longer than that of the female. As its name implies, sandy districts are its favourite haunts. The warmth of the sand assists reproduction, for the eggs are simply deposited in sand and left to hatch out. Insects of various kinds are the staple diet. This species is the only one of the three British mainland lizards which is an egg-layer, like the green lizard and the wall lizard of the Channel Islands.

The fact that the slow-worm or blind-worm (*Anguis fragilis*) has no external limbs is quite enough for most people to regard it as a poisonous snake and destroy it at sight. Not only is it perfectly harmless, but actually a very useful creature, because its favourite diet is the slug. It is, of course, neither blind nor a worm. Its bright little eyes have eyelids, which snakes have not. It often lies motionless, but its individual movements are not slow. It is the fact that it has only rudimentary limbs under the skin which cause the ignorant to persecute it as a snake. It is, indeed, an intermediate form between lizards and snakes, one of the many connecting links between separate groups found in nature, indicating the evolution from generalised to specialised types.

THE slow-worm is common in most parts of Great Britain, but absent from Ireland. A full-grown adult measures from 12 to 15 inches long. In females about half the length consists of tail. The skin is remarkably smooth, but quite dry. The tongue is notched. The tail is easily fractured, and this often enables the slow-worm to escape with its life from a snake or other enemy which has seized it.

There is great variation in colour. The young are silvery white above, with black bellies. Adults have grey, brownish or even coppery bodies, and grey bellies. Their food is mainly slugs, the common garden slug for preference, of which a dozen may be eaten in a very short time. The young are carried to full time, bursting the egg membrane in August or September to the number of four, six, or as many as twelve. They are from two to three and a half inches long at birth, and active at once.

The slough is cast periodically and hibernation begins rather later than in most of the reptiles.

The green lizard (*Lacerta viridis*) is not indigenous to England, Scotland, or Ireland, but is common in the centre and south of Europe. It is much larger than our other species, the adult reaching 12 to 15 inches long. The tail accounts for most of this, almost three-quarters in long males. The predominating colour is green, especially above. The back is often mottled with spots; the male throat is bluish in the breeding season. There is a semicircular collar on the neck, the head is flat, the eyes prominent, and the snout rather pointed.

It prefers rocky ground in the Channel Islands. Insects, worms, and snails are eaten. The writer once found a specimen of the sand lizard in the gullet of a smooth snake, the lizard's stomach being full of beetles, the three creatures forming a striking object-lesson in the struggle for natural existence. The females carry the fertilised eggs for a time, and then deposit them in a suitable warm spot, the whole period of gestation being eight weeks. The eggs are usually eight to ten in number.

THE wall lizard (*Lacerta muralis*), the other Channel Island lizard, is very common in South Europe as well as Northern Africa and Asia Minor. It is a small lizard from six to eight inches long, exhibiting great colour variation. Usually it is brown or greyish above, with white, yellow or pink belly, sometimes spotted. It gets its name from its habit of basking on walls. It is oviparous.

All the amphibians with which we have to deal have the following characters in common: they are cold-blooded vertebrates of a creeping habit. Thei skin is smooth and clammy and has no scales. Ther is a remarkable difference between the young and the adults, because the young live in water, in which they breathe by gills. In adult life they become as a rule land animals, breathing by lungs. The blood corpuscles are nucleated, oval and biconvex in shape. The limbs never take on the fin characters of fish. The fingers and toes have no claws.

In general appearance the tailed amphibians such as newts are not unlike some lizards, but the newts are very much slower in their movements. They are perfectly harmless creatures, in spite of various superstitions which attach to some of them. These are associated with the irritating properties of the skin, which has poison glands of a very mild character. This secretion is very distasteful to other mammals, and is the best defence of the amphibian. It feeds chiefly on insects, of which it consumes large numbers, capturing them by means of its sticky tongue. Frogs and toads are the most common amphibians, and are found practically all over the world.

THE common frog (*Rana temporaria*) is about three inches long. Teeth are present in the upper jaw and on the palate. The insect-catching tongue is notched. The fingers are free, but the toes are webbed for swimming. The hind legs seem very long in proportion to the rest of the creature, being more than half as long again as the body. In colour the frog is of varying shades of brown, with or without dark spots. Often the males are yellowish-white below, and the females a darker orange colour. The female is larger than the male. The colour changes to a certain extent with the surroundings. There is a nictitating membrane in connexion with the eye. The general habit is terrestrial rather than aquatic.

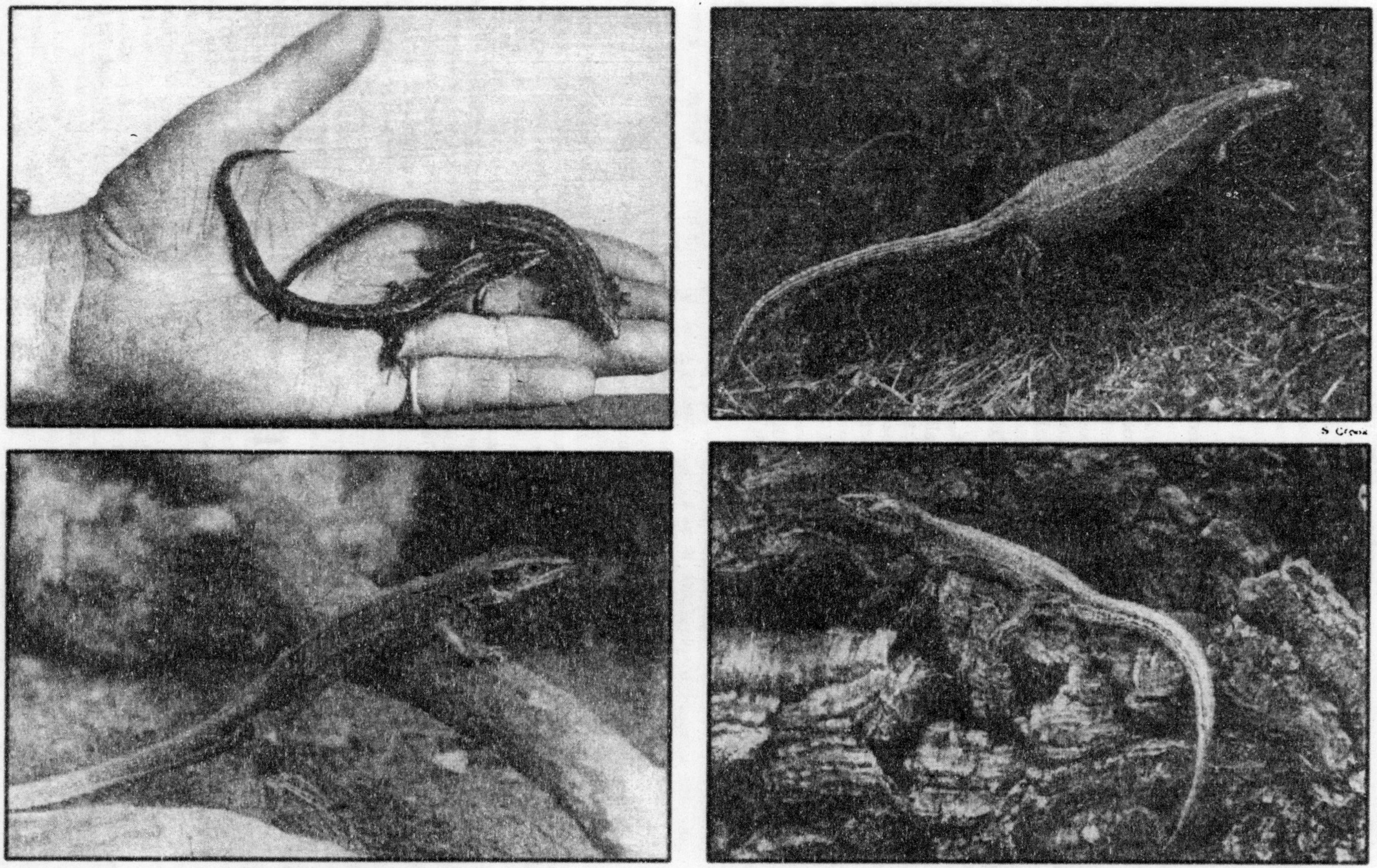

S. Crook

S. Johnson

GREEN LIZARD OF THE CHANNEL ISLANDS AND THE SAND AND COMMON LIZARDS

Great Britain has only three species of lizard but there are two other kinds found in the Channel Islands. Of these the green lizard (bottom left) is much larger than the others, growing more than a foot long. It is found in rocky ground and feeds upon insects, snails and worms. The sand lizard (bottom right) is sparsely distributed in the south of England and very rare elsewhere. Dorset and Hampshire are the places in which to find it most easily. The females are brown and the males green, and both sexes are spotted. The eggs are laid in the sand which the lizard frequents and allowed to hatch in the sun's heat. The upper photographs are of the common lizard. The two in the upper left photograph were captured in the Isle of Man.

In the breeding season the male develops a swelling on the fore-foot. The spawn is deposited in early spring in ponds, where it may be seen floating about in irregular masses. In about three weeks the fertilised eggs produce tadpoles, which at this stage are not in the least like frogs. Their metamorphosis is a fascinating study. At first they breathe by gills in a fold of the skin. They show a beak-like mouth, and possess a long tail. This tail gradually becomes absorbed and the mouth loses its beaky appearance. Then the limbs begin to develop, the gills disappear in favour of lungs, and the tadpole becomes a perfect frog.

The common toad (*Bufo vulgaris*) has a reputation which is not deserved. It is doubtless an unpopular creature, credited with a habit of spitting of which it is not guilty. It is not poisonous, but it has, as a means of defence, a dirty, whitish secretion in the pores of the skin which has an irritant effect. When excited the toad puffs itself out and exudes beads of this secretion.

It is a clumsily-built creature, three and a half inches long as a rule, but growing to larger dimensions. The large, flat head with gaping mouth, brown colour, and warty skin are familiar characters. There are swellings over the eyes like warts. The legs are shorter than the frog's legs, the hind ones being a little longer than the body. There are no teeth. The tongue is attached in front in the mouth, but is free behind; it is slightly cleft at the tip, and is an insect-catching apparatus of great perfection. The male toad is smaller than the female.

The toad is a terrestrial liver commonly found among stones in damp places. The slough is cast several times a year, and often swallowed. In addition to insects, toads feed largely on worms. Stories of toads having lived for years in stones, *without any air*, should be received with caution.

The natterjack toad (*Bufo calamita*) is much rarer than the common toad, and is absent altogether from the Scottish Highlands. It may be distinguished by means of a light-coloured line along the centre of the back, which has given it the name of Golden Back. In size the natterjack is about two and three-quarter inches long. It has a less clumsy appearance than the common toad, but the eyes project more and the eyelids are more elevated. The hind legs, in this case, are not so long as the body. Both sexes are of the same size. The general colour is greenish with spots, the under parts whitish, and often speckled with black. In habit this species is more active than the common toad. It feeds on insects.

All British newts are terrestrial in their habits, except in the breeding season. They spawn on or in the crumpled leaves of various water plants. They differ from the frogs and toads in that they retain the tail throughout their lives, as well as in the fact that they put on a special appearance in the breeding season. All newts are carnivorous. All are quite harmless, though somewhat unpopular.

The smooth or common newt (*Molge vulgaris*) is the most common of all newts in Great Britain, and is found in Ireland. It is about three and a half inches in length, green or brown in colour, profusely spotted. Below it is yellow with black spots. The chin is also yellow. In the male the lower surface of the flat tail is reddish, with bluish lines and markings. In the female it is yellow, without markings.

TOADS ON THE HUNT FOR FOOD
In spite of their slow rate of progress and awkward movements toads are by no means so sedentary and sluggish as is often supposed. Their gait, if unhurried, is very determined, and the photograph shows two of them off upon a voyage of exploration.

In the breeding season the male puts on a festooned frill along the crest of the back, and the female a smaller frill. The eggs are laid in strings of four or six. The tadpoles are dotted with yellow. Water is only sought in the warm months when the slough is cast.

The palmated newt (*Molge palmata*) is the smallest of our newts, being only three inches long. The chin is colourless. The male toes are webbed, and in the breeding season a filament appears on the tail.

The great water newt or crested newt (*Molge cristata*) is our largest newt, measuring five and a half inches in length. It is black or dark brown above and yellow underneath spotted with black. The female is slightly the larger. The toes are yellow, and are decorated with black rings.

In the breeding season the male is distinguished by a high, serrated crest along the back and a further crest along the tail. The eggs are laid in the water usually in May or June, and deposited in the folds of water plants or grasses. In from three weeks to a month the tadpoles hatch out, yellowish-green in colour with black stripes. The fore-legs appear first; the hind-legs follow some weeks later. In about six months, the gills having disappeared, the young newt leaves the water for a land existence and does not return for three years, when the male reaches maturity. After that a water life is lived annually for some three months during the breeding season.

The tadpoles of all newts are herbivorous, but in the adult life all the newts are carnivorous creatures. They feed largely on the tadpoles of frogs.

The crested newt is said to hibernate in companies of different ages, those over three years separating from the younger ones.

STAG AND ZEBRA OBEY THE LAW OF THE HERD

With animals that live together for mutual protection in herds, like deer (top) and the zebras (bottom), there are certain instinctive laws which are always obeyed. Any attempt at individuality or eccentricity in this matter is punished by ostracism or active persecution. These laws of the herd require that the females and the young shall be protected by the herd as a whole and the males in particular. Fighting is discouraged save for purposes of deciding leadership and at mating time, when the survival of the fittest obeys an obviously eugenic law.

Chapter XLVI

Law in the Animal World

By R. C. Macfie

I spoke as I saw,
I report as a man may of God's work—all's Love yet all's Law.

BROWNING

We are inclined to think of law, at least of law applicable to conduct, as essentially and exclusively a human institution, and we are apt to imagine that wild animals, outside the orbit and influence of man's will, are lawless anarchists. But all living creatures are products of chemical and physical laws: the chemical substances of which they are built have obeyed the laws of chemical affinity, and not only the voluntary actions of man but the physiological processes and instinctive actions of the lower animals obey certain rules of life. A world without law would be a chaotic world inhabited by lunatics. The reign of law in Nature is universal —not only law physical and chemical, but law affecting conduct; and though man and possibly other animals may guide and use law, they cannot escape from it, nor abolish it.

The term "law" is, of course, commonly used in several senses; it is used to denote a certain regularity of happenings—a certain invariable sequence of events. A stone thrown up in the air always falls down again, and it always falls at a steadily accelerating rate which can be noted in a mathematical formula. A man eating a sapid substance always secretes a certain substance called saliva, and it is always secreted according to certain known physiological and chemical laws; it has always certain composition, and is always produced by certain cells, in certain quantities, under certain definite conditions. Such invariable linked events are instances of what is called law. But the term "law" may be applied also to the something—to the power behind the events—that links them together.

God is law say the wise, but if He thunder by rule
The thunder is yet His voice.

In whichever of these senses we use the word law it still stands true that law is universal in animal conduct. In man there may be a force called "will" and in animals a force called "instinct" producing invariable sequences of conduct, but invariable sequences of conduct there always are and variation in these sequences—through a lapse of will, or through a lapse of instinct—are abnormal, and mean in the long run death. Rules of conduct, patterns of conduct, whether voluntary or instinctive are the *sine qua non* of life, even though we cannot see their vital value.

Even in such lowly organisms as the amoebas and the bacteria, we find that behaviour is according to law, that movements are not erratic and capricious, but always of such a character as to bring about certain general results, some of which at least are conducive to the welfare of the organism. We find, too, that the relation between stimulus and response varies, as in the case of man, in accordance with Weber's law. However lowly and minute the organism it is ruled by laws in obedience to which its welfare and indeed its very existence depend.

It is so, too, all along the animal scale. Among earth's most ancient animals are the insects and arachnids. Long before the vertebrates appeared, millions of years before the coming of man, they crawled over Silurian ferns, or flitted through Carboniferous thickets, or worried Jurassic dinosaurs, or were hunted by Jurassic pterodactyls. But even these early little creatures were communists, not anarchists, and to-day we find among them rules of conduct observed with a mathematical punctiliousness—rules of conduct which, whether consciously or unconsciously observed, were yet necessary for their survival. They are amongst the smallest of Earth's inhabitants; some are so small as to be invisible, and yet they have succeeded so well in the struggle to survive that taken to-day there are more than two million species which altogether outnumber and outweigh all the vertebrates. Only by following advantageous rules of life could they have thriven and multiplied in such an amazing way.

Take the spider, whose ancestors can be traced back to Palaeozoic times. We find that its conduct, though individualistic and bloodthirsty, is far from anarchic, that, indeed, it conforms persistently to certain detailed rules of life. Look with what mathematical accuracy, with what careful skill, with what ingenuity, with what patience, the ordinary garden spider spins its web! It might no doubt form a web good enough to catch flies by simply making a wild tangle of threads; but it proceeds like an artist and engineer; its web is made according to law, and is itself an exemplification of law and of the value of obeying law. Beginning by laying down a number of circumferential threads to mark out the area of the web, the spider next lays the radial threads which intersect in the centre. "Finally beginning at the circumference and working inwards the spider lays down the delicate viscid spirals on which the efficiency of the web depends. The primary spirals simply form a scaffolding, and are undone, in fact eaten up, as soon as they are displaced." The work is methodical according to plan, according to law: it is a precise adaptation of means to an end.

Or take the wax hive of the ordinary bee. It is built not anyhow, but in accordance with law, and by the combined and co-operative efforts of swarms of architects. Each bee does its own little lawful bit of work and no more, and all the bees follow the principles or laws of solid geometry. Together they make the cells regular hexagons because the hexagon is the most convenient and the strongest shape; also they make the bottom of the cells of three planes meeting at an angle which mathematicians have proved to be the very angle to economise both material and labour.

FURTHER, in the hive there is regular distribution of labour, as if by decree. There are workers, each with its proper task; there are nurses who look after the nymphs and the larvae; there are ladies in waiting who attend on the queen, there are "punkah" bees who ventilate the hive and evaporate water from the honey by fanning with their wings, there are architects who make the honeycomb, there are foragers who collect the honey and pollen, and salt, and water, there are the chemists who preserve the honey with formic acid, there are the sweepers who keep the hive and its approaches clean; there are the amazons who guard the hive and drive away all foes; there is the queen whose one duty it is to propagate the species. All these work in accordance with law as faithfully and definitely as the wheels of a watch. They obey law, and they obey it even when it makes demands that mean loss and unhappiness to the individual. Every year there comes the day of the great annual sacrifice—the sacrifice so brilliantly described by Maeterlinck, when the bees swarm and "the thrice happy city is scattered abroad in obedience to a law superior to its own happiness." He says:

> Never is the hive more beautiful than on the eve of its heroic renouncement. From the height of a dome more colossal than that of St. Peter's at Rome, waxen walls descend to the ground, balanced in the void and the darkness; gigantic and manifold, vertical and parallel geometric constructions, to which, for relative precision, audacity, and vastness no human structure is comparable. Each of these walls, whose substance still is immaculate and fragrant, of virginal silvery freshness, contains thousands of cells stored with provisions sufficient to feed the whole people for several weeks. Here lodged in transparent cells, are the pollens, love-ferment of every flower of spring, making brilliant splashes of red and yellow, of black and mauve. Close by, sealed with a seal to be broken only in days of supreme distress, the honey of April is stored, most limpid and perfumed of all, in twenty thousand reservoirs that form a long and magnificent embroidery of gold whose borders hang stiff and rigid. Still lower the honey of May matures, in great open vats by whose side watchful cohorts maintain an incessant current of air.

IN the centre "is the royal domain of the brood-cells, set apart for the queen and her acolytes; about 10,000 cells wherein the eggs repose, 15,000 or 16,000 chambers tenanted by larvae, 40,000 dwellings inhabited by white nymphs to whom thousands of nurses minister. And finally in the holy of holies of these parts, are the three, four, six or twelve sealed palaces, vast in size compared with the others, where the adolescent princesses lie who await their hour, wrapped in a kind of shroud all of them motionless and pale and fed in the darkness."

Out of this palace of beauty and luxury the bees are driven by the flaming sword of the law of sacrifice, against whose decree of banishment and exile there is no redress and no appeal, surrendering not only their palace but a store of honey representing twelve times the entire weight of the bee population. There could be no more dramatic illustration of the Law of Sacrifice that underlies life. Yet the massacre of the males that follows on the nuptial flight and impregnation of a virgin queen bee is, perhaps, an instance of sacrificial law even more striking. As is well known the chosen bee who consummates wedlock with the virgin queen dies in the act: it is law, there is no way out of it. But not only the chosen lover dies, but in time all his comrades. For one day the law of sacrifice ordains the death of all the males, and the "stern workers who recognize only Nature's harsh and profound laws" promptly massacre them without mercy.

These are instances of law operating *en masse* in mighty matters, but even in small matters there are codes that must be respected. A queen may never use her curved sting against any bee save only a rival queen; and no bee save a queen bee dare sting a queen. "For it is written that against a mother the sting may be drawn by a mother alone; only she who bears in her flanks close on two million lives appears to possess the right with one blow to inflict close on two million deaths." When a queen is to be killed by her subjects she must be suffocated in a "scrum," or held till she dies of starvation.

THE termites and the ants, like the bees, are social insects, are equally under law, and equally live their lives according to law.

The economic laws of some species of the termites are even more elaborate than those of the bees, and even more pervaded with the idea of self-sacrifice. Maeterlinck says "we find in the termite a whole-hearted, heroic, deliberative and intelligent sacrifice to an idea or an instinct—a sacrifice that is without limit and almost infinite. It brings the victims nearer to ourselves and makes them also our brothers, and from certain points of view causes these wretched insects, more than the bee or any other living creature on earth, to become the heralds, perhaps the precursors, of our own destiny."

It is a vulnerable, defenceless insect and only by means of organized law has it succeeded in surviving and making for itself a kind of insect society and civilization. There are four main classes of termites—workers, warriors, and males and royalties; and the males are starved to death after the nuptial flight is accomplished.

The wonderful social organization of the ants, too, depends on a faithful obedience to salutary laws and the same dependance can be illustrated from the lives of beetles and many other insects. What is behind the economic laws which these little organisms obey is a mystery, but the fact remains that they do obey laws and that on their obedience their very existence depends.

We have specially insisted on law in the insect world because insects are especially social animals, and law in the truest sense of the word means certain general rules of conduct implicitly followed by the members of a community for the common weal.

E N.A

MUTUAL TOLERATION OVER THE VITAL MATTERS OF FEEDING AND DRINKING

Despite their extreme ferocity which, it might be thought, would cause endless strife, the lionesses, which live all together in one cage at the Paris Zoological Gardens (bottom), have learned to behave themselves even over the vexed question of food. Each one settles down to its own share in obedience to the only rule which could make life tolerable behind those relentless iron bars. Above we see some wild animals in the Kruger National Park, Africa. They consist of zebra and wildebeest and are sharing a waterhole.

But there is, of course, equally a reign of law in the case of the larger animals.

Take, for instance, the migration of birds. The migratory birds all migrate by law, at a fixed time, in a fixed direction—"The stork in the heaven knoweth her appointed times; and the turtle and the crane and the swallow observe the time of their coming." So regular are the dates of migration, that in India some of the months used to be named after migrants. So unanimous is the response to the inner call of the unwritten law that the flocks of birds move *en masse* like army battalions. So imperious is the law that some birds cover in their migration a distance of thousands of miles. The stork flies between Germany and Natal. The curlew and sandpiper fly from the far north to New Zealand. The dotterel passes to and fro between the North African steppes and the Arctic tundra. The Virginian plover and the warbler journey between Labrador and North Brazil. The Arctic tern beats them all by alternating between Maine and the Antarctic zone.

But even in the egg the bird acts by rule and not by caprice. The chick, in order to break the egg-shell, always chips round in a circle moving from left to right. It works quite uniformly and regularly and consistently.

In the nest, too, law and order is always preserved. For a week or two, perhaps for seven weeks, the mother bird will sit patiently on the eggs while the father bird forages for food and protects the nest. Often the mother has an hour or two of off-time, and the father takes her place.

SIMILAR law and order is exhibited by birds in many situations of life. The pelicans, says Kropotkin, "always go fishing in numerous bands and having chosen an appropriate bay, they form a wide half-circle in face of the shore and narrow it by paddling towards the shore and catching all fish that happen to be enclosed in the circle. On narrow rivers and canals they even divide into two parties, each of which draws up in a half-cricle and both paddle to meet each other, just as if two parties of men, dragging two long nets should advance to capture all fish taken between the nets when both parties come to meet. As the night comes they fly to their resting-place—always the same for each flock—and no one has ever seen them fighting for the possession either of bay or resting-place. In South America, they gather in flocks of from forty to fifty thousand individuals; some enjoy sleep while others keep watch; and others again go fishing."

That is social law practised for the good of the community. In the case of all animals that live in flocks, and packs, and herds, there have to be social rules and laws, though they are not so marked as in the case of the communal insects. Children and mothers are looked after and protected: there is no fighting permitted between members of the clan except at mating-time, or to establish leadership. In many cases there is a sentinel set to keep guard when a flock or herd is liable to be attacked by an enemy, and movement is usually *en masse.* Offenders against the unwritten law are punished, and eccentrics are liable to be ostracised.

Even in the jungle there is jungle-law. "The law of the jungle," says Kipling in "The Jungle Book"—"which is by far the oldest law in the world—has arranged for almost any kind of accident that may befall the Jungle People till now its code is almost perfect."

What exactly the jungle-laws are, not even Kipling knows, but he is probably right when he declares that in time of drought a "water-truce" is declared, and tiger, bear, deer, buffalo, and pig all drink together.

> The pools are shrunk, the streams are dry
> And we are playmates, thou and I,
> Till yonder cloud—Good Hunting—loose
> The rain that breaks our water-truce.

THE laws of animals are, of course, based not on reason, but on instinct, and they all make on the whole for the health and preservation of the individual or of the race. It is obedience to these unwritten laws that enables any group of animals to survive, and disobedience and lawlessness mean death. But the laws are meant to deal only with average and normal situations: they fail when novel emergencies arise, and obedience in such circumstances to the laws of the instinct may and often does mean disaster. The lemmings driven on by an instinctive urge are drowned: the moths perish in the candle-flame.

Man is one of the animals, and he, too, is under the laws of certain animal instincts. The instincts to eat, to propagate his kind, to kill his enemy, to hunt, to play, have the force of laws with him, and if they weaken or if he fails to obey them, the race of man will perish. But man has discovered that these instinctive laws are not sufficient to guide his life in *all* cases, and that there are cases—as in the lower animals—when obedience to them must be ruinous or fatal, and so he has supplemented Nature's laws, with other laws meant to meet the special conditions of a complex civilization, and man to-day has to obey not only the laws of his nature, but the laws of God and the laws of the land. He cannot always, he need not always reason out a course of action, he has these extra general laws to guide him, and they are the laws that have made civilization and that have lifted him above the level of the other animals.

MAN from the first has been a creature of law especially requiring laws because of his communal character, and any endeavour now to emancipate himself from law, and live at his own sweet will, as an uncompromising individualist or anarchist, must be fatal both to the individual and the race.

Yet each man is an individual: the human community is more than an ant-hill or a bee-hive; and, subject always to the safety of the community, each man should be as little law-bound as possible, and should be given liberty to go his own way and live his own life and develop his own individuality.

Neville Kingston

ADVENTURES OF A SECRETARY BIRD THAT BROKE THE RULE OF "BIRDS OF A FEATHER"

One day at the London Zoo the secretary bird, that lives among a number of other species, safely separated by bars, succeeded in getting out of its pen. Next door were a couple of cranes (top) which immediately showed by their behaviour that the visit was not merely unwelcome but intolerable. The secretary bird got itself away from those dangerous beaks by flying out of the frying-pan into the fire of the next cage, where a stork lived (bottom). Luckily help arrived just in time to restore the unpopular visitor to its rightful place.

Neville Kingston

PIKE AND EELS, EVERY MOVEMENT OF WHOSE GILLS IS SEPARATING OXYGEN FROM THE WATER

Nature constructed one of her greatest marvels when she invented the gill. On examining the gills of a pike—a very unsafe operation until the fish is dead, since the mouth is furnished with a surprising quantity of teeth—a number of scarlet leaves are seen when the gill cover is pulled back. These leaves contain capillary blood-vessels and are arranged so that the greatest possible number of these can be presented to the water, so that the oxygen may pass into the blood stream. There is a clear passage from the open mouth to the open gill cover save for these red breathing surfaces. The pike and eels seen above were photographed in the Aquarium at the London Zoo.

Chapter XLVII

The Fight for Oxygen

By Joseph Barcroft, C.B.E., F.R.S.

Professor of Physiology, Cambridge University: Author of "The Respiratory Function of the Blood"

THE flame of life. Why the *flame* of life? The comparison of life to a flame is no mere rhetorical conceit; there lies underneath it some measure of material truth. The flame can only be supported as the result of incessant chemical activity and the same is true of life. But that is not all. The type of chemical activity in each case is similar: it is the oxidation of organic material. The chemistry of this flame is simple and intense, the chemistry of life is complicated and subdued; the flame burns, the body only smoulders, the flame is hot, the body is only warm; but whether in the flame or in every living cell, material is continually being consumed, it is continually giving out heat, it is continually undergoing the process known to chemists as oxidation, and for this reason it is clear that it must be fed with a sufficient and continual supply of oxygen.

This dependence upon oxygen is true of the humblest as well as the most highly organized forms of life. Whence comes this oxygen? For the furnace it comes from the draught of air without which the fires would go out; life depends upon the atmosphere as well. So far as *animal* life, at all events, is concerned there is no other source of supply. Fortunately there is no chance of this oxygen supply petering out. There are over five million tons of oxygen in the atmosphere over each square mile, and as no one in his lifetime uses more than about a ton, and most people very much less, there need be no apprehension about the supply.

The question is not is there enough oxygen in the universe, but by what means is it to be acquired? The most lowly forms of animal life are to be found in water, and indeed life itself is supposed to have had its beginnings not on land but in the ocean. The earliest forms of life were then divorced from the atmosphere; how were they to obtain oxygen? How were they to obtain *enough* oxygen?

As regards the path by which oxygen reaches them, fortunately that gas is to some extent soluble in water. Each time a wave breaks, some of the air in the foam becomes dissolved in the water, unless indeed this water is charged to the full extent possible under the circumstances. As the water all becomes mixed up and as in any case the dissolved gas can pass about through the water, it has no difficulty in reaching any living organism which is not situated at too great a depth.

But how to get enough? Fortunately the needs of these mean creatures are very limited. They themselves are extremely small, perhaps no bigger than the head of a pin, perhaps much smaller, so that the amount needed by any one cell—any unicellular organism—is rather trifling. Being so minute, every part of the cell is very near to the water in which the oxygen is dissolved, so the oxygen just soaks into the cell from the water outside much as the coffee in our cup soaks into the lump of sugar we put into it.

But the oxygen requirements of unicellular organisms are small not only because of the diminutive size of the creatures themselves. Even for its size such a thing as the amoeba demands but little oxygen and for at least two reasons: firstly because it is cold and secondly because it is inert. Of these considerations more will be heard later; here it is merely to be noted that size for size the warmer the temperature of an animal the more oxygen it requires, and also that its demand for oxygen increases rapidly in proportion to its activity.

J. J. Ward

BREATHING TUBES AT WORK

The water scorpion has two respiratory tubes, so that if one gets blocked it can still breathe. These are attached to the tail-end and are pushed through the surface film to the air.

For the moment, however, let us keep to the cold and humble animals which live in water. As they developed and became more complicated it almost goes without saying that they became larger. The sea-urchin, for instance, does not rank very high in the scale of creation. Yet the sea-urchin has attained to quite a considerable size even in this country, whilst abroad there may be found sea-urchins of sorts about as large as the head of an average baby.

Oxygen never could soak into these creatures from the water in which they live in the same sort of way as the coffee soaks into the sugar. The process of soaking (or diffusion, to give it its proper name) is too slow

J. J. Ward

GNAT LARVAE AT THE SURFACE

It was the knowledge that gnat (or mosquito) larvae breathe by thrusting a tube through the surface of the water that made human life possible in malarial places. A little oil on the surface clogs the tubes and suffocates the larvae.

and the distance to be traversed by the oxygen would be too great, for the oxygen is wanted all over the body of the sea-urchin. A plan has therefore been devised by which the water can be circulated through the urchin in canals so that no part of the body is very far from the circulating water. Thus the creature inside is, as it were, irrigated by a system of canals in each of which water is circulating and in each of which the water is either carrying oxygen to some part of the body or is returning for a fresh supply of it

The fluid spoken of as circulating in the channels of the sea-urchin has been spoken of as water. Essentially and for the present purpose it may be regarded as such, for its power of dissolving oxygen is much the same as that of sea water, but in reality it is something more than water, for if shed into a vessel it will clot. It is, in fact, a very primitive type of blood.

To turn to a much more highly developed form of marine life, the lobster, you are confronted with an animal of much greater activity, as may be evinced by the power of its claws. This power is the expression of a background combustion and therefore of oxygen used. It is therefore only natural to find that the provision for the oxygen supply of the tissues of the lobster is on an altogether more compendious scale than the primitive irrigation of the sea-urchin.

The fundamental principle of the system of oxygen supply in the lobster is still one of irrigation. The advance wrought is largely one of degree. In the first place, the fluid which is driven through the various channels—channels which we may now definitely term blood vessels—is propelled by one definite pump, the heart. In the second place, there are very complete arrangements by which the blood can pick up oxygen from the sea water in which the lobster is living. These arrangements are gills of sorts, and may easily be seen.

The shell covering the back of the lobster is continued down over the animal's sides as two shields which, on their inner surfaces, are quite free from any attachment to the body. These shields of shell may be broken away and underneath them will be found numerous bodies which look like plumes. Each fibre of these feathery bodies contains delicate blood vessels within it. The blood is continually circulating in these, and is only separated from the sea water by a membrane so delicate that the oxygen has no difficulty in soaking through from the water into the blood of the lobster. The blood therefore comes from tissues where it has been denuded of oxygen, replenishes its store in the feathery gills and is driven once more to the tissues.

But the whole story has not yet been told, for in the blood of the lobster and others of its kind is to be found the germ of one of nature's most ingenious devices. Oxygen is rather insoluble in water; at best, when shaken up with air, water will only dissolve a little more than one two-hundredth part of its own volume of oxygen. Pity the poor lobster's heart, therefore, which, were it not for the provision

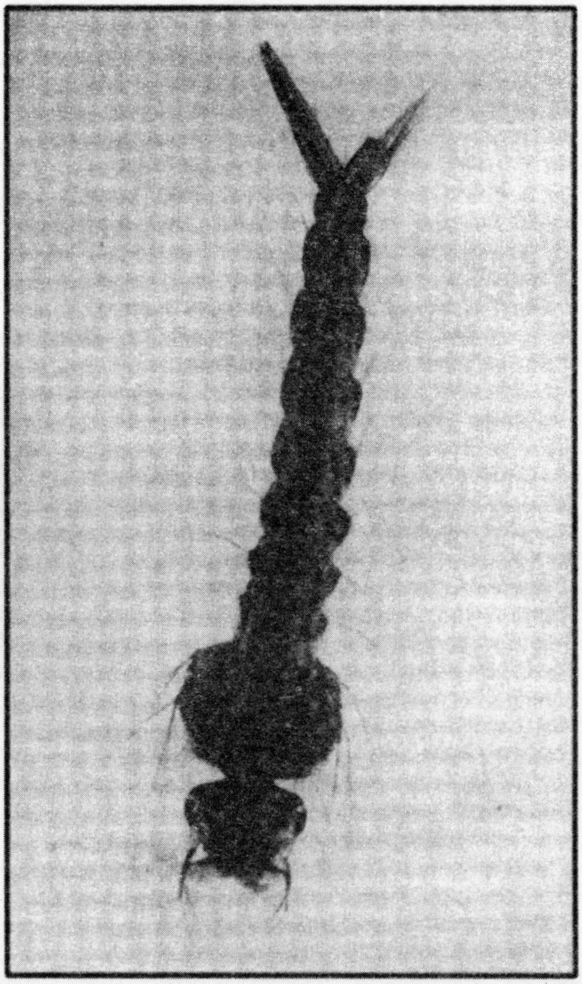

J. J. Ward

THE GNAT LARVA AND ITS BREATHING TUBE

The breathing tube of the gnat larva is joined to the eighth or penultimate segment of its body, and ends in five flaps. These, spread out upon the water, act as floats to keep it at the surface and also as breathing holes. The flaps are closed for diving.

W. S. Berridge

SALAMANDER THAT CHANGES ITS BREATHING APPARATUS

For many years the real life history of the American salamander, common in Mexico and found also in the Rocky Mountains, was not guessed at. It came as a great surprise to naturalists when the discovery was made that a creature called the axolotl, considered to be allied to the newts and living in the water, was really one and the same animal in an early stage of its development. The axolotl breathes under water by means of gills. But on leaving or being deprived of water the axolotl sheds its gills and breathes air.

which I am about to describe, would have had to propel quantities of water round the body, out of all proportion to the amount of oxygen which was transported therein.

NATURE found a chemical absorbent which could be dissolved in the water, and which when dissolved increased many times the quantity of oxygen which a given quantity of water could carry. This substance has the further remarkable property, namely, that when it arrives in the blood vessels of the tissues it generously gives up the oxygen which it has acquired in the lungs. The name of this chemical absorbent is haemocyanin, and it is a compound of copper.

In reality these arrangements for the absorption of oxygen and its transport are so efficient as to be capable of absorbing much more oxygen than would be in stagnant water immediately in contact with the gills. Therefore, the lobster has had to devise some way of securing a consistent stream of fresh oxygen carrying water over the surface of the gill-plumes. It has, so to speak, to ventilate the gills not with air but with water which contains air in solution. This ventilation is carried out in an extraordinarily ingenious way. The gills are situated, as we have already said, in a sort of tubular chamber which is formed of the body wall on the inside of this shell. On the outside, this tube is open at the front, or head, end, and also at the hinder end. Near the front end of this tube, attached to one of the legs, there is an object which bears some resemblance to a paddle—it is called a scaphognathite. This paddle is never at rest. Ever swaying, it maintains a constant stream of water over the gill-plumes.

The fight of the body for oxygen in all the higher animals, though much sterner, presents the same three-fold problem as in the lobster. First, how to provide a suitable site for the transference of the oxygen from the outside air or water into the blood. Second, how to transport the oxygen from that site (be it lung, gill, or skin) to every nook and cranny of the body. And third, how to ventilate the respiratory apparatus with sufficient oxygen for the blood to pick up. The problems of the respiratory system are no other than the problems of any system of intensive supply. You classify the provision of food for a large town along precisely the same lines. A means of bringing food to this place on a large scale—the railway corresponding to the ventilation; a site for its transference to some means of internal transport—the goods station; and a system

J. J. Ward

DRAGON-FLY NYMPH BELOW WATER

At the hinder end of the dragon-fly nymph's body there are three pointed appendages which, when open, admit water to the region of the body filled with blood channels, where oxygen is extracted. The used water is then expelled and, if necessary, with sufficient force to drive the nymph violently along.

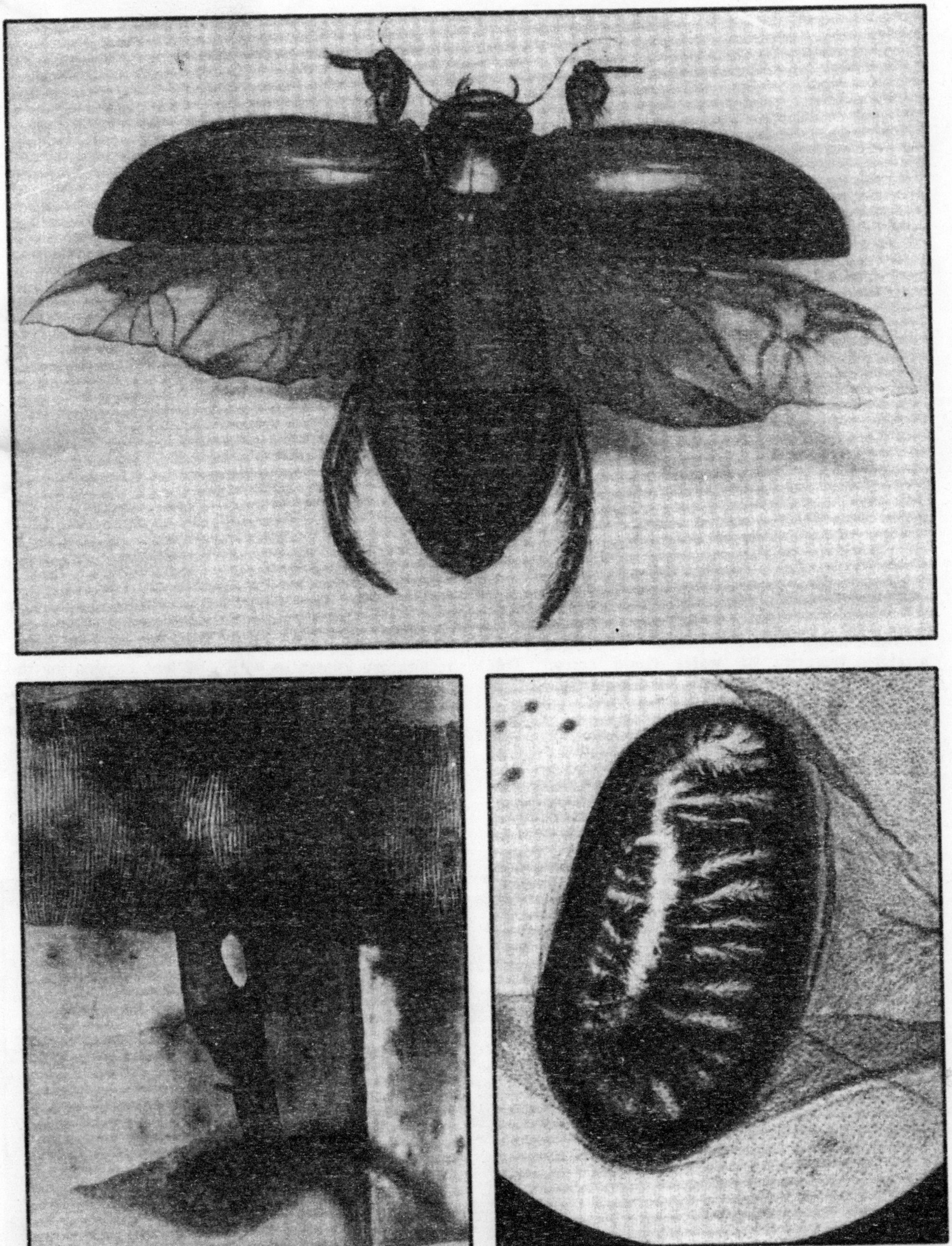

H. S. Cheavin

RESPIRATORY METHODS OF A WATER BEETLE

One of the common inhabitants of an English pond is the dyticus beetle (top). When it wishes to breathe it rises to the surface and waits there with the end of its abdomen in the air. It then raises the elytra or wing case and exposes a surface of its body covered with spiracles or breathing holes. The lower right photograph shows one of the spiracles, and the lower left illustrates the connection between the spiracle and the main tracheal tube in the wonderful breathing system of this creature of the pond.

of distribution which is capable of carrying it to every house in the town—the streets, vans, lorries, and so on—corresponding to the blood vessels and the blood circulating through them.

The necessity of adequate provision of all three components of the system of respiration may be judged from the fate of a certain section of the animal kingdom, which forgot one of the three.

THE insects are not so far removed in relationship from their jointed legged neighbours of the lobster family, but the insects "made the plunge," if I may be excused so inverted a metaphor, from life in the water to life in the air. By doing so they came into much closer touch with oxygen in bulk, but clearly the respiratory system which was designed for life in the water—the scaphognathite, the gills and the rest—were of no use for the air, so another system must needs be devised. The insect did rather the obvious thing. It laid down a system of minute air tubes all over its body. Such a tube, starting from the surface of the body, spreads into the interior like the branches of a tree (but hollow), ending in terminal blind twigs. The tubes are prevented from collapsing by a spiral of hard material in the wall. A very beautiful system, you say, extending to the furthest interstices of the body; true, but note there is no provision for getting the air in and out of the tubes!

When I go to my friend the dentist, I see a little flame on his table and in his hand an instrument which consists of a tube, the open end of which he puts in the flame; but the other end is fitted with a rubber ball. He gives the ball three or four squeezes, during which the hot air rapidly traverses the tube, and then the instrument is fit for use. Then I feel inclined to go to the insect with great deference, take off my hat and say: "Sir, why did you not put just such a ball at the blind termination of your breathing tubes, so that by making it pulsate you could perpetually be clearing the tube of the old air and introducing new?"

Well, I reflect that to suggest anything to nature would be an impertinence; but still the fact remains that if the dentist closed the end of his tube at which the ball is situated, the air could only change very slowly in the tube, and so it is with the insect, only in the part of the tube which is quite close to the orifice does the air change at any rate that is worth while. Therefore, to be of any use to the insect, every part of every tube must be near the orifice, consequently the insect never can become anything but small. The dragon-fly is among the largest of insects, but even it has a very "thready" body, long indeed but thin to a degree. Yet the insect life, though capable of great activity, must always be small because the insect has no provision for the ventilation of the air pipes.

It is when we consider the life of the higher animals—those with backbones—and especially the warm-blooded animals, that we see the provision for an oxygen supply on a grand scale. To take in three

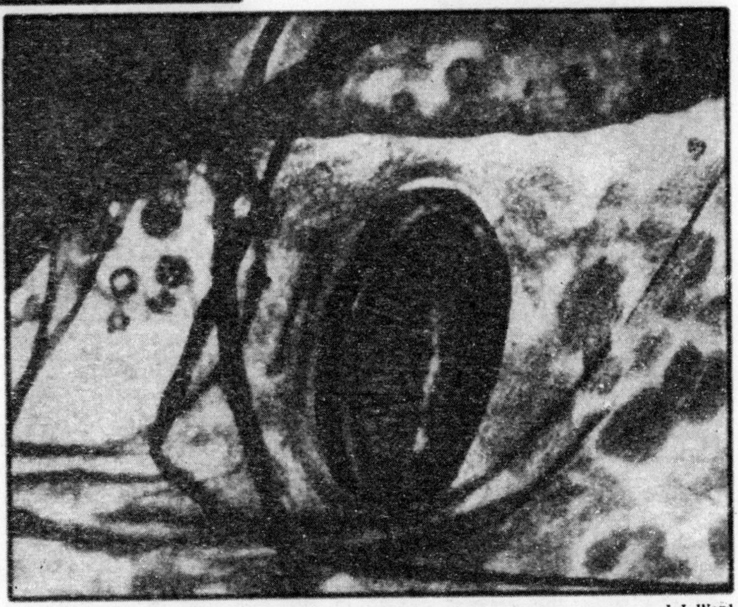

J. J. Ward

ORGANS WHICH SUPPLY THE BLOOD WITH OXYGEN

These insects take in the air from which the oxygen is to be separated by a series of apertures, called spiracles, on either side of the body. In the lower photograph are spiracles of the gipsy moth. Above is a silkworm spiracle showing how the tracheal tubes branch from the spiracle itself into finer tubes and spread to all the body.

J. J. Ward

SPIRACLES OF BORDERED UNDERWING CATERPILLAR

In the caterpillar the spiracles by which it breathes are plainly marked all along the side of the body. This simple but very efficient arrangement allows the air free access to the blood supply without the intervention of any lung organ. The mouth is thus purely for feeding and, in the caterpillar's case, ever-busy

cardinal points, firstly as regards the seat of oxygen-exchange between the air and the blood, that in land animals is the lung. Each lung in man is essentially a number of bags into and out of which the air can be driven, but the wall of each bag is one vast honeycomb of minute air-cells into which the oxygen diffuses from the general cavity of the bag, and in the walls of which is a network of minute blood vessels. A vast area of blood, estimated at nearly a thousand square feet, is at any one time spread out in these vessels and separated from the air in the air-cells only by a delicate film of material sufficient to keep the blood from leaking out, but yet porous enough to allow of the passage of air.

THE arrangements for inflation and deflation of the lung differ in different forms of life. In all cases they are carried out by some sort of rhythmic muscular movement operated by the brain. The frog fills its lung by filling its mouth with air, shutting its mouth and nose and then gulping the air down into the lung. The lung is deflated when the nose is opened, by its own elasticity. Possibly it is just because this method is primitive and not to be relied upon, that nature in the case of the frog is not prepared to risk too much on it. At all events, the frog can breathe through its skin and, therefore, is not confined to pulmonary respiration. The mechanism by which birds inflate and deflate their lungs is a little mysterious. The bird's lung, unlike the human lung, is not at the end of a tube, but consists really of numerous little lungs packed along the sides of a tube which again recalls the air syringe of the dentist. For at the end of this tube there is a large air sac which goes down the body, and indeed the bird has quite a system of air sacs. It is supposed by many that the bird, especially when it flies, draws air in and expels air from its air sacs with each rhythmic movement of its body muscles, as the dentist expels it from the syringe with each squeeze of his hand. Incidentally, the tubes on the way to the air sacs and the lungs on their walls become ventilated. It is not surprising that the birds have a very powerful respiratory apparatus. To force air out of the lung when flying at sixty miles an hour up wind cannot be an easy affair.

THE animals with warm blood do not force air out of their lungs—at least, not to any great extent. They draw it in and, in a measure, allow it to come out of itself. In them, as in the birds, interest concentrates largely on the brain's respiratory rhythm. The part of the brain which is responsible for the respiratory rhythm works automatically like a fly-wheel. If the respiration is too violent, the blood will alter in composition, and the altered blood when it arrives at the brain soothes it and makes the respiration more quiet. Again, if the respiratory efforts are not strong enough, the composition of the blood again suffers, and the impure blood stimulates the brain to drive the respiration with still greater energy.

A few words in conclusion about man himself. In him the fight for oxygen is more exacting than in any other creature, for man lives to a much greater extent on his wits than do the brutes. By his " wits " I mean the accurate and detailed action of the thinking parts of his brain, and it is these which suffer first if there is deficient oxygen supply. So sensitive is the brain to complete deprivation of oxygen that consciousnesss can only last a few seconds. After all, oxygen has been prevented reaching the brain. There is in the lungs about two minutes' supply of oxygen and perhaps a minute's supply in the blood, so that the faculties can be maintained for a short time after the complete cessation of respiration.

The persons who carry the fight for oxygen to its most extreme limits are the pearl divers of the South

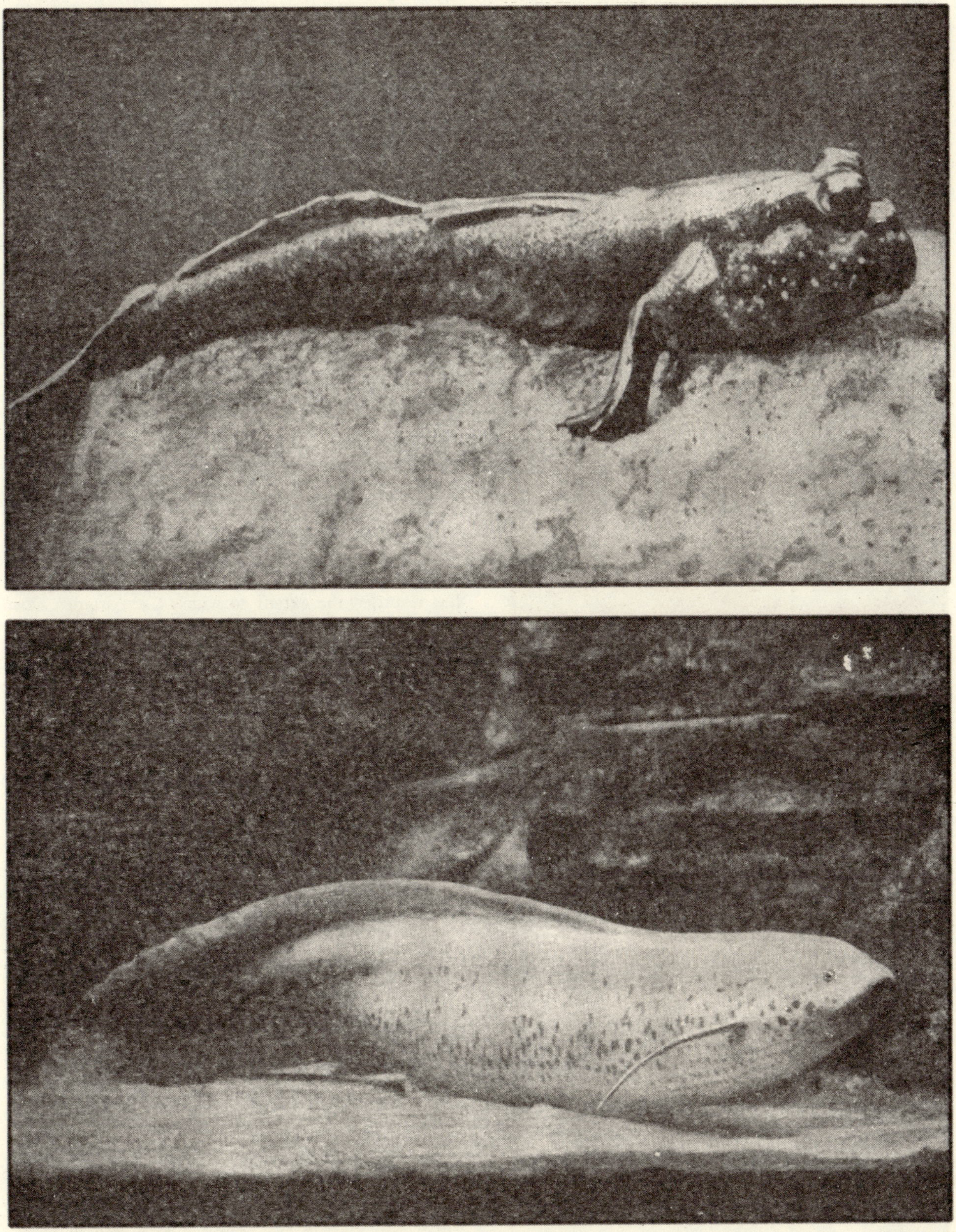

Neville Kingston

REMARKABLE FISH WITH DUAL SYSTEMS OF BREATHING

The lung-fish have adapted themselves cleverly to circumstances. The rivers in which they live dwindle to a greater or less extent in the dry season, and leave only a chain of pools. Species like the African mud-fish (bottom) make a hole in the mud with an aperture at the top and breathe air, remaining dormant till the rain shall fill the rivers again. They use the air-bladder common to all fish as a lung. The mudskipper (top), also African, walks and skips about ashore and is said to use its tail as a respiratory organ by leaving it hanging in the water.

FEATHERY GILLS OF YOUNG NEWT

During its early life the newt breathes by means of gills which are feathery-looking appendages. We see them here at their greatest development. As it gets older these gills disappear until the newt finally leaves the water and becomes air breathing.

WATER CREATURES THAT BREATH AIR

While being essentially of the water the sea lions (bottom) have not, in the wonderful course of evolution, made any attempt to adapt their breathing apparatus to under-water conditions, but must rise, just as the turtles must (top), to the surface for air.

Sea Islands—the woman pearl divers to boot. A traveller reaching one of these islands in a yacht has recorded the extent to which these women have reduced oxygen want to a fine art. They dive to the bottom of the sea, search for the pearls and time their stay with such nicety as just to have reached unconsciousness when they are at the surface. Still unconscious, they are dragged out of the water, laid out on the beach to regain their faculties, and, having done so, they smilingly make another excursion to the bottom.

BUT the fight for oxygen is not left to savages; civilization fights as well, and in the following way. Man is ever trying to push upwards, even in the literal sense of the word. The spirit of conquest impels the ascent of Everest, the search for rich mineral deposits drives him to carry out mining operations 16,000 feet up the Andes. Victory over the air sends him far above the clouds in 'planes. As he ascends he is ever getting into rarer and rarer atmospheres—that is to say, into atmospheres which contain less and less oxygen per cubic foot. Then he fights. The deficiency of oxygen in his blood drives his brain so that he pants, and in time he achieves a partial success; the want of oxygen also drives the factories of his blood so that it becomes richer in the red pigment, haemoglobin, that in all higher animals acts as an oxygen carrier; herein he achieves another partial success. The poverty of the air also makes him expand his chest, so that the races which live high in the Andes appear almost to be deformed, so large is their chest development—a third success. And other more subtle changes take place, all of which are, in one way or another, the response of the organism to deprivation of its most immediate necessity—oxygen.

Chapter XLVIII

The Mystery of the Salmon

By Hamilton Fyfe

"THE salmon," wrote Izaak Walton in his "Compleat Angler," "is accounted the king of fresh-water fish." He wrote with careless, happy assurance. He was confident that he knew all about the salmon; that it was beyond question a fresh-water fish. Yet in his day very little was known about it and in ours not much more.

The title which he gave it has not been disputed. It is a king of fish, a favourite equally with anglers and with those who enjoy the pleasant flavours of food. There are some who say that salmon is difficult to digest. Perhaps it has been blamed sometimes when the cause of trouble lay in reality elsewhere. Mr. Snodgrass (in "The Pickwick Papers") murmured on one occasion in a broken voice: "It wasn't the wine, it was the salmon," when it really was the wine and not the fish. There is no doubt that salmon is highly nourishing; there is little danger of its causing digestive trouble if it be eaten moderately and not mixed with other rich substances.

It is to-day found on a very much larger number of tables than ever before. Its pink flesh, once a luxury for the well-to-do, has become an everyday article in the diet of the poor. True, the fish which are canned in enormous quantities on the Pacific Coast are not like those which are caught in Scottish or Irish rivers or in Norwegian lakes; they are smaller, they have not the same flavour. Yet they are salmon, they belong to the same species, there is the same mystery about them.

In the animal world are many unexplained wonders. We find certain creatures with habits which are peculiar to themselves, habits which they must have acquired for some reason now only to be guessed at. For example, the huanaco (or guanaco), a South American animal something between a goat and a deer (not at all like a "camel without a hump," as it is described by some writers) goes always to a particular place to die. No one has been able to trace this instinct to its origin. The suggestion has been made that in past ages when the South American continent was colder, the huanaco may have been driven by storms to shelter among the reeds and trees growing beside rivers in deep valleys, and that now it still seeks its Valley of Death when it feels discomfort and pain arising from causes other than the climate. But that is no more than a surmise.

Not any less puzzling is the salmon's habit of living partly in fresh water, partly in the sea. This is made even more difficult to understand by the fact (if it be a fact) that salmon do not feed while they are in fresh water, or at any rate feed very little. The usual emptiness of their stomachs when they are caught has been attributed to their vomiting from fear or anger as soon as they feel the hook in their jaw and are being dragged towards the bank against their will. But this remains a suggestion.

It has been pertinently asked: "Why, if salmon do not feed in rivers, do they snap at the fisherman's fly?" The reply made to this by the naturalists who maintain that they live on their own fat during the periods of their absence from the sea is that they take the fly merely from curiosity. That again is but a theory. Against it has been set the probability that if they snap at an artificial fly they must be accustomed to snapping at real ones, and therefore to feeding. Yet the examination of stomachs has shown pretty conclusively that it is not their custom to take

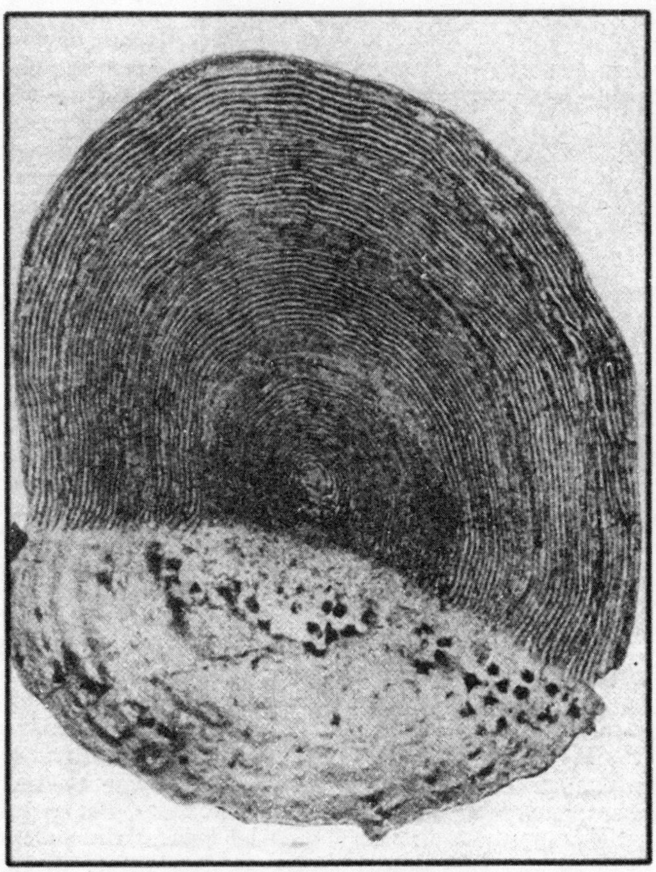

E.N.A.

SCALE FROM A SALMON

This scale was taken from a mature male fish in its fourth year. The rings, shown clearly by the magnification, are an indication of the age of the fish. The tint of the scales varies considerably, being bright before, and dull after, spawning.

W. S. Berridge

E.N.A.

EARLY STAGES OF THE SALMON'S LIFE

The salmon fisheries being a very important industry the eggs are carefully collected and sent from rivers where the fish are plentiful to those worse stocked. About 100,000 can be packed in one of these cases (bottom), and the eggs can remain for several weeks if kept moist and cool. Above is a salmon in the " parr " stage.

nourishment regularly in fresh water. Another doubtful point is whether salmon return always to the rivers where they came into being, and where their first year of life was spent. They seem to do this as a rule, but the rule appears to be variable.

One thing seems sure among many incertitudes. The eggs of salmon will not develop in salt water, nor even in large bodies of fresh water. They must be deposited near the source of a stream, in pure water flowing quickly over a gravelly bed. This explains the astonishing determination shown by salmon in ascending rivers. Nothing more resolute than their will to reach a suitable spawning place is known in nature. It is usual now in Britain to assist them by putting in salmon ladders or passes wherever a sudden rise in a river level makes ascent specially hard. Even with such help they cannot go forward at a rate more rapid than from eight to ten miles in a single day.

Their leaps are prodigious; from their trick of jumping clear of the water they get their name (Latin, *salire* to leap). In the rivers flowing to the Pacific Ocean, where they ascend in dense masses, their struggles are pitiful. Vast numbers leap out of the water and die on the banks. In the water they are in places so thick that they appear to be a solid body. So imperious an instinct is rare. It is among the most arresting wonders of animal life.

The career of the salmon is on this wise. It begins as a wriggling, shapeless, tiny creature, not unlike a tadpole. Since it has no mother to suckle or feed it, it is provided with a bag from which it draws its nourishment. It is called an *alevin*. After two or three weeks it has grown to the length of an inch and become a *samlet* or salmon fry. For centuries these have been in England under the protection of the law. As far back as 1533 an act of Henry VIII declared that " no manner of persone shall take at the tayle (tail) of any mylle (mill) or were (weir) the yonge fry of salmon." Thanks to this care for their welfare and the fact that they are so small, the baby

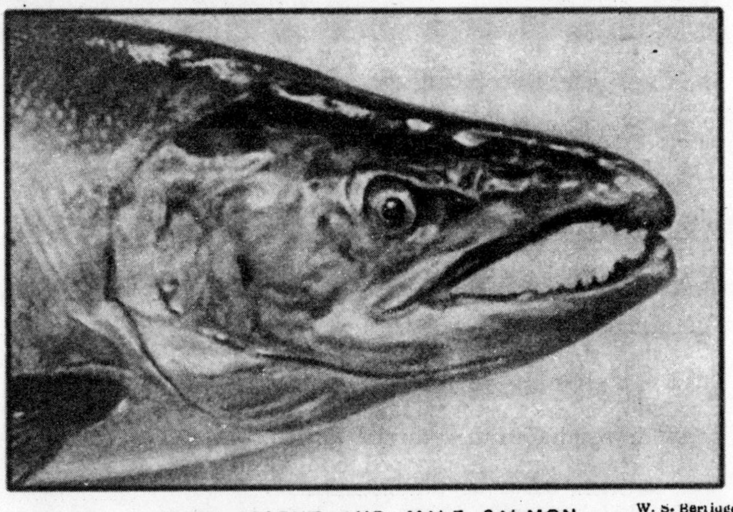

W. S. Berridge

ADOLESCENT AND MALE SALMON

When the fish are ready for spawning the male becomes very pugnacious and develops a great hook on the lower jaw (bottom). After spawning is done the jaw loses this asymmetrical appearance. The upper photograph shows a young salmon. At the end of three years the fish loses its parr markings and becomes a silvery "smolt."

salmon seldom fall a prey to man. They are frequent victims, however, of fish; their own species even is said to devour them, though this is another topic of controversy. Other fish certainly do. But there are a great many samlets; large numbers escape all perils and at the age of a month or six weeks they grow into *parr*, four inches long and very lively.

Until less than a century ago parr were believed to be a separate species of fish; only in 1837 were they discovered to be growing salmon. They grow steadily but not rapidly. Their life settles down to a long, gradual development. Not until they are from fifteen to eighteen months old do they reach the next stage and become *smolt*. Now they make their first journey to the sea, where, if they are lucky enough to reach it, they soon have silvery scales and begin to look like grown salmon.

But the perils of the journey reduce their number to a meagre fraction of that which set forth. At first they are snapped at by voracious pike; herons drive at them with rapier-like beaks. Then gulls swoop down on them and large hungry sea-fish harry them. Only the strongest and the most fortunate escape from so many fierce and greedy foes. Those which do find themselves safe in deep water, for which they always make at once, grow in a few months' time into *grilse*, their last stage but one.

Many salmon in this stage leave salt water and go up rivers along with the fully matured fish, in order to breed as a rule, though not, it is said, invariably for that purpose. Other grilse, not so precocious, remain in the sea until they are mature.

The salmon which ascend rivers are divided into *baggits* (females) and *kippers* (males). Both have in the period before spawning a most unpleasant appearance. The females are almost black and are bloated and bulky in shape. The males are of a dirty red colour, spotted and slimy of skin. Their shoulders have shrunk, making their heads seem enormous. Their jaws have lengthened, they display dangerous-looking teeth, they have formidable curved beaks. These are for no other purpose, it would seem, than

E.N.A

GROUP OF SALMON TAKING A DOUBLE FALL ON THEIR WAY TO SPAWN

When the rush and drive of these boiling waters, swollen high with winter rains, is seen, then the amazing energy of the salmon can be understood. For months the fish has been swimming the sea—its true home—laying up fat and strength for the great trial. But when the hour comes the fish seems to exult in its own strength and the task before it. Here we see that not only one jump must be made but, immediately upon regaining the water, another to surmount this double obstacle.

to fight with. Combats between the kippers are frequent. Darwin noted in the "Origin of Species" that male salmon had been observed fighting all day.

The female prepares a nest for her eggs by making a deep trench in the river bottom with her tail, then she lays them gradually, the kipper fertilises them, and as soon as they have undergone this process they sink into the gravel. Eggs which are not fertile float and are snapped up by fish which wait for them below the salmon nests.

The hatching takes from seventeen to twenty weeks; the warmer the water, the shorter the time. The tiny creatures which emerge from the eggs stay for a fortnight or so under a rock or stone for protection. They get no help or instruction from their parents. They have to shift for themselves. The older fish do not even wait to see how they get on; as *kelts* (in Ireland *slats*) they go down stream as quickly as they can to recover themselves in the sea after spawning. When they have regained their handsome appearance, they are known as "clean" salmon. They remain "clean" until they are again under the influence of the urge to reproduce, which sets them ascending a river again (though some, it is contended, go up without spawning).

Many do not feel this urge a second time, very few a third time. It is held to be very uncommon for a salmon to "run" more than twice. The great number probably go up rivers to breed only once. This can be learned from their scales, which tell something of their life history. It has been discovered in this way that sometimes they stay in the sea for as long as three years before being seized by the impulse to seek fresh water. This is felt in the autumn or winter. The spawning season is from September to January. In British rivers salmon spawn usually in November or December, sometimes as late as January.

There is a belief among certain naturalists that adult salmon do not "run"; that fish in the grilse stage are the only ones which ascend rivers, and that they do so for the sole purpose of spawning. But this view obtains little support. It is mentioned in order to show how diverse are the opinions concerning salmon and how little there is in their life history about which all who have made a particular study of them are agreed.

One statement may be made without fear of contradiction. Pacific salmon furnish the most valuable catch of fish in the world. Not even the herring, a poor relation of the salmon, can compete with it as a source of wealth. The Pacific variety is distinct from the European. It is called sometimes the hump-backed, sometimes the dog salmon. There are many slightly differing types of it and these are netted in vast quantities; they are canned on the spot and sent to many lands.

SALMON FIGHTING ITS WAY UP THE FALLS TO SPAWN

The Pacific salmon are of no interest to anglers. They do not rise to a fly in the rivers, as European salmon do. Their flesh is not so delicate; it is red rather than pink (both colours are the result of eating certain kinds of shellfish); they are not so "kingly" in their aspect. The scenes in the rivers and on the banks of rivers when the salmon are in spate have been noticed already. A British Columbian writer says they actually stop the course of mighty streams.

E.N.A.

SALMON THWARTED BY A LANDSLIDE: SPAWNING FISH

Below is a silver horde whose invasion was stayed by a landslide into the creek up which they have been making their way. Construction operations on a Canadian railway were the cause. Above are some thirty fish engaged in spawning in gravelly shallows. Salmon eggs must develop in cool water and this they get in the upper waters.

LAKE salmon are found in Canada, in the State of Maine, and in Norway. These have the same habits as those which live mostly in salt water. They ascend rivers to spawn, evidently being aware, as the others are, that they must lay their eggs on the gravelly bed of a shallow river. This seems to point to the probability that the salmon was originally a river fish which somehow or other acquired the habit of going down to a large body of water, either salt or fresh, to recuperate after the exhaustion of spawning.

Yet here we are met with the difficulty of explaining why the salmon does not feed in fresh water (unless it is an inhabitant of a vast lake). Its practice of living for a long time, while it is in a river, on what it has stored up during a period of roaming in more ample waters, suggests that it must originally have been a sea fish. But if we accept that view we have to supply reasons for (*a*) its invariable custom of ascending a river in order to spawn; and (*b*) the fact that its eggs will not develop in sea-water.

Thus, whatever hypothesis we are disposed to adopt, we find ourselves still wandering in perplexity. No theory seems to fit all the circumstances. The problem of the salmon, a mystery over which naturalists have argued for years, remains unsolved.

"RUN" OF SALMON MAKING UP-STREAM IN AN ALASKAN RIVER

Where food is plentiful there the fish are plentiful, and a good rule for judging the possible abundance of salmon is "the larger the river the more and bigger the fish"—other things being equal. In the rivers of North America the Pacific salmon teem. A good idea of the amazing number which appear in these streams can be had from a study of this photograph. They are resting in a pool below the falls preparatory to continuing their strenuous way to the upper reaches where their exhausting and prodigious journey will find its end.

IN SCOTLAND OR ALASKA THE SALMON'S URGE UP-STREAM IS ALL POWERFUL

Where in the British Isles one may see a single salmon leaping, in a North American river which flows to the Pacific one may count a hundred. Indeed the numbers are so great and the urge, which drives this furiously struggling mass towards its destiny, so strong that hundreds get stranded in shallows and upon the banks where the wild animals snap them up. Below is a Scotch salmon making its leap, and above a fall at the outlet of Lake Brooks, Alaska, where it is estimated that twelve hundred salmon make the leap in an hour.

Neville Kingston

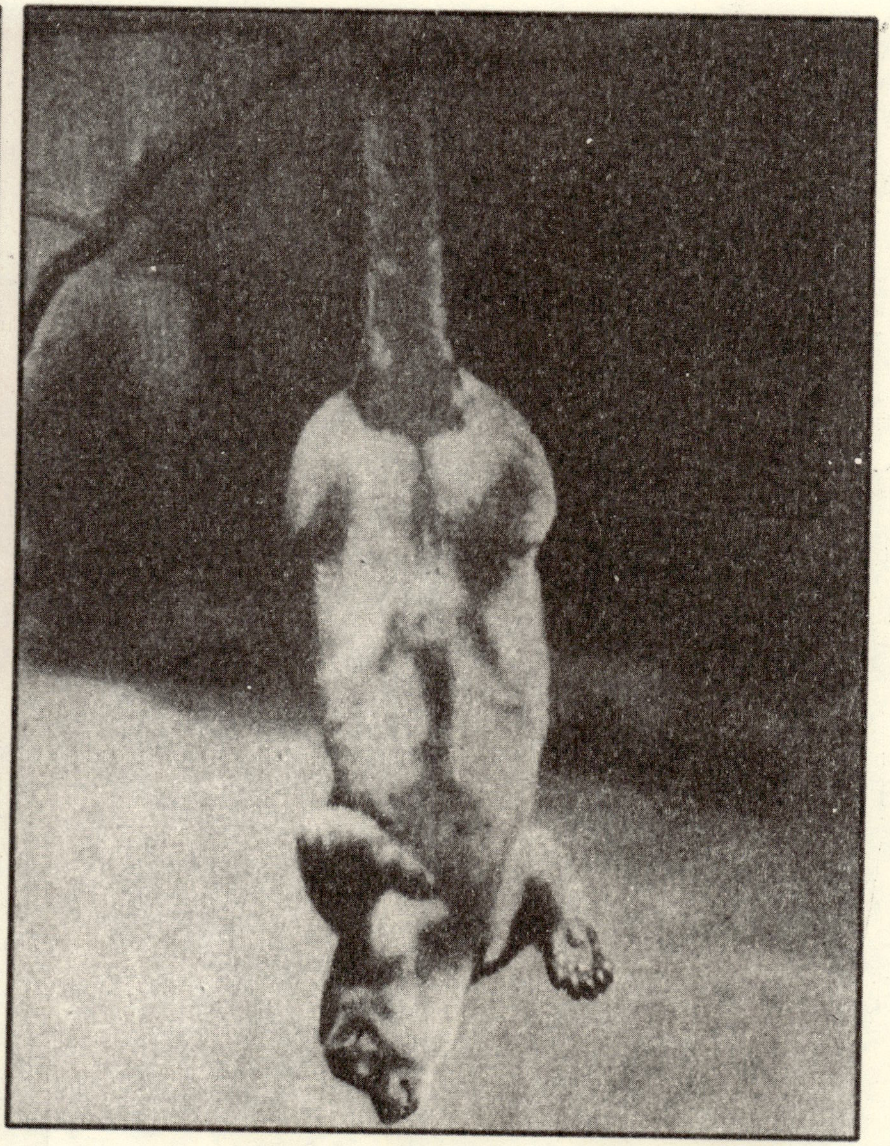

W S. Berridge

ANIMALS THAT HANG THEMSELVES UP ON THEIR TAILS: OPOSSUM AND KINKAJOU

Opossums occur in America only, though from fossil remains it is evident that their distribution was almost world-wide in other ages. Nearly all the various kinds possess long prehensile tails which serve them as an extra limb in their arboreal life. Notice that the specimen here (left) is unconcernedly supporting its whole weight with its tail as it hangs from its keeper's finger. The kinkajou is also peculiar to the New World, and is confined to Central and tropical South America. We see it in a typical attitude, hanging by its tail from a branch. The animal is about the size of a domestic cat, and is covered with a soft, yellowish fur. In Australia the name opossum is given to the phalanger.

Chapter XLIX

Strange Tails and their Many Uses

By Frances Pitt

Author of "Wild Creatures of Garden and Hedgerow"

MANY and strange are the tails of the animal world, varying from tails big and useful, such as that of the kangaroo, tails wondrously beautiful, such as those of some of the birds of paradise, to little insignificant tails like those of the deer and rabbits, which for all their insignificance are of importance, their owners using them as danger signals. Then there are tails which are weapons of offence, such as the powerful one of the crocodile, and the armed one of the sting ray; tails that are used to give warning, the rattle of the rattlesnake being a good example; tails with which the owners balance themselves; tails that are used as rudders; and last but not least the bird's tail as used in flight, when it becomes both an elevating plane, a brake and a rudder.

It is impossible to exaggerate the importance of the tail in the animal world, or the myriad uses to which this appendage is put. It is at no time more conspicuously useful than when it becomes a fifth hand, as in the prehensile tailed monkeys, in which it is as sensitive as a tendril, being used to wind round the branches and anchor its owner, while he uses his paws for one purpose and another.

It is curious to meet the prehensile tail again in a creature so far removed from the Primates as one of the rodents, yet the tiny European harvest mouse, a wee animal not so big as your little finger, has a wonderfully sensitive tail, which it uses to good effect when indulging in acrobatic feats among the corn. I have seen this tiny sandy-coloured mouse sitting on a swaying ear of wheat, its tail around the corn head, happily washing its face.

In the kangaroos and their allies the tail becomes a jumping pole rather than a fifth leg, its strength and springiness enabling the animal to take enormous bounds. There is a somewhat analogous development of the tail among those little desert animals the jerboas, which have a long tail and use it to take what, in consideration of their size, are very long hops.

Both the jerboa and the kangaroo use their well-developed tails as supports, taking their ease by resting upon them as we do upon a shooting stick, and certain birds use their feather tails in the same manner. I am alluding to the woodpeckers, tree creepers and their relatives. In these species, the tail feathers, though comparatively short, are very stiff and strong, and do not "give" when the bird presses its tail against the bark of a tree and rests its weight upon them.

With a few exceptions tails are a great feature in the bird world, being often marvellously decorative as well as useful. Sometimes they are more beautiful than useful. The peacock's train is, of course, the best known example; that great feather fan, with its array of gleaming eyes, which he erects in an iridescent halo about him, and sets a-quiver until every eye seems alive, is indeed a marvel. To be accurate the peacock's train is *not* a tail. The true tail consists of plain grey, rather stiff feathers, behind the ones we admire so much, which latter are really tail coverts, but so developed and elongated as to have lost all likeness to the uninteresting feathers that serve that purpose in most birds. But for practical purposes we may call the peacock's train a tail, and a marvellous one at that.

Why has the peacock got such a wonderful tail? The generally accepted theory is that it is to please his mate, and that the peahen always chooses the most beautiful cock; hence selection by the female has brought about the handsome

W. S. Berridge

RING-TAILED LEMUR FROM MADAGASCAR

Lemur tails are never prehensile, but the ring-tailed lemurs have very handsome tails which serve to balance them among the boughs in which they live. They are nocturnal, and the name lemur, which in Latin means a ghost, is an allusion to their stealthy ways.

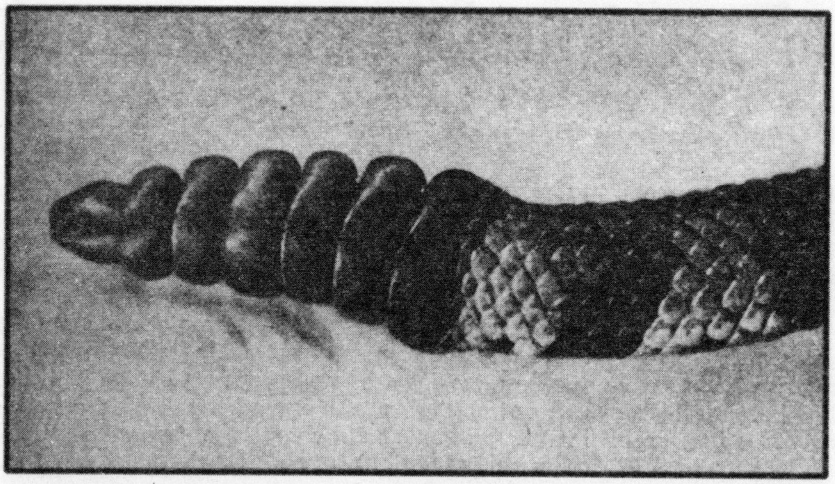

F. W. Bond

W. S. Berridge

WARNING RATTLE OF PORCUPINE AND SNAKE

To warn all who may approach near enough to suggest attack, the porcupine can rattle the quills in its tail (bottom). The rattlesnake is famous for the warning apparatus on its tail. The snake does not want to waste its precious poison to defend itself if the rattle will do as well. The rattle itself consists of a number of horny cups, loosely but securely attached to the tail.

appearance of the male. In any case, it is unquestionably a rule of Nature that if a cock bird has fine feathers, he must let his lady see them, and this especially applies to fine tails. Many cock birds spread their tails fan-wise when displaying before the female; the turkey and black cock or black grouse are examples.

Some of these decorative bird tails are lovely as regards shape, but others owe their beauty to colour alone. The well-known African grey parrot has an ordinary tail as regards length, but it is of a beautiful rosy hue. The lyre bird gets decorative effect by the peculiar development of its tail feathers, as is the case with some of the birds of paradise, and others, but these latter often combine colour and form with most striking results.

One of the strangest of tails is that of the Japanese long-tailed cock, wherein the curved feathers, seen in the tails of the cocks of our poultry runs, grow many feet in length. This long-tailed fowl is a freak, or mutation, which has arisen under domestication, and we may surmise that it is due to the loss of some factor regulating feather growth in normal birds.

Reverting to useful tails, one has only to watch a bird in flight to realize how essential the tail is to it, enabling that bird to steer and turn, descend and rise again, check itself, and alight gently when it wishes to come down. I watched a kestrel hanging in the wind, maintaining its position on quivering wings, the while it scanned the ground beneath for mice, and I noted particularly the part played by its tail, widespread and a-quiver all the time, the bird using it as much, if not more, than its wings.

But important as the tail is to the bird, it is of even greater utility to the mammal, the fish, and other vertebrates. They put it to such an extraordinary diversity of uses. As a striking example, take the fat-tailed sheep kept by the natives in some parts of Africa, which, when it has plenty to eat, not only gets plump about the body, but lays up quantities of fat in the tissues of the tail, where it is retained as a useful store of nutriment when food is scarce and times are bad.

Perhaps no mammalian tail is more truly useful than the fly whisk of the horse and of the ox. Watch cattle and horses on a summer day and note that their tails are in incessant motion, ever swinging to and fro, whisking here and there, and keeping the worrying hordes of insects from their owners' flanks. A few moments' observation of horses and cattle when turned out in the fields will convince any one that their tails are not only most valuable appendages but possessions they can ill afford to part with, and that the docking of horses is a cruel fashion, especially in countries where flies carry horse diseases, and the docked horse is entirely at the mercy of his winged foes. Now the thick-skinned animals, such as the

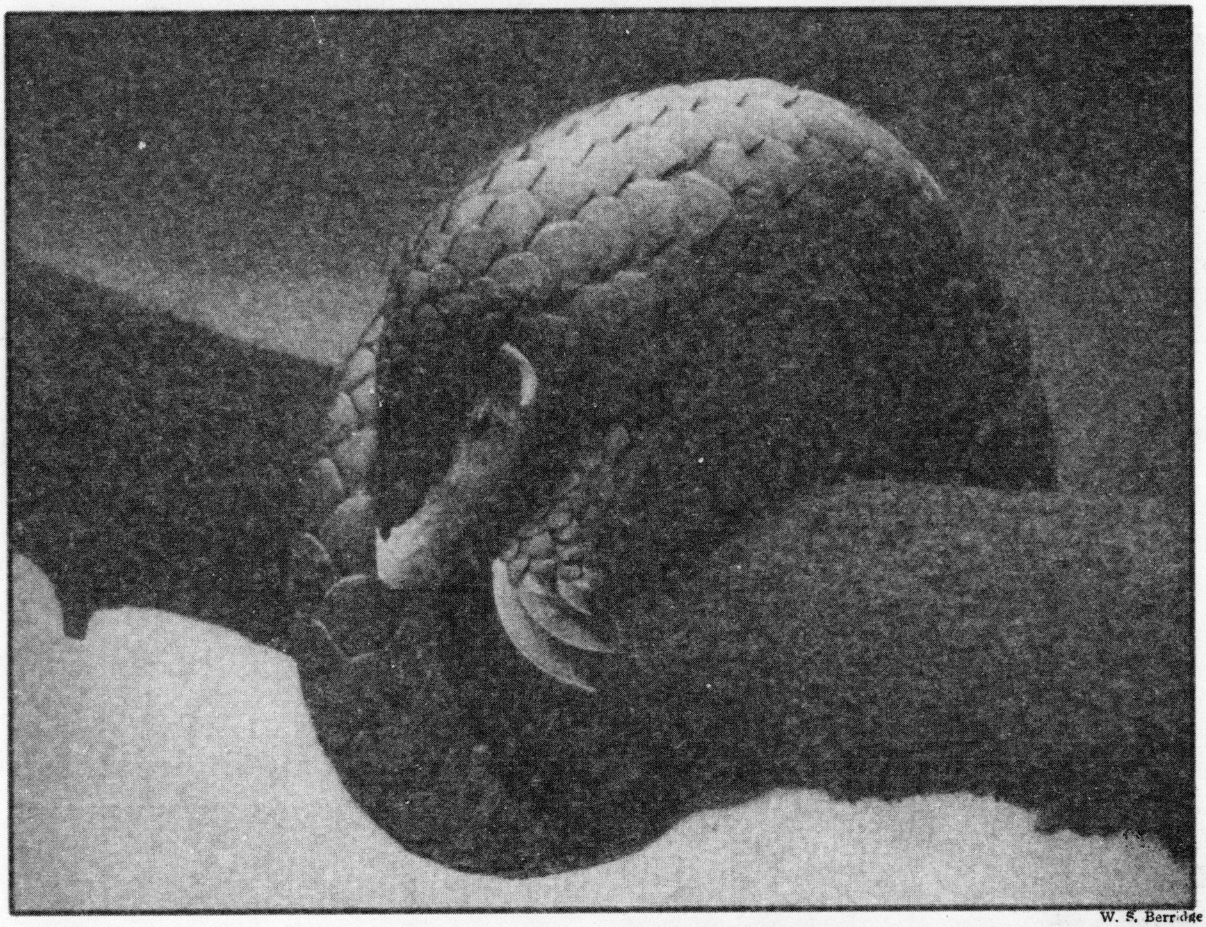

W. S. Berridge

elephant and rhinoceros, do not suffer so much from the worrying attentions of flies, and so in their case the defensive fly whisk is reduced almost to vanishing point. It is the same with the familiar pig. It has a good thick hide and flies are no menace, so its tail is correspondingly reduced.

THE fashion that calls for the removal of a terrier's tail is quite as silly as that which leads to a horse being deprived of its fly whisk. It is true that the tail is not so essential to the dog as the horse, but it is extremely useful none the less, being a great help in balancing and turning quickly, to say nothing of its function as a danger signal in emotional outbreaks. The angry dog who advances growling with his bristles erect and tail up lets his foe know how seriously annoyed he is, and it is that " flag " which helps to convey the information and, incidentally, intimidate the approaching enemy.

It is the same in the case of the wolf, and the full brush of the fox is a particularly good rudder, the word " rudder " signifying here that it helps the animal to turn ; in the case of the otter and certain other aquatic animals, the tail helps tremendously as a steering instrument. But for its long, thick, strong " pole " the otter would not be able to turn under water as it does. As it is, it turns, twists, and doubles in its own length, much like a fish.

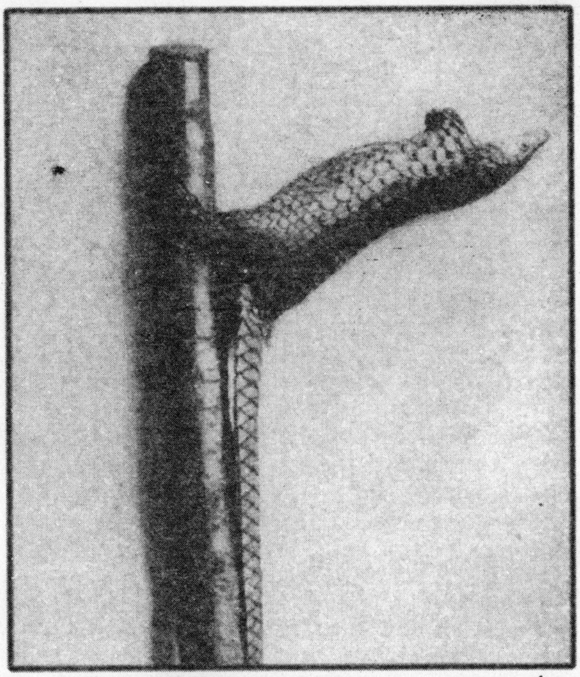

E. J. Manly

HOW PANGOLINS USE THEIR TAILS

In this extraordinary posture the African pangolin (bottom) takes its ease, and it can be seen how the very long tail makes this possible. The characteristic pose and use of the tail of the Chinese pangolin (top) is, however, quite different.

Neville Kingston

KING CRAB, DOG, AND ALLIGATOR, AND THE TAILS THEY HAVE

The king crab (bottom) puts its tail to a very practical, not to say a vital, use; for, while it is almost invulnerable when the right way up owing to its formidable shell, when turned over it is at the mercy of the first enemy. Therefore the crab uses its steel-strong tail as a lever by means of which it can turn itself over. Above is a record of a strange and amusing meeting that took place in Los Angeles some time ago between a dog and a baby alligator. This provided a real contrast in tails.

W. S. B[illegible]ridge

GAVIAL AND IGUANA WHOSE TAILS ARE WEAPONS

Besides its long, slender snout the gavial (bottom) has another and better weapon of defence in its tail. This is thick, heavy and capable of extraordinary vigour, and, in addition, is armed throughout its length with dangerous-looking spikes. This long serrated edge, switched rapidly to and fro, is something from which every wise animal beats a hasty retreat. But the gavial, unlike the rest of the crocodile family, rarely attacks land animals, but prefers fish. The tuberculated iguana (top) has a tail like a strong whip.

... S. Berridge

TAILS USEFUL, USELESS, AND ORNAMENTAL IN THE ANIMAL WORLD

The great islands of Sumatra and Borneo and the Malay Peninsula are the homes of the pig-tailed monkey (bottom left), which has discarded altogether the use of a tail for gripping or prehensile purposes. The famous fat-tailed sheep of Africa (bottom right) uses its tail for economic purposes. When there is plenty of food about the sheep lays up a store of fat in its tail. There is in Africa also a mouse (top left) which does the same thing. By the winter the mouse has covered its whole body and its tail with a thick layer of fat to last it till the spring. The tail of the squirrel (top right) is as graceful to watch as it is useful in keeping balance during the little animal's caperings up and down the tree-trunks.

W. S. Berridge

KING BIRD OF PARADISE AND THE MOTMOT THAT DECORATES ITS TAIL

The king bird of paradise (left) is of small size and wonderful colouring, in which emerald green contrasts with brilliant scarlet. The formation of the tail feathers is extraordinary, the quills being bare almost to the tips, where they coil into a beautifully vaned spiral. The racket-tailed motmot (right) is unique among the birds, for it deliberately alters the appearance of its tail, presumably for decorative purposes. The middle pair of tail feathers are longer than the rest, and the bird nibbles away at them until the quills are quite bare save for a tuft at the ends. The motmots are found in the New World between Mexico and Paraguay. This specimen is from the island of Trinidad.

W. S. Berridge

BARE AND HAIRY TAILS OF BEAVER AND ANTEATER

In the beaver (bottom) the tail is particularly conspicuous in that it is flattened laterally and quite bare, whereas the rest of the animal is covered with thick fur. The tail acts as a rudder in swimming. The anteaters all have useful tails, and the great anteater (top) uses its long and fan-like tail for warmth when asleep.

keel of silvery hairs along its under-surface, so that it forms the neatest and most efficient of little rudders. Quite a different type of rudder is the broad, flattened tail of the beaver, but apparently this serves its purpose just as well, for the beaver is as expert a swimmer as any of the creatures that habitually spend their time in and out of the water.

Advertising tails, such as the dog's, are not uncommon in Nature. That of the rattlesnake is a good example of the tail used for warning purposes. The snake is a dangerous creature, but there is no advantage in the use of its poison when biting some animal it cannot eat. The reptile carries, however, a rattle of horny plates on the end of its tail, and when any person or beast comes near it vibrates this implement, which acts as a warning, letting the world know of the snake's presence and, which is more, that it will be as well to let it alone.

The plume-like tail of the skunk is also a warning one, helping, in conjunction with its owner's conspicuous coloration, to let the world know the animal is coming. Many animals, such as the cat, when angry and frightened, and therefore in a desperate mood, fluff their tails out to double the

There is another aquatic creature in which the tail is especially adapted to serve as a rudder, namely, that quaint little mammal the water shrew This smart black and white shrew, which haunts streams and ditches, has a tail about two inches long, with a

E.N.A

normal size. This serves the twofold purpose of letting the foe know they really are ready for anything, and bluffing him into thinking they are bigger and more powerful than they are in fact.

In the case of cats, from the domestic puss up to the lordly tiger, the tail affords a valuable clue to the creature's state of mind. The bottle-brush tail, just referred to, indicates anger mixed with fear, but the twitching tail tip of a cat that has heard a mouse squeak in its hole betokens tense excitement. A sideways movement of her tail also indicates annoyance, as when a kitten persists in teasing its mother, and her tail begins to twitch ere she deals her offspring a reproving smack.

Old writers on natural history invariably wrote of the lion as " lashing itself into a fury " with its tail. What they really meant was that when excited its tail was as liable to twitch as is that of a cat.

W. S. Berridge

PEACOCK'S REAL TAIL AND A LONG-TAILED COCKEREL

In the lower photograph we see the real tail of the peacock supporting the great fan when it is expanded. This fan is actually formed of the tail coverts enormously enlarged for display purposes. For practical purposes the train is regarded as part of the tail. Above is a Japanese cock with an abnormally long tail.

It is strange, yet nevertheless a fact, that the dog and its kindred also express emotion by means of their tail, but use the same gesture to signify pleasure that the cat uses to exhibit annoyance. A dog, as we all know, wags its tail when pleased and holds it stiff when annoyed, just the contrary to what the cat does. Reverting to tails that are of undoubted use to their owners, the lovely plume-like tails of the different squirrels are for balancing purposes. Take the European red squirrel as it dashes along its

Neville Kingston

ALBINO PEACOCK UNFOLDS ITS WONDROUS "TAIL" FOR ADMIRATION

As an example of a tail in the animal world that has been evolved for ornament instead of use, the peacock's is as remarkable as it is pre-eminent in beauty. This particular bird is one of the rather rare albino peacocks. The brilliant colours of the ordinary peacock are due, not to pigment in the feathers, but to prismatic formations in the feathers which break up the light into the colours we see. The albino, for some reason, lacks this feather structure, and so appears white. Although of so great a size when fully expanded, the tail folds up compactly, and when the bird is walking, trails out behind in true pheasant fashion, for the peacock is related to the pheasant. But when the bird is flying the long feathers hang down, and seem rather to impede flight.

Neville Kingston

HANDSOME TAIL OF A ZOO LEMUR

All the lemurs are expert climbers of trees and all are characterised by an immobile face as opposed to the highly expressive faces of the monkeys, to whom they are related. While some have long handsome tails, others are quite without them.

overhead highway, racing along one branch, taking a flying leap to the next tree, to land upon the outer twigs, and run on, now down a tree trunk, up another and anon leaping from bough to bough. It balances with perfect ease on the swaying branches, never hesitating or losing its head. That beautiful tail is better than any balancing pole, and enables its owner to indulge in acrobatic tricks to its heart's content. It is noteworthy that the martens, creatures allied to the otters, polecats, and ferrets, are great climbers, and to aid them in their tree-top excursions they sport a tail as lovely as that of the squirrel.

To jump from mammals to reptiles, most of the lizards have long and conspicuous tails, in some instances adorned with prickles and spines, but in the majority of cases they do not seem to put them to any particular use, though there are exceptions. Some of these exceptions are lizards that use their tails as a means of escape from danger. They break them off, and leave a wriggling tail to engage the enemy, while the lizard itself glides away into safety. The so-called glass snake (really a legless lizard) of Southern Europe is a case in point. When startled it discards its tail, a sudden contraction of the muscles bringing about the amputation. The thrown-off member lies wriggling on the ground, muscular action persisting for some time, even up to an hour, while its owner glides away to grow a new tail in peace and security. The common blindworm, another legless lizard, has the same capacity.

The most formidable of reptilian tails are those belonging to the crocodiles and alligators, for they are powerful weapons of offence, the great reptiles using them to deal their enemies a blow that sweeps them off their feet and into the river, after which the victims are not likely to take much interest in tails of any description.

So far we have dealt with what may be termed important tails. Among these must also be classed the all-important tails of fish, as important to them in the water as a bird's tail is to it in the air; and

Neville Kingston

ARMOURED TAIL OF THE PEBA ARMADILLO

Not only does the armadillo guard his body with very hard, bony plates, but also the tail as well, and the upper part of that tail almost resembles a piece of well armoured hose in the method of its construction.

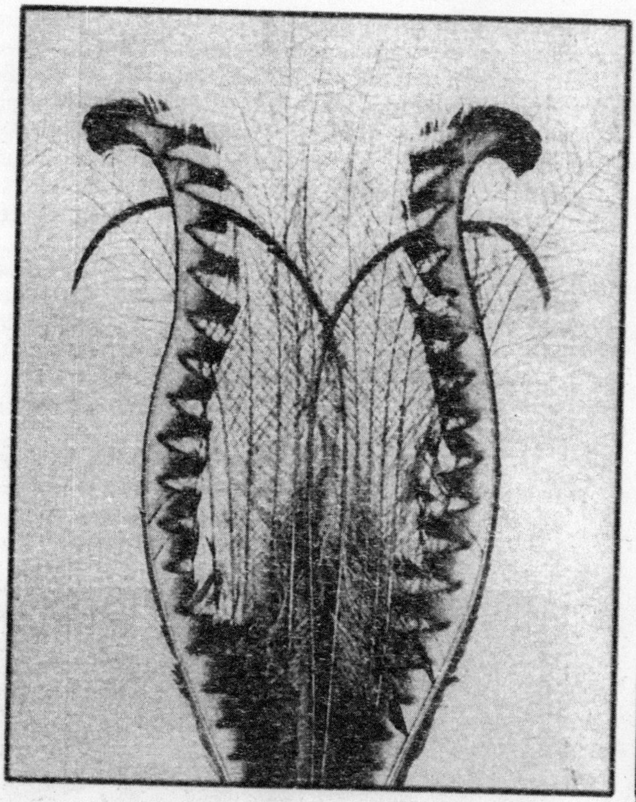

caudal appendage, leaving only a ridiculous bit of a tail that makes but a shabby contrast to the handsome tails of other cats. As long tails seem to be advantageous to the majority of the carnivora, it may be that the diminutive tail of the lynx is an accident of evolution ; some cause ot which we have no idea has brought about the reduction of the tail, and this big cat has gone on prospering in spite of the absence of a tail, not because of it.

In some cases, however, the absence of a tail is clearly an advantage, those strange water birds the grebes and divers being good examples. These birds, most expert of aquatic species, are marvellously specialised for life in the water. Their legs are so near the extremity of the body as to be perfect propellers (though no good for walking, the divers in particular being as helpless on land as a fish), but these propellers could not do their work as they do if there were a long, feathery tail in the way.

the curious tail of that queer little thing the sea-horse, which is at once its support and its anchor, enabling it to retain its place among the swaying seaweeds. But what of tails that are not obviously important to their owners ?

SOME of these tails are not quite so unimportant as they look. The rabbit is a good example, for its little white button of a tail is not at all startling ; yet when a rabbit flees for home, racing across the meadow with tail bobbing on high, that white button does catch the eye, and there is good reason to believe that it catches the eyes of other rabbits as well, thus acting as a danger signal. Certainly when a rabbit wishes to slip away unviewed by friend or foe, it holds its tail down, so that only the dark upper part is visible, and there is nothing to draw attention to the owner. The deer's white tail serves a similar purpose, for if alarmed by anything it dashes off with its short white tail erect, when the patch of white hair on the rump is exposed, the whole forming a white star that cries "Danger!" to the rest of the deer as emphatically as if the word were shouted aloud.

But what of the tails which not only look unimportant, but really are not of any special utility to the animal ? The mole's little stumpy appendage is undoubtedly superfluous, for what good is a tail to a creature that spends its life in a narrow tunnel ? None whatever but that tail is already reduced to the point when it is not in the way. Certain cats, to wit the lynx family, have also bobbed their

FEATHERED MARVEL OF THE LYRE BIRD

What virtue the lyre bird has expended on its tail it has lost in its wings, for it is a poor flyer. The resemblance of the two outer feathers to the shape of the primitive form of harp is remarkable. The lower illustration is from a drawing.

W. S. Berridge

TREE PORCUPINE AND OPOSSUM WHOSE TAILS MAKE FIFTH LIMBS

In the forests of tropical South America the tree porcupine is common. It possesses a prehensile tail to help it in its life up in the trees, and thus, if necessary, it can employ all its legs for other purposes, secure in its grip with its "fifth limb." Unlike the porcupine of the Old World, these American tree porcupines are active during the day. Above is an opossum with its young clinging to its back. With all this extra weight the clinging tail, coiled like a tendril round the branch, is of great importance.

Neville Kingston

TAILS OF THE GAMBIA GIANT RAT AND THE KINKAJOU

Rats put their tails to a unique use when, for the purpose of carrying an egg too large to be held in the jaws, one animal will lie on its back while others pull it along by its tail. In this way the rat makes itself into a kind of trolley. The Gambia giant rat (bottom) has a tail in keeping with its immense size. It is restricted to one part of Africa: the Gambia territory. The tail of the kinkajou (top) is the sturdiest part of the animal, and is about equal in length to the head and body.

M. H. Crawford

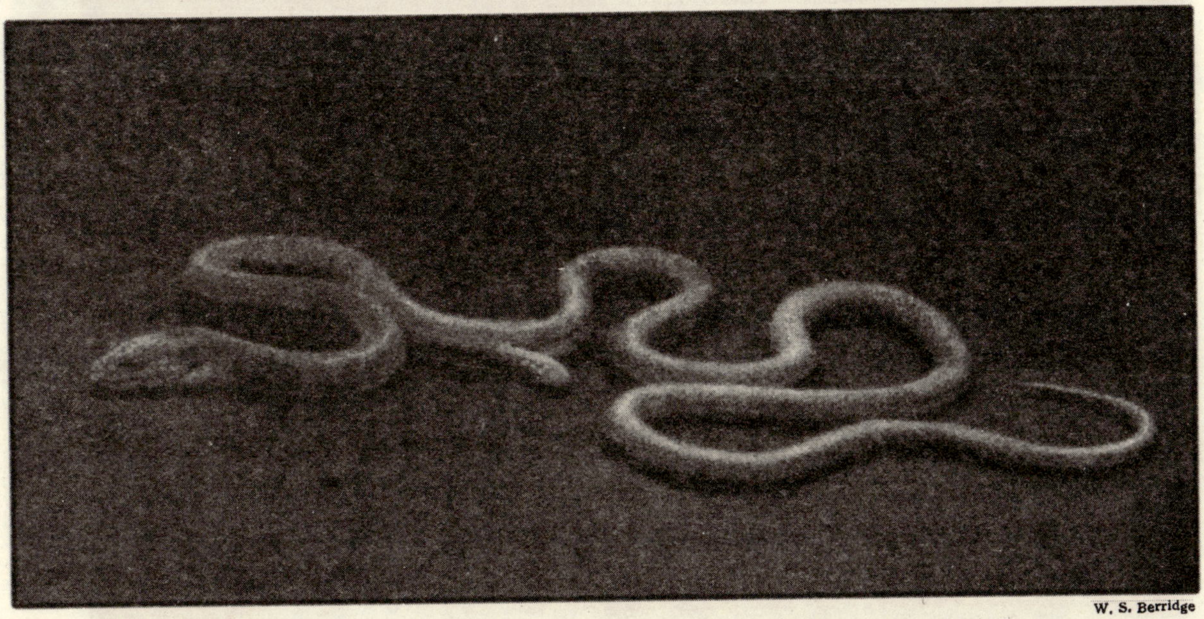

W. S. Berridge

HOW BODY MERGES INTO TAIL IN THE GREEN AND SCALE-FOOT LIZARDS

The body of the green lizard of the Channel Islands (top) merges insensibly into its tail so that, for the total length of the creature its fore and hind limbs seem to be set very far forward. In the scale-foot lizards of Australia and Papua the tail is twice as long as the head and body together (bottom). In this species it is even harder to see where body ends and tail begins, for the hind limbs are so rudimentary as to form mere scaly flaps hardly suggesting legs at all.

The very fact that there are bobbed-tailed birds and beasts, and animals without any external vestige of a tail, including many of the apes, does but emphasise the prevalence of the tail throughout animal life, and draws attention to its widespread importance. The uses to which the tail has been converted, its extraordinary developments, have been but hinted at in this article. It would take a volume, or rather many volumes, to tell of all the tails of the animal world, to say nothing of the tails of past ages, when the prehistoric monsters walked the globe dragging their great scaly appendages behind them.

REMARKABLE WARRIOR AND PARASOL ANTS THAT LIVE IN BRITISH GUIANA

South America is the home of some of the most formidable ants in the world. The warrior ants (left) go about in battalions a hundred thousand strong, carrying their eggs and young ones with them. As they go their presence is often announced by the noise of the ant thrushes, birds which follow the army for the sake of the pickings. Insects form the bulk of the warriors' food, and if an army should visit human dwellings it will make a complete clearance of all vermin, spiders, and so on, without harming human food stuffs at all. The parasol or leaf-cutting ants (right) have a nest below the ground to which they carry sections of leaves. These are laid down to form a kind of bed upon which a special fungus is grown—an instance of ant "agriculture."

Chapter L

The Amazing Life of an Ant City

By C. K. Ogden

Translator of Forel's "The Social World of the Ants"

NOT very long ago a picture appeared in the papers of a strange and complicated invention: a new kind of automatic machine. Hitherto man's inventions have been almost exclusively confined to extensions of his senses, like the telescope, or extensions of his limbs, such as engines and aeroplanes. They have enabled him either to perceive more or to do more; to accomplish, in fact, what he would if he had been endowed with better eyesight, or with more or stronger arms and faster or longer legs. But all have been dependent on the human brain; they did not, like the human organism, stop, reflect, and take some action suitable to changing conditions.

A few years ago, however, the age of Robots dawned. The possibility of doing mechanically what has hitherto been done only by a brain began to exercise the imagination of inventors; and this new device, a sort of chemical Robot for softening water, goes far beyond anything yet achieved. It can make the most elaborate adaptations, and the inventor, Dr. Hatfield, has written a book on the future of mechanical man which recalls the old controversy about the ants.

Have they actually become mechanical Robots and progressed beyond us, so that their present condition indicates a stage which we shall inevitably reach when we have efficiently satisfied all our needs; or have they merely evolved a form of society which we can avoid if we take warning in time? Certain it is that more than a hundred million years before man appeared on the earth the ants, after more than a hundred million years of experiment, had perfected the organization of their social life, had decided in favour of the "specialisation" on the verge of which we are hesitating to-day, and have remained in the same condition throughout historical time.

Our understanding of the wonders of insect life has made great advances of late. The expository gifts of Fabre, the mystical appeal of Maeterlinck, the social wisdom of Wheeler, have all played their part in attracting attention to the crawling, creeping and buzzing universe. But the greatest single influence has undoubtedly been that of Auguste Forel. Forel began his ant studies at the age of five, and the cause of his early interest makes a charming story, worthy even of Victorian England. He tells us how, in a little village on the shores of Lake Geneva, his mother would sit at the piano, playing Beethoven's sonatas, while he, outside on the terrace steps, was watching the ceaseless turmoil of black, red, and yellow ants, cooperating, fighting, transporting. Why did these peaceful and industrious creatures sometimes fight so savagely? That was his first question, and the problem of war and peace remains his chief concern to-day, as it is the chief concern of Geneva, near which he still dwells, the fierce enemy of alcohol in the midst of the vineyards of Yvorne, the ardent apostle of peace in the centre of a war-weary continent.

He began collecting insects alive, and then, since that was regarded as cruel, dead ones. But the mystery of ant enmities grew deeper, till at the age of eleven his grandmother gave him a book by the famous naturalist, Huber. "There," she said, "I will make you a present of this book, written by my old flame Huber. He was not cruel, like you, for he scolded me when I killed the ants that were eating my jam. I have never been able to get through his book. It isn't my style."

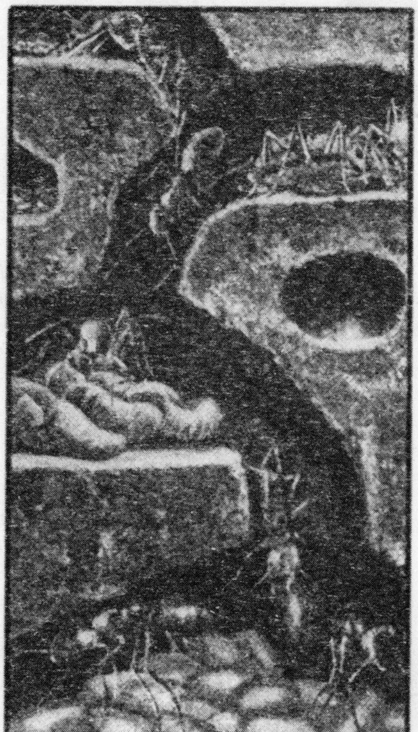

SECTION OF AN ANT'S NEST

This illustration from Forel's book shows the complicated gallery system of a nest with its highways and branching byways, with eggs deposited and being attended by the "nurses."

The child found that he had already made discoveries about robber ants which had escaped Huber. But the mysteries were revealed, and he vowed he would devote the rest of his life to the science of entomology; and thus the labours of seventy-five years have gone to make his two wonderful volumes, "The Social World of the Ants." For, in spite of all his other preoccupations, his studies of the insane, his investigations of the brain, and the researches embodied in his most popular work, "The Sexual Question," the ants have remained his dominating interest; and to-day, though paralysed and unable to afford a secretary, he is besieged by requests from all over the world for information which he alone could, yet is unable to, give.

Fortunately, his masterpiece is now available for future

ANT USING POISON SQUIRT

Some of the ants, instead of being armed with a sting, have a poison apparatus at the hinder end of their bodies through which they can squirt formic acid over an enemy, often causing death. This illustration is from Forel's "The Social World of the Ants" (Putnam).

inquirers, and, apart from its value as an introduction to the sympathetic and inspiring personality of the author, it provides the best guide to the amazing life of the ant city in English. And we need a guide not only in order to avoid misinterpreting what we see, as nearly everything about the ants has usually been misinterpreted, but in order to see anything at all. For the ant nest is one of the most difficult things in the world to study under natural conditions, and only the most skilled observers can profit by the opportunities of the artificial constructions in which ants are usually kept. The rest we piece together, often by inference, from discoveries all over the world during the past wonderful century of science.

SUPPOSE that, like Gulliver, we could live for a while as minute denizens of an ant city, what would be our most unexpected impression? In the first place, although their work is often carried on in the midst of filth, ants are fastidiously clean both in their persons and as regards the nest, and all refuse is at once deposited in a special dump or midden outside. Perhaps, therefore, we should be most surprised at the amount of time spent by the ant on her toilet; sometimes, cat-like, attending to the face, sometimes licking and polishing either her own shining armour (chitin) or that of her companions. But more probably the methods by which food in various stages of digestion circulates through the community would fill us with astonishment, if not with disgust.

Not only do ants derive intense satisfaction from the liquid exuded by their offspring, but in their own crops or "social stomachs" they carry a variety of viands ready for regurgitation to other ants or to guests. These latter are so numerous and ingenious that it is surprising an ant ever has anything left for herself. The guest, perched it may be on the back of her head, has only to tickle the host judiciously, and instead of purring, the latter at once most obligingly disgorges a meal.

Yet all the while other small creatures are being reared in stables attached to the nest. These are the ant-cattle, kept to suck plant juices, to which the jaws of the ant, as a biting apparatus, have no direct access; and they are tended with the same care as is bestowed on mushroom-growing or harvesting by species which keep gardens or fill their granaries against an evil day. One peculiar method of storing food is that by which "nurses" swollen to enormous size, are suspended like bottles from the ceiling of the nest, and tapped, as occasion demands, for honey.

It is chiefly for food, of course, that the ceaseless warfare of the ants is waged, though their pugnacity is closely related to other activities, which the gentler entomologists deplore. Some kinds are slavers on a large scale, and their slave-raids are as bold and efficient as the Gold Coast ever knew. It has been maintained that the slaves of the ants should more properly be regarded as auxiliaries, since they are quite unconscious of their lot, and have never experienced any happier state. But as Forel points out, the same was true of many children born to negroes in America, and none the less slaves. Young ants are captured and tamed to live in enemy nests, whose odour they then acquire, proving that instincts are capable of considerable modification, at any rate in some species; though the stupidity of the harvesting ants, whose foresight excited the enthusiasm of Solomon, and their failure to adapt themselves to combined work, have impressed many keen and interested observers.

It was long supposed that Solomon had allowed his moral fancy to run riot; for ants in northern countries, where most scientists carried out their researches previous to 1870, go to sleep in the winter, and it was supposed that harvest granaries were everywhere out of the question. But it is now known that Solomon was correct, and it is for the dry, hot season that they "prepare their meat in the summer."

Groceries, then, are no less prominent a feature of ant life than of our own, and it is probably to differences in diet, whether as regards time or quantity, that we must attribute those differences in form and sex on which ant-specialism depends. Apart from the act of fertilisation, however, the male ant plays a very small part in the life of the nest. The workers are all neuter females, whether they function as soldiers or in some civil capacity; but the fertile female, or queen, will retain the male element in a special receptacle for years, using it as she requires.

THE actual nuptials, the marriage flights, and the swarms which sometimes darken the August sky, have not awakened the enthusiasm of poets like the pursuit of the virgin queen by her admirers among the bees. Forel quotes Maeterlinck's account of the aerial scene, as the queen bee rises through the blue air of the morning. Drunk with her wings she seeks the heights:

"To some lonely region must she soar unhaunted by birds that might profane the mystery. Still upward she climbs, and now the ill-matched crowd beneath her dwindles and scatters. The weak, the infirm, the aged, the unwelcome, the starveling brood of sluggish or impoverished cities, all renounce the pursuit and disappear in the void. All that remains is a small and tireless group hung in infinite opal. She exacts of her wings one supreme effort, and lo! the elect of the incomprehensible forces reaches her side, seizes her, conquers her; and borne aloft by their two-fold impetus, the ascending spiral of their intertwined flight spins for one second in the hostile delirium of love."

THE ants, too, perform their nuptials in the air; but as they are polyandrous and not monogamous like those of the queen bee, they have not yet inspired their poet. Entomologists, with the notable exception of Miss Adèle Fielde, whose brilliant researches were

WAR BETWEEN RIVALS OF THE SAME SPECIES

Ants fight furiously not only with other species, but with rival colonies ot their own kind. Here is a fight in full swing between two armies of *Formica pratensis*. Separate duels are going on over stones, up the tall grass stems, and in all sorts of attitudes. This drawing comes from "The Social World of the Ants," by Forel (Putnam).

FIERCE BATTLE BETWEEN GIANTS AND DWARFS OF THE ANT WORLD

Wars in the ant world are caused by territorial infringement. One colony will covet the part of a field used by another colony or perhaps a tree which has a supply of the little aphides which supply the ants with a kind of nectar. Above is an illustration from Forel's "The Social World of the Ants," depicting a strange fight between giant and dwarf ants. The dwarfs are trying to overwhelm their adversaries by crawling up their legs and antennæ, seeking vital spots, while the giants are crunching the little foes with their powerful jaws.

responsible for most of what we know about the sense of smell in ants, are mostly males, and regard polyandry as prosaic. Maeterlinck, however, has lately given us a graphic picture of the swarming of the white ants or termites, the hereditary enemies of the ants; and the tragedy of the male ant, whose fate it is to crawl about till death overtakes him after his descent from those dizzy heights, while the queen carries on the life of the race and founds a new city, is no less worthy of a poet's pen.

THOUGH many of them are now vegetarian, ants are, for the most part, carnivorous, and a difference of smell is all that is required to provoke a fight. Their battles will go on for days, the vanquished being torn in pieces, their stores seized, their brood devoured. The courage and pertinacity of victors and vanquished alike have been admired by the bellicose throughout the ages; their stings, their poison squirts, the mandibles with which they bite, their agility, and their rescue work are proverbial. Nor must we forget their ceaseless warfare with nature and with other creatures, particularly the ant-lions and scaly ant-eaters. Indeed, Forel has found several species of ants, hitherto unknown, in the stomachs of their enemies. One of these (as one might call a baby found alive in a whale "Jonah") he christened "esta," which means "eaten"; and by that name it will be known to science probably as long as our present system of nomenclature lasts.

It is a relief to think that though ants "can certainly feel pain," their suffering must be infinitely less than ours; for they will greedily eat honey a few moments after their abdomens have been severed. How they feel pain—with what nerves—we do not know. Can they hear? We have no definite evidence. Smell? "They are able to recall smells as round, square, elongated, hard, soft and so on, and as having a certain height and being in a certain direction." When we perceive odours, on the other hand, they come as a disorderly medley to the back of the nose, giving us no clear image either of time or of space. We have largely lost our sense of smell, and only by a study of creatures like dogs and ants can we realize how vast is the extent of the possible worlds which we are condemned to ignore.

Take the case of sight. We are so accustomed to staring at things in front of us with just two eyes that we forget how many other ways of seeing there are, and how many creatures get along without seeing at all, in our sense of the word.

Ants, for example, though they dwell most of their lives in the warm darkness of the nest, have two kinds of eyes; but in order to see, or rather to

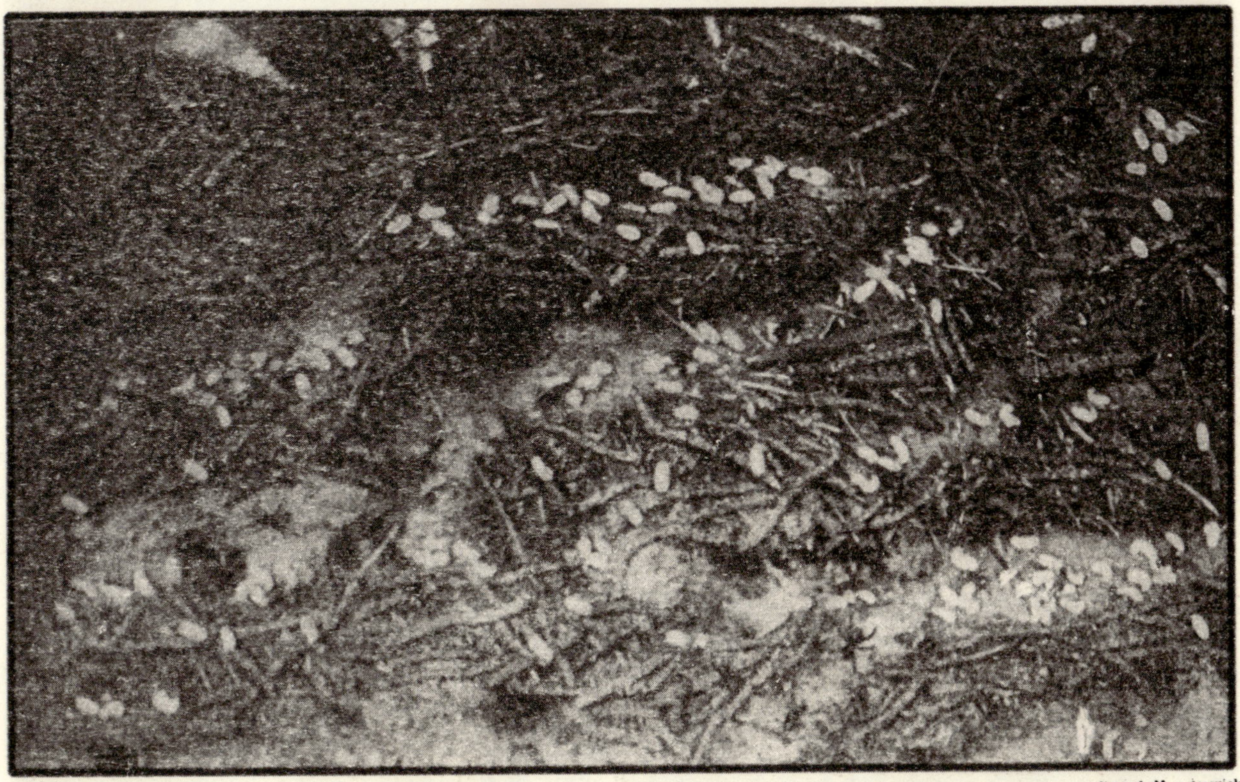

Rev. S. N. Sedgwick

ANT CITY AND PART OF ITS INTERIOR REVEALED

From the outside the nest of a community of wood ants seems to be just a rough pile of pine needles or twigs, although the dimensions of that pile are surprising when the size of the builders is considered. But when part of the ant city is removed with care (bottom) an intricate system of galleries is revealed. There are places for the larvae and the cocoons, and some of the unlit, and, to the ant, vast chambers and thoroughfares of the city go far into the ground beneath the apparently simple and artless superstructure.

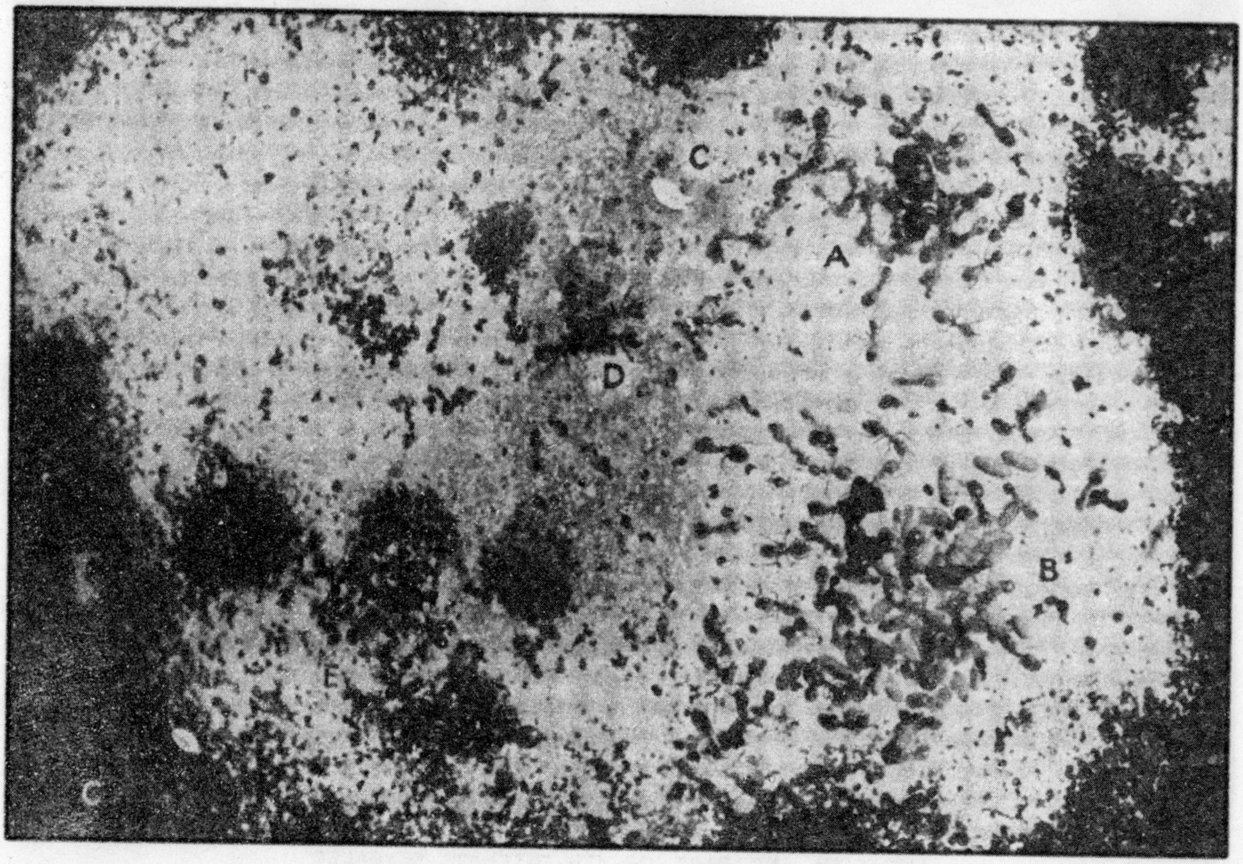

Rev. S. N. Sedgwick

LOOKING DOWN UPON A NEST OF MEADOW ANTS

The lower photograph shows the inside of a nest of meadow ants which is lettered to make plain the important features. "A" marks where the queen stands with her courtiers; "B" the nursery for pupae and their attendants; "C" two of the insects called Platyarthrus Hofmanseggii which are domesticated by ants; "D" a nursery containing eggs and "E" a number of larvae and their nurses. The upper photograph was taken from above as the human would see it. The concealing grass has been removed.

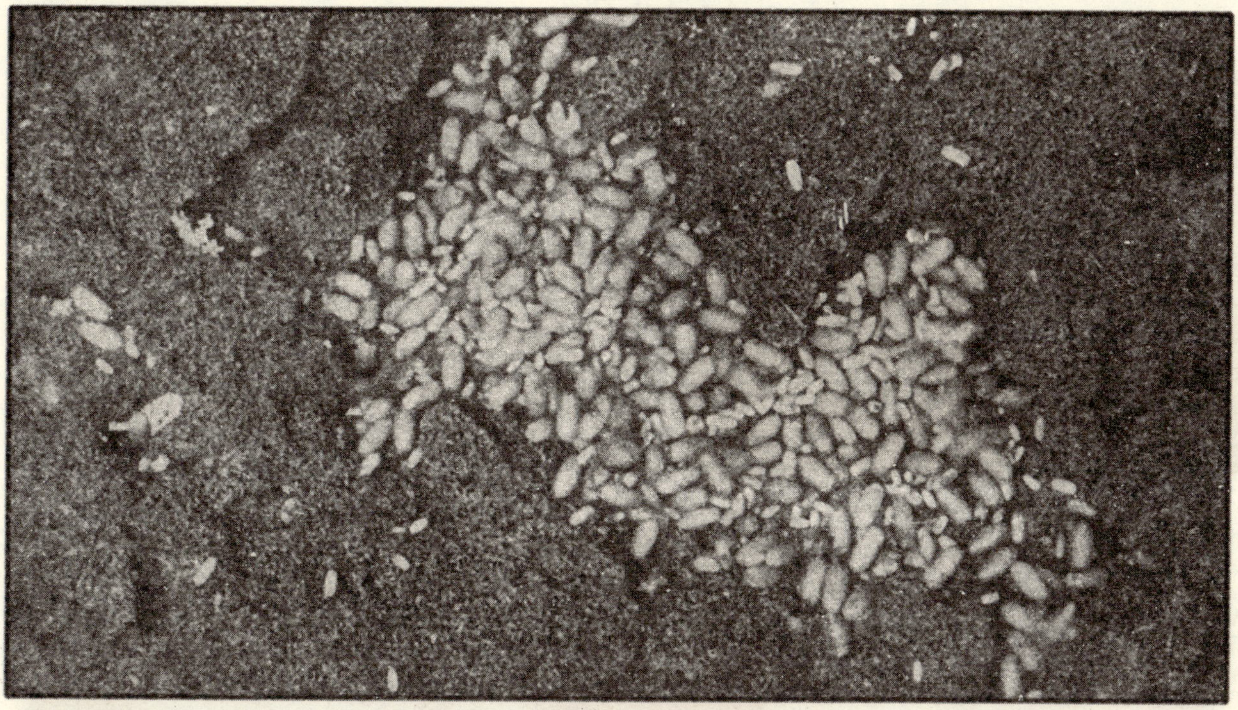

Rev. S. N. Sedgi

IN THE NURSERIES OF BLACK AND WOOD ANTS' NESTS

Certain apartments within the city are set apart as nurseries and hither the eggs are carried so soon as they are laid by the que The eggs adhere to each other in little clusters and are picked up and transported in the mandibles of a nurse. When the hatc larvae spin cocoons the nurses still have to carry them about to different parts of the nest for the benefit of heat or perhaps to esc injury owing to damage to the nest. Above is a black ant nursery and below some wood ants with cocoons.

An Ant City

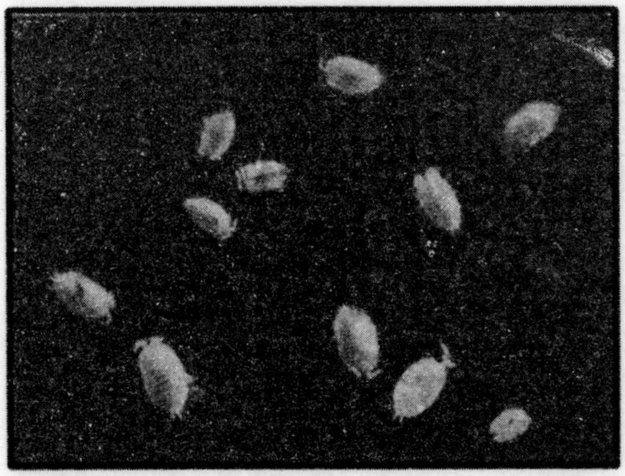

S. N. Sedgwick

ROYAL FAMILY AND ATTENDANTS: AN ANT "STABLE"

In the lower photograph we see the princes and princesses of an ant city just emerged from their cocoons with the help of the nurses. These nurses accompany their charges to the outside of the nest whence the males and females will soar into the sunlight for the nuptial dance. Above is a " stable " for the aphides or green-fly.

perceive, they combine sight, touch, smell, heat and so on in ways which at present we can only dimly realize. Very soon it will be possible to make a film magnifying ants to the size of men, so that we can see all parts of their bodies a thousand or even a million times as large as we do at present. If a man the size of St. Paul's could be observed by a physiologist, a lot might be discovered about parts of the skin, the eye, or the brain which is at present a complete mystery. By studying the ant similarly enlarged, we might discover facts about its behaviour which would be of great service to those suffering from blindness.

But there is another interesting thing about sight. The eyes of the ant are, for the most part, constructed like those of the dragon-fly or the butterfly out of thousands of tiny facets. The dragon-fly has over twelve thousand such facets, and this fully explains its skill in poising itself at the precise distance which is beyond the reach of a hand or a net. Such eyes are sensitive chiefly to moving objects, for ants cannot rest the retina by blinking as we do, and anything stationary is, therefore, visible to them only for a very brief moment. That is why their behaviour may repay more careful study, for, after all, our eyes are only a special part of the skin which has gradually come to be used for the function of sight. In some creatures the skin is sensitive to light; they actually see with their skin. And this fact suggested to a French writer, Jules Romains, that our skin, too, might still have some of its original powers if only we could learn to revive them. So he set to work to experiment with Eastern methods of concentration to make use of some of that mental control which enables certain people to alter the rate of the pulse, to blush, or to twitch muscles at will. Eventually he claimed to have taught blind people to see with the skin, and to have trained friends to see with almost any part of the body. They could even read newspapers with their chests.

M. Romains, however, is known as a poet, a dramatist, a satirist, and a wit; and people suspected a hoax. But he was in earnest, and a serious controversy arose, a bitter war of words with the professors. In due course he persuaded Anatole France that he could prove his case. After translating his book into English, under the title " Eyeless Sight," I found that Professor Forel had also been greatly interested, and though, as he remarks, the interpretation of the experiments is contrary to all our present ideas, he is prepared to consider the claim seriously. As a result of his life-long study of the eyes and brains of ants and men, he had even gone so far as to experiment with blind people before he knew that others were already engaged in work of the same nature. At the moment the controversy is still in progress. A blind American lady who went to Paris to practise " eyeless sight " has written a book stating that she succeeded; but this is more than doubtful, and the matter remains a tantalizing speculation. The great majority of scientists regard the objections as at present insuperable.

THERE is, however, another speculation which is more promising. The most important sense organs of ants are their antennae which, like a cat's whiskers, tell them a great deal about the outside world. How do ants communicate with one another? They tap out messages in various ways with their antennae. The Jesuit Father Wasmann and Forel are in agreement on this point, if on nothing else,

H Bastin

ANTS THAT HAUNT THE FORESTS OF TROPICAL AMERICA

On the left of this trio we have the celebrated sauba or parasol ant of tropical America which cuts sections of leaves, stores these in the nest until they ferment and rot, and then, on the leaf mould so formed grows mushrooms for food. In the centre is the acana ant from the Amazon valley and, on the right, a winged foraging ant which belongs to a fierce, predatory species whose members make no settled abode, but wander in their thousands, raiding other nests. The ants in these photographs are shown magnified.

and no one will accuse the former of going out of his way to make ants resemble human beings.

This tapping code is used in eight different circumstances; as a signal for collective work, passed from one to another; to secure honey-dew; to indicate the direction of a trek; to give information about a source of food; to incite to attack or flight; to warn of danger from some special quarter; to calm a case of nerves; to initiate a slave-raid.

Here again the possibilities of an ant film are suggested. With ants the size of a man, every movement of the antennae could be closely observed, and repeated at will, like semaphore signals which we fail at first to understand. The behaviour of all concerned before and after the incident could be minutely examined in the light of what we have already discovered concerning bees, beetles and cicadas, all of which make known their doings in surprising ways. Any sounds caused by the tapping could be amplified by the same methods which have enabled a heartbeat to resound like thunder. Perhaps Dr. J. G. Myers, whose studies of the cicada's songs have been so successful, will one day help us here. But the solution will probably come from the tropics, where ants are larger, more numerous and, presumably, noisier.

Of the architectural and engineering feats of the ants it is impossible to speak without elaborate diagrams, but the nicety with which they judge distances and stresses and the speed with which they inspect works begun by their companions, in order to co-operate or correct errors, present some uncanny problems for the student of instinct.

The same is true of the accuracy with which they judge direction outside the nest, for there seems no

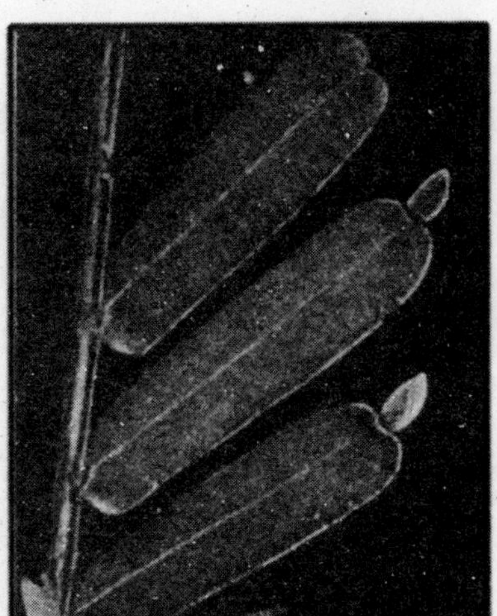

H. Bastin

ANTS THAT GO TO PLANTS FOR THEIR MEANS OF LIVELIHOOD

Certain ants who are neighbours of the saubas inhabit acacia bushes. Each ant bites a hole through one of the acacia thorns (left) and eats out the soft core. It then has a fine home and, furthermore, a constant food supply for the acacia exudes a liquid from its leaves (centre) of which the acacia ant is very fond. These leaves also possess special tips containing nourishment for these ants. The right-hand photograph shows an ant trying to reach the flowers of a wood sponge which are inside the leaf.

necessary they work in chains, only the two end members of a chain being actually in contact with the leaves. This use of one living creature by another as a working tool is only paralleled, except amongst humans, by the old fable of the cat's paw.

"Consider her ways, and be wise." We can learn what to do, but we can also be wise in time. Those who have devoted most thought to the foibles of ants and men see in our Universities, for example, one of the chief mechanisms by which we stifle the originality and vitality that might save us from becoming ant-equated, if the term be permitted. Here is the verdict of Professor Wheeler, on whom Forel relies for much of his American material:

doubt that they are often guided by the sun; and it has lately been suggested that the moon and even the stars may play a part. Anyone who has disturbed an ant track must have marvelled at the speed with which the procession was resumed, and in some cases the ant army moves for considerable distances. Migrating species change their abode every few weeks, and the expedients they adopt to overcome obstacles include the formation of their army into a solid ball which can be carried over water.

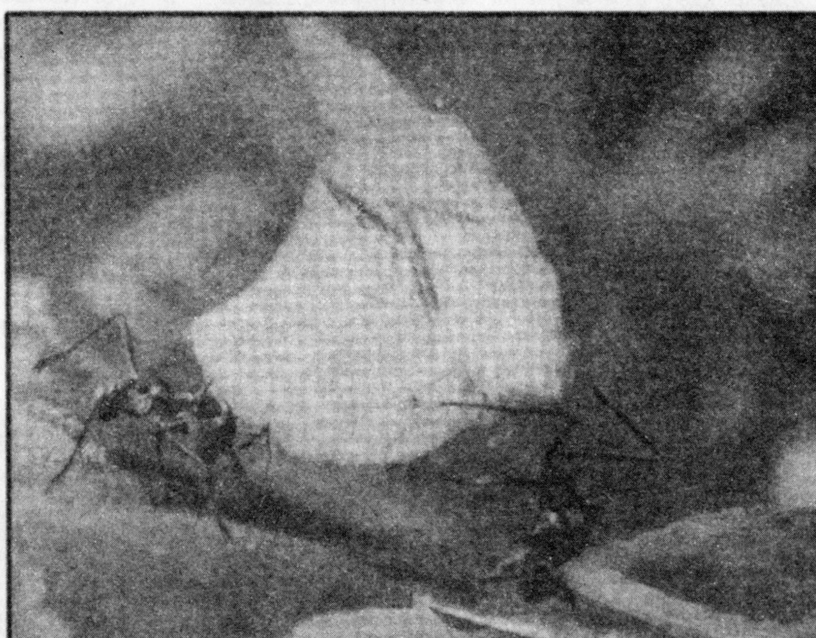

LEAF CUTTING ANTS AT THEIR WORK

In obtaining the pieces of leaf from their fungus beds the sauba ants display most workmanlike methods. The lower photograph illustrates how the leaf section is raised into a convenient position. This is an excellent example of ant cooperation. Above is a pair of ants returning with their loads. Photographs by P. G Howes, of the Bruce Museum, Greenwich, Conn.

The leaf-cutters of South America, as they return from their labours each with a leaf many times larger than itself, have all the appearance of a vast procession protected by sunshades, and for this reason they are often described as "parasol" ants.

Perhaps the most curious of the industrial habits of the ants are those connected with weaving. In order to produce the finely woven silk of which their nests are composed, certain Indian ants use their own larvae as a weaver uses his shuttle. A whole squad will set out, each carrying a larva to a place between two leaves, and fix their mouths to the edge of one leaf, while another squad pull the leaves closer and closer together. If

To us morontic schoolmarms in trousers, who have flown from reality and have slowly succumbed to autistic thinking, with defective eyesight, doughy musculature, brittle ossifications, demoralized intestines . . . and atrophied interstitials, there comes every year a small army of freshmen very properly so called—in the late teens and early

CARPENTER ANTS RESTING AND WARRIOR ANTS ON THE MARCH

Even the ants rest sometimes. The carpenter ants (bottom) are quite at ease hanging upside down in this fashion. They make their home in the solid timber and carve long galleries in it. The warrior ants (top) carry their eggs and larvae with them and are thus independent of any headquarters, while they subsist by attacking the strongholds of other species and eating the garrisons. These photographs are much enlarged to show detail and were taken by P. G. Howes, of the Bruce Museum, Greenwich, Conn.

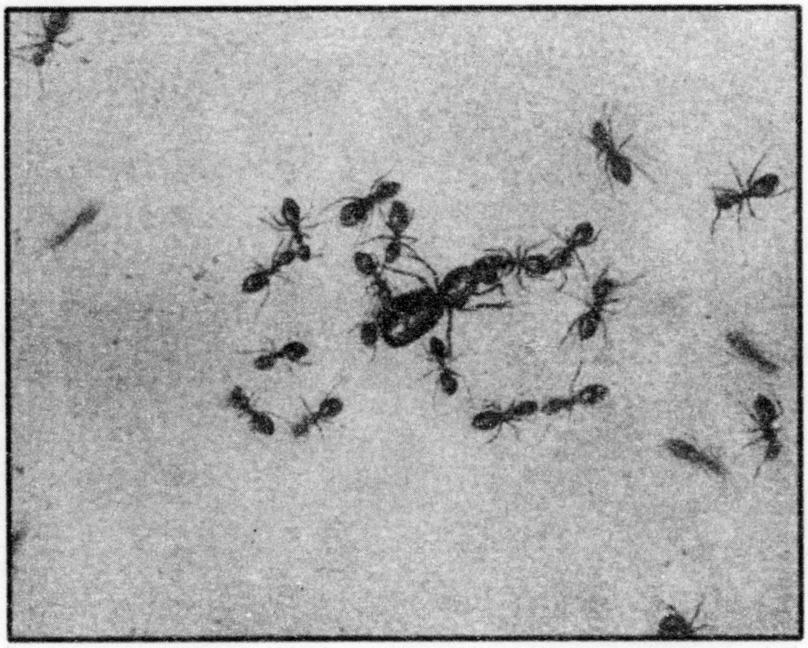

ment, to the elaborate toilets already mentioned, or to snoozing quietly until they are roughly awakened by taps of the antennae to new industry or new conquests.

Have they any sluggards, dissentients, contemplators? We do not know. But at least they have no scruples about sacrificing the inefficient. With such a population problem the possibilities of humanitarianism are small, for ant figures are as staggering as those of the astronomer. There are over five thousand distinct species of ants, which cannot interbreed any more than tigers and rabbits among animals; but there are probably ten thousand different kinds—as different as English and Chinese. No

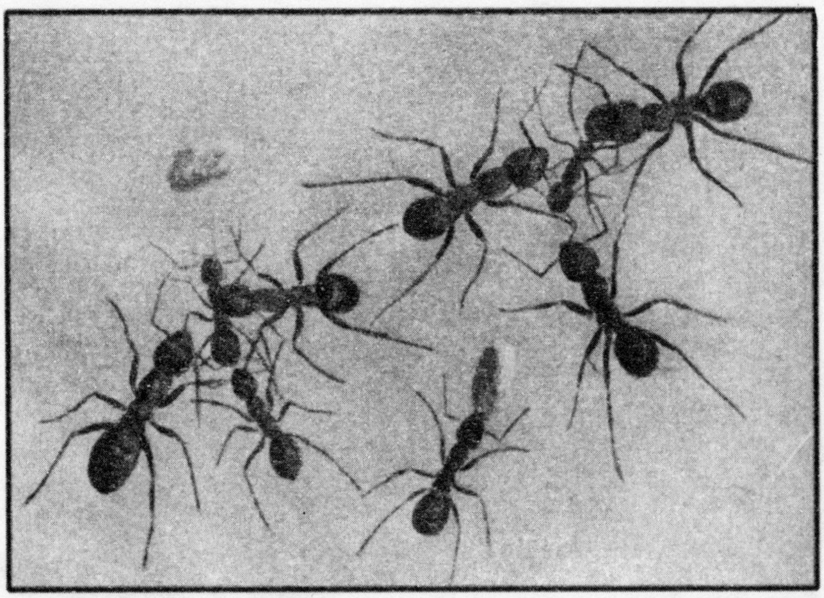

H. Bastin

SLAVE RAID AND FUNERAL PROCESSION IN THE ANT KINGDOM

Here (bottom) is a slave raid in progress, the larger ants making away with the cocoons of the smaller. The ants which hatch out of these cocoons will be trained in the service of their masters. When ants die the corpses may be removed from the nest or buried in a special part Above some black ants are taking the body of a queen which has died outside back to the nest.

twenties, burning for impact with reality, with exquisite sense-organs, superb bones, muscles and alimentary tracts . . and what do we give them? "

The same writer, in discussing the alarming inroads of "organization," and its effects on research, has contrasted the few means of escape from schedule and routine still available for the human mind with the complete "efficiency" attained by the ant. He suggests that:

> As the earth becomes more densely covered with its human populations, it becomes increasingly necessary to retain portions of it in a wild state, free from the organizing mania of man, as national and city parks or reservations to which we can escape during our holidays from the administrators, organizers and efficiency experts and everything they stand for, and return to a Nature that really understands the business of organization. Why may we not regard scientific research, artistic creation, religious contemplation and philosophic speculation as the corresponding reservations of the mind, great world-parks to which man must resort to escape from the deadening, over-specializing routine of his habits, moods and occupations and enjoy veritable creative holidays of the spirit?

We have seen that even the ants find time to play, though we may suspect that their play is designed to lead to greater efficiency. There are signs, too, that on occasion they give themselves over to enjoy-

wonder entomology has become one of the most specialised and exacting forms of science, for to the ordinary eye most of these ten thousand are as much alike as a flock of sheep.

Whoever tries to deal with the ant statistically will have no easy task, for, though no ant is so prolific as the termite queen, which is capable of producing over a hundred million children, there may be

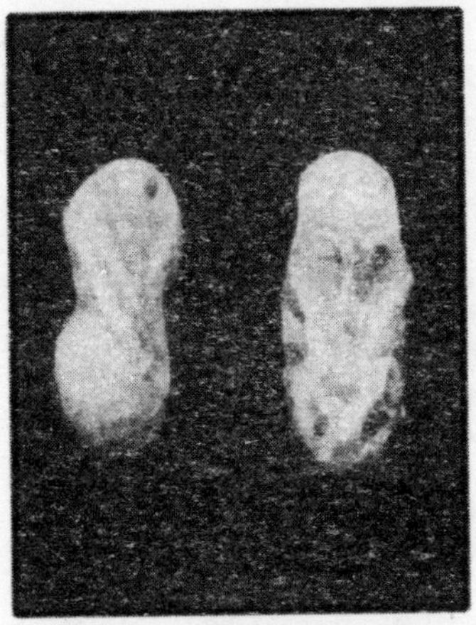

Pupae

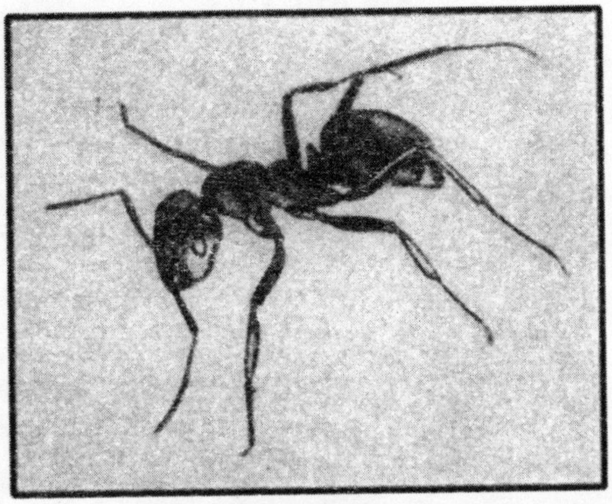

Worker

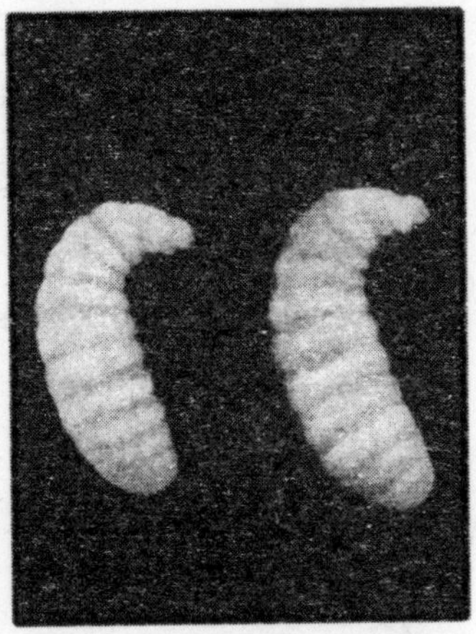

Larvae

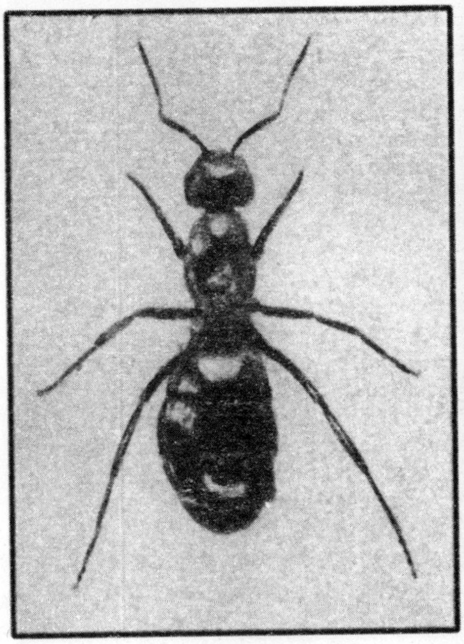

Queen

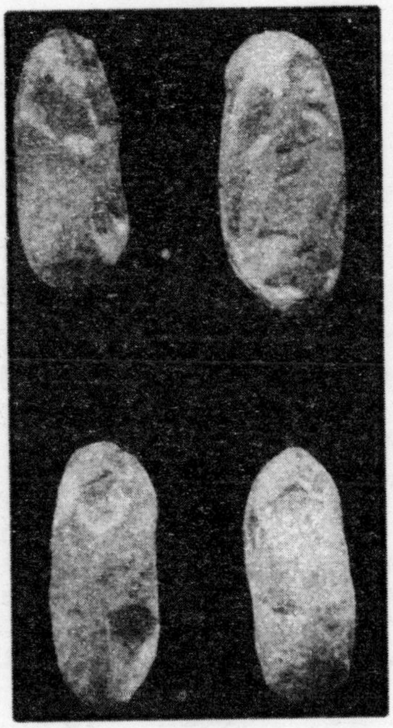

Cocoons

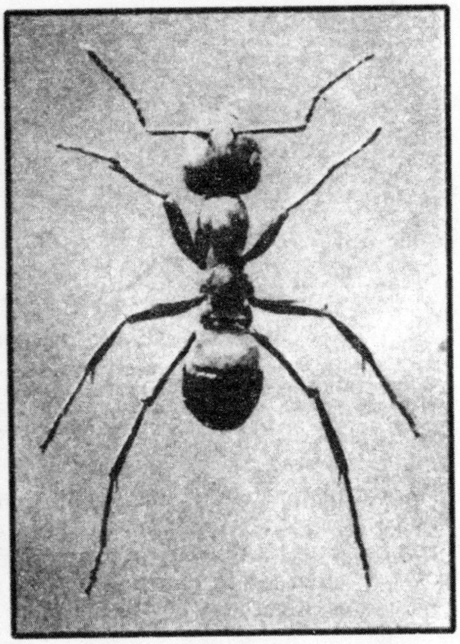

Worker

Winged Male

Winged Princess

INDIVIDUALS IN THE DRAMA OF THE ANT CITY

At the head of the ant community is the royal family, consisting of the princes (bottom, left) and princesses (bottom, right). When the mating flight is over, the princesses lose their wings and settle down to carry on the race, while the princes die sooner or later. The workers, sterile females, do the labour of the city. The familiar "ants' eggs" are really the cocoons spun by the ant larvae. Out of these cocoons the emerging ants have to be helped by the attendant nurse workers. These photographs of wood ants are by H. Bastin.

H Bastin

SLAVER AND HOUSE ANTS

On the left is one of the slaver ants with the smaller species which it breeds as its servant. On the right we see a queen and a worker of the house ants, a species which appears to be tropical in origin and which cannot live in the open.

more than the total human population of the globe in a single settlement. Thus, unlike ourselves, their younger generations cannot complain of any lack of opportunities for promotion.

It was Goethe who first diagnosed the tendency which threatens us with the stagnation of the ants, when he made the cruel remark that the funerals of public men do not succeed one another with sufficient frequency. Professor Wheeler has even offered to draw up "a list of fifty well-meaning superannuated reactionaries who, within recent years, have done more harm to civilization than any equal number of criminals one might select." Forel is not so harsh, for he believes that if we could abolish wars between nations (and, be it always understood, find harmless means of slaking our thirst) we should have plenty of incentives to further effort and perfectly adequate resources to realize our ideals. Be that as it may, each of us may draw his own moral, according to his political convictions, his religious traditions or his personal predilections. Forel, himself a radical and a visionary, admires the communistic institutions of his little friends, tries to defend them against the charge of militarism, and urges us to imitate their virtuous, orderly, and self-disciplined habits before it is too late ; before alcohol has enfeebled our overworked brains, or before the next war shall put back the clock still further towards the Dark Ages ! We are to set to work to build up a "supernational human formicary," a world-organization which the ants have never imagined and because of their size can probably never achieve, though they have blindly taken so many steps on the road we seem bound to travel.

As Forel says :—" One human formicary, united throughout the world, and at the same time divided into a host of multi-cellular individuals, townships, nationalities and States superimposed upon one another, but supple in their restricted liberties, will replace the barbaric conditions of our ancestors and all their warlike anarchies. It will free humanity from a great deal of distress, without, however, realizing the Utopian ideals of certain visionaries for a quickly-approaching earthly paradise in which all men suddenly become angels. No—we shall always have need, alas, of laws, tribunals and police, even prisons and madhouses, by reason of the pitiless heredity of our innate feelings. But all these things must be completely reformed. Many lunatic asylums have already set us good examples in this respect. We may hope that the eugenics of the future, if well applied, will even be able to improve by small degrees the quality of our higher races."

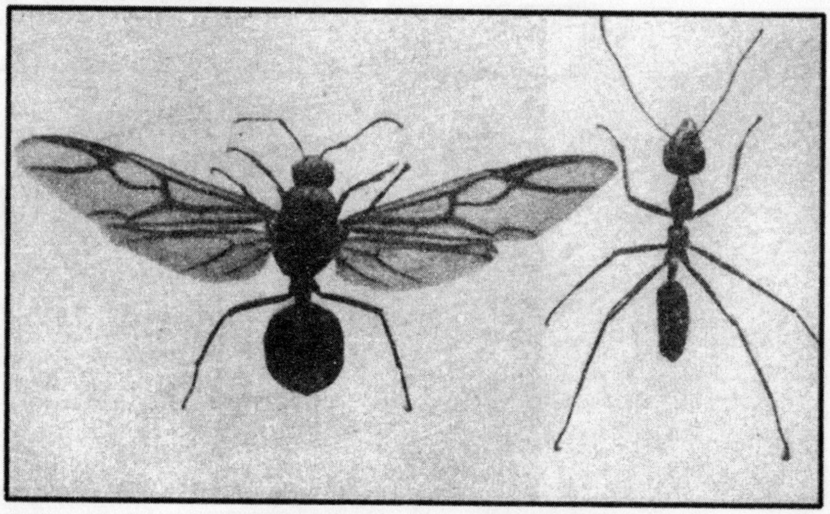

H. Bastin

WINGED ANT AND A WORKER

Among the ants it is only the males or princes and the princesses who are equipped with wings. These they use in making their nuptial flight, for the mating takes place in the air, never in the nest. Furthermore, when a princess is mated and becomes a queen she loses her wings The worker (right) never has wings and has no need of them, spending her life in the nest

Chapter LI

Gluttons of the Sea

By Dr. William J. Dakin

Professor of Zoology, Liverpool University

When we hear stories to the effect that the daily fish requirement of a single seal costs as much as would keep a man at the Ritz Hotel, that a cormorant can go on swallowing fish as often as they are presented to it, and that there are fish which are six times bigger after they have fed than they were before their meal, we are naturally liable to jump to the conclusion that there are some appalling gluttons in the animal world—even if we allow that the stories have been fishermen's tales!

It must be remembered, however, that we regard a glutton as a person who eats excessively and it is very doubtful if the normal appetite of any creature in nature can be termed gluttonous. The portly gentleman who develops what is subtly called a "corporation" is not liable to be chased by an enemy with an axe although he may die of apoplexy in his study. The life of one of nature's "voracious" animals is too much a struggle to permit of excess.

The fact is that every creature requires a certain minimum amount of food to provide it with energy and material for the upkeep of its body. This minimum may in some cases appear extraordinary to us, for there are several causes which may make the food requirements of an animal very large.

In the first place the actual nutriment in quite a large bulk of some particular kind of food may be small or much may be indigestible. An animal would have to eat a lot of this stuff to cover its needs. Again, these needs may be unusually great. Probably no creature eats more in its existence than a silkworm caterpillar, which devours 4,700 times its own initial weight. This is because it must store up nutriment for a long resting period when no food is eaten. A vampire bat has a very short intestine and probably requires very little food, for blood requires little digestion and must be regarded as of high nutrient value. A huge boa-constrictor may swallow a mammal of relatively extraordinary size, but it goes a very long time before its next meal.

It is true that some of the most voracious appetites are exhibited by sea creatures or by animals closely associated with the sea; they are particularly interesting creatures, too, far more exciting than the fat caterpillar steadily munching leaf all day long. Let us begin with the fish.

Most fish are restricted in some way so far as *kind* of diet is concerned, that is, their mouth apparatus, jaws, teeth, and so on, are definitely adapted to one type of food. Thus the sardine, the herring, and hosts of others, feed upon microscopic floating creatures which they filter out of the water by comb-like structures on their gill supports. You might not think that these fish could be gluttons, because if you take up a glass of sea-water you would not see much in the way of microscopic life in it, but hundreds of thousands of tiny organisms have been taken from the stomach of a sardine, and heaven only knows how many little copepods, each the size of a pin's head, may be found in the stomach of a herring. These fish can evidently filter a large amount of water.

R. W. Stemson

WALRUS, GLUTTON OF THE COLD SEAS

When it is realized that a full-grown male walrus may be as much as twelve feet long and weigh three thousand pounds, the size of the meals necessary to sustain this great mass and the energy required to move it may easily be surmised.

Another type of food restriction can be illustrated by the sharks. We certainly regard them as voracious and also their relatives, the rays. Some rays can only feed upon shell-fish; their teeth are flattened and specially adapted to crushing shells, whilst on the other hand the really

W. S. Berridge

Natural History Museum

ATLANTIC SWALLOWER AND A DOG FISH

Of all the monsters of the sea which are remarkable for their eating the swallower heads the list It has so expansive a stomach, compared with its size, that it can swallow fish larger than itself. The stomach stretches until it is so thin as to become transparent. Above is a dog fish, a species of small shark.

dreaded sharks have rows of sharp teeth perfectly fitted for a hasty snap at a slippery fish and equally horrible as a trap for a human leg. These fellows would find it impossible to eat shellfish. The shellfish eaters are by no means less greedy because of their diet; they can put away huge quantities and have been regarded as one of the causes of the depletion of the pearl oyster fisheries of Ceylon and other oyster beds. The author once watched a shark (of the man-eating species) at very close quarters tearing huge chunks off a floating half-decayed whale. It made it easy to appreciate Melville's description in "Moby Dick." "If you have never seen that sight" (that is, ravenous sharks round a dead whale moored to a whale ship at night-time) "suspend your decision about the propriety of devil-worship, and the expediency of conciliating the devil."

But the palm for fish voracity must be given to the fish which are four or five times bigger after a meal than they were before it, and this because they have swallowed a fish much bigger than themselves. This is not a fisherman's story; it is an actual fact and can be easily verified by a visit to the Natural History Museum in London. They are rarely seen by man for they live in the ocean at depths of from three to six thousand feet—think of having always a mile of heavy water over your head! There is practically no light, and therefore no vegetation. Food is scarce and consequently the most has to be made of it when chance brings it. These "Gastrostomids" from the depths of the Atlantic are practically only great trap-mouths with a stomach and a whip-like tail—when empty. They can, however, extend their stomachs outside their body and so capture and take in fish larger than themselves. They do not hesitate to eat their own kind either!

Some fish, including the sharks, seem to take a delight in killing far more than they can eat, perhaps the nearest approach to real gluttony. The teeth of these predaceous fish are slender, very sharp-pointed and adapted for capturing swift and slippery prey. It follows that they are not suitable for chewing food. Possibly also their owners have no time to do so. The prey is disposed of as quickly as possible by swallowing, and it is not surprising therefore that the booty should reach the stomach of the capturer alive. In fact, it is on record that a fish so swallowed has eaten its way out through the stomach wall and actually escaped!

EVIDENTLY, amongst the fishes themselves, life is either *Je mange* or *Je suis mangé*, and at times these habits become distinctly annoying to fisher folk. Off the coast of Western Australia the fishermen could not use a common English mode of fishing, that of setting "long lines" with hundreds of baited hooks at intervals. Probably each hook would catch its fish, but these would immediately be removed by useless sharks which might in turn be caught by the hooks. In nearer waters the thresher

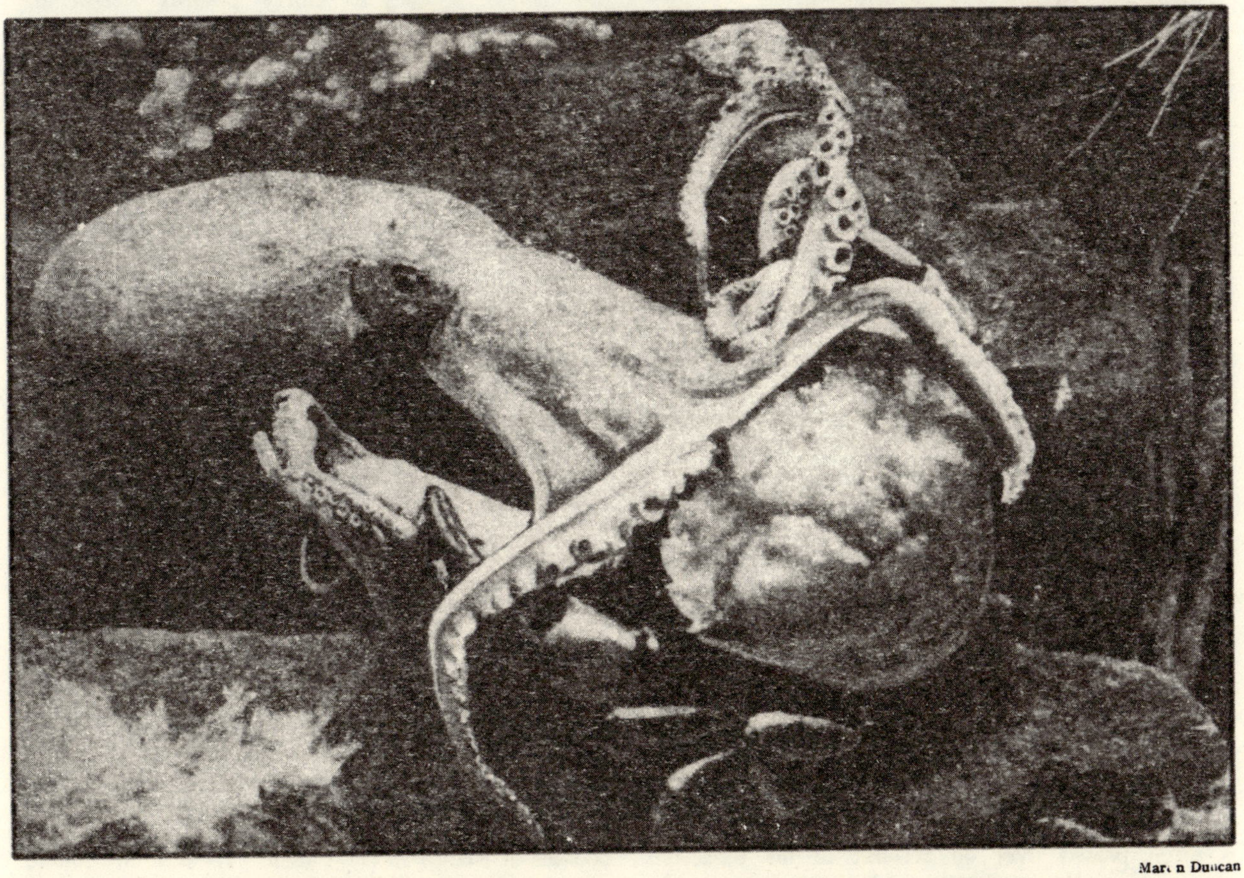

Mar‹ n Duncan

OCTOPUS AND JOHN DORY THAT GET THEIR MEALS BY STEALTH

With eight strong tentacles, each equipped with many suckers, the octopus (bottom), hidden among the rocks, seizes its prey and conveys it to the mouth. The curious John Dory (top), which is esteemed highly by gourmets, has an enormous mouth and a corresponding capacity for small fish such as sprats. These it obtains not by superior speed, but apparently by keeping end on to the fish it means to devour, when the dory's extraordinary flatness makes it an inconspicuous and unalarming line in the water.

Gluttons of the Sea

Natural History, N.Y.

NURSE SHARK AND ITS DREADFUL TEETH

Nine rows of teeth in one jaw make for quick eating (bottom) and this is the equipment of the nurse shark. The shark is curious in that although its young are born alive, they are believed to develop in an egg covering, this forming an interesting example of transition between egg laying and bringing forth young alive. The nurse shark swims in American waters.

shark preys upon shoals of herrings, pilchards, and sprats and destroys incredible numbers, swimming round and round a shoal in ever decreasing circles, violently beating with its enormous tail (hence the name, thresher) until its victims are conveniently huddled up together.

THE voracity of fish may, however, be even more clearly seen in the restricted waters of rivers and lakes, where numbers are limited and other factors tend to weigh the balance against fish life. For an example, we cannot do better than study the pike of English rivers. He is rather popular, indeed, as a fish except perhaps with those whose trout waters have suffered from his depredations. There is an element of mystery in the pike, whose ferocity is often passed over on account of his tenacity and pluck. He is a true fresh-water fish, found over a wide range in Europe, Asia, and North America. Many stories have been told about both the size and the voracity of the pike. For a long time Ireland was looked upon with grave suspicion on account of these tales, but there seems no doubt now that fifty-pound monsters are to be taken occasionally in its waters. Plenty of twenty to thirty pounds weight are to be found.

Not disdainful of a minnow, the pike has been known to attack ducks and even rats, and, of course, every kind of fish. I believe one has been discovered with its head jammed down the throat of another. Naturally, this fish—which, by the way, is very prolific—is not a desirable guest in trout waters. In fact, one small pike in such a spot might do more harm in a season than all the poachers of the district together could do.

So much for the fish themselves. Let us turn for another example of voracity to the birds who are interested in fish life. The fact that we sometimes impolitely decorate certain undesirable specimens of the human race with the term " old cormorant " at once brings this bird to mind. To realize the full possibilities of the cormorants one has to see these birds where they congregate in their thousands; or, conversely, to see the trained cormorants of the Chinese catching fish with their masters. They used to be employed in England, but for a gentleman's sport. Probably very few of our home gardeners realize that when they use Peruvian guano they are supplying their plants with nitrogen produced as excreta by the cormorants, pelicans, gannets, and boobies of islands in the Pacific. Its ultimate source was therefore the flesh of Pacific Ocean fishes.

The birds in these regions move in flocks like clouds, and it has been estimated that on one small island of less than one square mile area there were

E N.A.

STRANDED GLUTTONS AND SHORE SHARKS IN AN AQUARIUM

At Port au Prince, capital of the republic of Haiti, these sharks (bottom) had the misfortune to be stranded, thus giving an excellent opportunity for studying their size and gauging their feeding capacity. The New York Aquarium often obtains some fine sharks, and those seen here (top) are shore sharks caught off Sandy Hook. They attain a length of six feet or so, and are said never to attack human beings. They are attended, in their tank, by some dog fish—also very voracious in their habits.

GANNETS THAT WORK HAVOC WITH THE HERRINGS

Widely distributed throughout the globe and common on the rockier coasts of the British Isles, the gannet or solan goose is a large bird, three feet long, and in British waters takes great toll of the pilchard and herring shoals. The birds fly along and then suddenly close their wings and fall headlong in the sea—and very seldom dive in vain.

probably ten million cormorants. It would require from four thousand to twenty thousand tons of fish per day to sustain that colony! It seems almost incredible, and yet a cormorant has been known to devour seven pounds of fish per day. That is what it can do in a zoological garden if given the fish. Still more extraordinary is the way the cormorants capture their fish. They leave the surface of the sea where they have been swimming, descend into the water and, using wings as paddles, conduct hunt and capture whilst submerged. Photographs showing this will be found on pages 370 and 371. They return home at sunset, and what a sight it is with lines and lines of birds crossing and re-crossing, and with but very few clashes!

It has been estimated that a single flock of cormorants observed on one of the Peruvian guano islands would consume each year a weight of fish equal to one quarter of the entire catch of the United States fisheries, and this has been going on for ages. The young birds which stay at home feed by thrusting their heads down the parents'

Neville Kingston

throats. This is also the case with the pelicans, which are close relations of the cormorants. There is no doubt about the greediness of the young birds; they swallow the fish whole without even withdrawing their heads from the mouth and gullet of their mothers! In fact, it seems that if it were not for their wings, the young might disappear altogether down into the depths of the parent.

CORMORANTS and gannets fish actively around the British coasts, especially the rocky coasts like those of the Isle of Man and Scotland. They enjoy the herring shoals, but it is questionable whether they do serious damage anywhere unless they move inward into more secluded waters.

There are other birds which take their toll of fresh-water fishes, but here we are treading on dangerous ground, for the bird-lover will never agree with the angler. The stately heron is one of the sinners, and that cheerful bird, the king-fisher. The heron loves the marshy flats as well as riversides, and takes up its residence where clear waters are well stocked with fish.

E. N. A.

SKUA GULL, SCAVENGER OF THE SEA, AND THE PENGUIN

Four species of skua gull (bottom) occur in the north of Britain, and there is also a special breed in the Antarctic. These birds are the bullies and scavengers of the coasts they frequent, preying insatiably on other gulls and eating offal that may be floating or cast up on shore. The penguin (top) hunts its food under the sea.

Herbert G. Ponting, F.R.P.S., Copyright

Neville Kingston

SEA BIRDS THAT ARE GLUTTONS OF THE COAST LANDS

The herring gull (bottom right) is said to have received its name from its habit of following the herring shoals, but it is much more a robber of nests in gull colonies. This is a real glutton among sea birds, for it often comes inland and attacks the turnips in the fields. The black-headed gull (bottom left) is also rather loosely named, for its head is rather brown than black. Like the herring gull, it is fond of coming inland and it eats great numbers of grubs. The Antarctic skua (top) preys upon the penguins' eggs as soon as it sees a nest unattended.

SEALS POSSESSED OF GARGANTUAN APPETITES FOR FISH

Prodigious is the only word that describes the appetite of a seal. To keep a mammal, a warm-blooded animal, active and well in the sea needs a great deal of food from which the necessary heat and strength may be obtained. Fishermen often complain of the ravages of seals among the shoals and, locally, the animals may appreciably affect the fish harvest for men. But, in general, fish are so prolific that even such great eaters as the seals cannot diminish the supply. The lower photograph shows a seal in company with some penguins.

Its numbers must have been very much reduced in the British islands during recent years, for, in certain parts, where it was formerly quite common, it is now rarely seen

THE kingfisher, a very delightful bird, beautiful in plumage and interesting in its habits, has always been an object of interest. It is the subject of many old superstitions, and is conspicuously mentioned in the classics. Its usual method of fishing is to sit motionless on a branch or other perch (its feet are not adapted for walking), looking down into the water. So it may sit for hours until, when a victim happens to show himself, there is a lightning-like descent, the fish is captured on the dive, and the bird flies away to a suitable spot to swallow it. The kingfisher catches only small fish, but unfortunately its appetite is large. The famous laughing jackass of Australia is a kingfisher, but not necessarily a fisher of fish. Its sardonic laughter may be heard in the depths of the Australian bush, where its favourite food is small lizards and snakes.

No description of the enemies of fish could be complete without reference to those of the highest group of vertebrates, the Mammalia. It is almost as great a matter of surprise that quadrupeds so closely adapted to life on land should have returned and become fitted for life in the sea, as it is to see a cormorant swimming under water. The seals, for example, and their very, very close relations, the sea lion and walrus, are really marine dogs. They belong to the group of animals known as the Carnivora, to which the dog, cat, wolf, lion and the bears belong, but how different their habits. They are wonderful swimmers, and not nearly so much at home on land as in the sea. Yet their real mammalian nature is obvious. They must return to land to breed, they give milk to their young, and if they were kept too long under water they would drown.

THE capacity of a Zoo seal for fish seems inexhaustible, yet when we remember how active these creatures are and the fact that they are warm-blooded like ourselves and therefore must expend energy in keeping a high body temperature in the cold waters of the sea, the fact is not surprising. A story is told of a sea lion in the London Zoological Gardens which happened to be "just handy" when a keeper left the entire day's fish supply for the whole of the fish-eating denizens of the gardens on an untended truck. The keeper was not away more than a few minutes, but the whole supply went and, what is more, the animal seemed prepared to present himself for attention when at great trouble some more fish were obtained. A sea lion not full grown will take forty pounds of fish in a day.

A telling description of the sea lion was given by Peck in 1853, which is well worth quoting :

"But of all created things and monsters in the world, I think there can be none that when seen near at hand wears so horrible a face and shape. . . . Nothing can be conceived more unnaturally hideous. They are the embodiment of despair. Along with the look of fierceness and cruelty, they have one of agony and suffering that makes them altogether appear to be the compelled agents of some diabolical spell or inevitable doom, like the wicked afrites and genies of the Arabian Nights. Their breathing is always like sobbing, their cries are wails; who knows what they could reveal if they could speak? The depths of the sea and the monstrous creatures that inhabit there are familiar to them, and so are the darkest recesses of the great caverns. They were created to be destroyers. There is no doubt that to support their lives they must devour an incredible number of the small fishes."

Seals occur round the English and Scottish coasts, and at one time were quite plentiful on the Northumberland coast. Complaints were received from the fishermen who believed that they caused destruction to the salmon.

The reader of this chapter will now be in a position to ask why indeed there are any fish left at all in the sea, considering the vast toll made upon them, quite apart from the ravages of man. The truth is that the sea is remarkably productive. If we look around us anywhere on land, especially where life is more abundant, we find vegetable life predominant. What would be the appearance if the waters of the North Sea suddenly disappeared, leaving the whole mass of living things lying on the sea bottom? We should see a vast, almost level plain literally carpeted with animal life. Everywhere there would be a glittering mass of fish, and hordes of worms, crabs, starfishes, and so on, would be mingled with them.

IT would seem that the sea was much richer in animal life than the land, and this is actually a fact. The reason is not far to seek. On land the ultimate source of all food is the green plants. This food supply is limited by products which can only be obtained from the surface layer of the soil. In the sea microscopic plants can live as far down as light penetrates and that would be the whole depth of the North Sea, which is not very great. No parts of the sea are sterile, and some of the richest regions are in the icy latitudes where land life is most sparse.

The whole world's fisheries have been estimated at £200,000,000 per annum, and we can guess from that the amount caught, possibly not far from 16,000,000,000 pounds per annum. Yet it is doubtful whether even this attack is causing serious reduction. Certainly the natural enemies we have been describing occasion no diminution in the fish life, for quite a definite balance exists between productivity and destruction. The number of fish present in the sea must be enormous when one can capture three thousand million herrings in one season in the North Atlantic, that being only a tiny percentage of the total number present. Perhaps the explanation lies in the fecundity of the fish.

Chapter LII

Herds, Packs and Colonies

By H. Mortimer Batten

Author of "British Wild Animals and Their Tracks"

For everything in the world of men and women there is an exact counterpart in Nature, but there are many things in Nature beyond the region of our understanding. The optimist, the bully, society's victims who have tried to victimise society (and perhaps succeeded), the professional thief, the ne'er-do-well, even the altruist—every deceit and catch-penny device known to mankind has been practised for ages past, and will be practised for all time, by the children of the wilderness.

Before the days of Adam many of the highest sciences, to which we have only just awakened, or to which we may have yet to waken, existed, and were worked out in Nature. Stream-lining and camouflage, the rudimentary principles on which the whole wheels of modern evolution revolve, might have been learnt from Nature countless centuries before the Picts. Man shivered for ages on his rush mattress while the white ants were cosy in their centrally-heated palaces yet when we come across this, that or the other in Nature which seems to draw a wild creature nearer to our own lives, we throw up our hands and exclaim—"How uniquely human!" Human, indeed!—and we are only just beginning to learn many of the vast sciences which in the so-called lower world were worked to an efficient conclusion before man thought even of wearing clothes!

The herd instinct in animals should be a subject of special appeal, since we of all creatures are herd dwellers. In the wild we have two kinds of herd dwellers, those which do not need to travel for their food and therefore live in colonies, and those whose demands necessitate a wandering existence — in other words, the gipsies and the townspeople.

GRACEFUL FLOCK OF FLAMINGOES

One of the most beautiful spectacles to be seen, so far as companies of animals go, is a flock of flamingoes when they make a rose-pink cloud above the shallow water where they stand. Close by, as here, the necks seem to form naturally into a very decorative pattern.

Of one thing we may be certain, however, that no wild creature travels more than its food requirements demand. Of none is this more true than of the eagle and the falcon, commonly considered the world's greatest wanderers. Having fed, these great birds of prey are perfectly content to sit for hours till their food is digested, and if fresh food were within immediate reach, they would repeat the performance of feeding and resting throughout life.

In the days when the buffalo thousands trod the prairies, north and south each spring and autumn, from the plains of the Red River and Saskatchewan to the regions south of the Missouri, it was not restlessness which led them, but the necessity for food. It may be said that the life of the buffalo herds consisted of one gigantic migration.

Let us try to picture the massing of the buffalo herds. Spring has just come to the plains of the Mississippi, and over every ridge black streams of buffaloes are pouring. Herd joins herd till the valleys are full of them, every buffalo with its head towards the north, every buffalo obsessed by the migration fever. Still the black rivers feed the black sea, till an incredible army of buffaloes is moving across country; an army perhaps fifty miles in width and over a hundred miles in depth—the whole area black with them, shoulder to shoulder. Overhead countless birds of prey are wheeling and soaring, and in the train of the great army, ready to cut out the stragglers or to pull down the weak, prowl the timber wolf and the grizzly.

In these days it is almost impossible to imagine such a gathering of wild creatures, but the facts remain. Northwards the buffaloes moved, leaving the landscape strewn with their dead. The

Neville Kingston

COLONY OF COYPUS WHICH YIELD THE FUR CALLED "NUTRIA"

Along many of the larger rivers of South America the banks are riddled with the burrows of the coypus, furry rat-like animals, a little less than two feet long as a rule, and not unlike the beaver in general appearance save that the tail is not flattened but rounded like the rat's. Their food consists of water plants, both roots and leaves, and the under-fur is in great demand commercially, being known in the trade as "nutria." The coypus outer coat, however, is very long and harsh in quality.

rivers were still snow-coated, and there was nothing to indicate the rottenness of the ice—nothing, indeed, by which the hollow might be recognized from a general feature of the landscape. Out trod the vanguard of the great army, then came a thunderous boom as through they went—thousands being crowded to their doom, tier after tier and line after line of them forced on, by the surging mass behind, till the living were veritably ploughing their way across a bridge of the dead.

Thus thousands of buffaloes were drowned and trampled in the great prairie rivers every spring and autumn, and it is a fact that islands exist on the Mississippi and the Missouri which were built up by the uncountable stranded buffalo hulks. For several weeks each spring these mighty waterways were unapproachable owing to the stench of the buffalo carcasses piled along their banks in ridges for many hundreds of miles.

The buffaloes most certainly left an indelible trail behind them, an imprint on the face of the country from which man wiped out their thousands in the space of eight years, for by ages of travelling, the buffaloes had learnt the best routes through the hills and over the mountains. Thus the buffalo trail became the pack trail, and the pack trail the trail of the Red River cart, and to-day the Continental railways, with their Pullman saloons and their observation cars, thunder through the passes by the very routes once trodden black by multitudinous hoofs that have long since disappeared.

These great armies of buffaloes consisted of individual herds, or clans, which normally lived their lives scattered over the country, each herd keeping to itself. An average herd might number between twenty and fifty, and it may be taken that they were all related, great-grandmothers, grandmothers and mothers with their respective offspring. I am inclined to think that most wild creatures which live in herds do not so easily lose sight of their relatives. Recently, in the Forest of Atholl, I was watching a herd of red deer hinds numbering fourteen. The leader of the herd, obviously the mother mind, was an old grey hind, and the others were watching her, waiting for her decision, waiting for her to lead, and as I took stock of them, I saw the unmistakable family likeness from hind to hind, the grey markings and the distinctive features of the old leader. She, no doubt, was the great-grandmother of that clan, for though in the wild, as in our own world, the males show a tendency to wander off and seek their fortunes in distant ranges, the females cling to the mother, hence the herds.

If this is true of the deer, and in my own mind I am certain that it is, it was proven of the buffalo. There existed a certain buffalo robe which was much treasured by the Indians on account of its silky and curly texture. This robe was of the great-grandmother of the clan, so beloved and respected by her children that one or other of them was forever licking her coat, hence its particular texture. If an old grandmother was killed or wounded, the other buffaloes would hang around, refusing to leave her.

AMERICAN BISON WHOSE VAST HERDS FORMERLY ROAMED THE MISSISSIPPI PLAINS

When the time for migration arrived, the huge herds of bison (often inaccurately called "buffalo") used to form a moving mass, shoulder to shoulder, that might cover an area a hundred miles long and fifty miles wide. In the spring the ice covering the rivers would be getting thin so that as these tramping thousands crossed, the thinning surface would crack and the vanguard of the huge army drown. But the rest crossed on the piled bodies of those in front. These photographs are from the film "The Last Barrier."

HERD OF SCANDINAVIAN REINDEER AT THE HEAD OF A NORWEGIAN FIORD

During the summer the reindeer of Norway are to be found feeding on the grass of the valleys, while in the winter the herds go up the mountains and eke out a living on moss and various kinds of lichen. Wild herds are scarce now in Norway and only occur in the wilder parts. Outside that country the reindeer wanders through Lapland to Eastern Siberia. The wild herds are not large and contain only a few adult males, who act as sentries. But in the domesticated state the reindeer flourishes, for it has been kept by man for centuries in Scandinavia. At one time it occurred in England, and seems to have been hunted in the north of Scotland as late as the twelfth century.

J. D. Melhuish

TROOP OF GIRAFFES FOLLOWING THEIR LEADER AS THEY FLEE IN ALARM

Giraffes have greatly dwindled in numbers in South Africa, and it is only their extraordinary ability to exist for months at a time without drinking that has kept them from extermination in certain districts. They retire to waterless regions like the Kalahari Desert, where the herds have been found numbering perhaps fifteen or twenty head, while herds of seventy or more have been seen in the past. Our photograph shows a herd which has been alarmed by the approach of a photographer, and is making off in single file, as these creatures do when frightened. The leader of the herd will take them through the thickest bush unhurt, where no man might go on account of the thorns. But the giraffes, hides are impervious to such things.

J. D Ratton

HERD OF SEALS BASKING ON ONE OF THE SHETLAND ISLANDS

This remarkable photograph of a seal herd was taken in the Shetlands, and shows a sight not often to be observed, much less caught by the camera in the British Isles. It will be seen that one or two of the animals have noticed the presence of the photographer, perched high above them on the cliff and they are lazily turning their heads towards the camera. But the bulk of the herd is undisturbed and lies quite peacefully on the craggy ledge raised a foot or two above the water.

even though they remained at the cost of life. The passing of the buffalo was, indeed, a story as full of drama and pathos as any great history of wild Nature, but, alas, it could not be otherwise. The buffalo had to go. Imagine in these days the trampling of such unmanageable multitudes through the heart of a settled country!

OFTEN in the seeming folly of creatures which dwell in herds there lies the seed of a great wisdom. We in our ignorance are too apt to criticise and to compare the ways of animals with our own ways, but we must realize that though this creature and another may be an absolute fool with regard to the ways of mankind, it may yet stand out as wonderfully wise in its own world. How would the wisest of us fare, I wonder, if we had to change places with some of them?

As an example, sheep are generally set down as the most stupid of creatures, but, believe me, there are few animals more sagacious than the wise old ewe of the hill flock, chosen as leader because the rest have learnt that where she leads it is safe and wise to follow. The saying " blindly follow each other " has passed into an idiom of contempt, but among such creatures as dwell in herds, the rule of follow the leader is an inflexible and universal rule of life. As well might the soldier break formation as the herd-dweller break the line. The leader, I say, is chosen by common suffrage because she is best able to lead, and where she goes in a moment of danger the others will follow, be it over the brink and into giddy space. Thus, the panther lying in ambush is trampled down or beaten aside; even the grizzly cannot face the battering-ram assault of the breaking herd, whereas, if the individuals scattered they would be hunted down one by one and slain. You will notice that when a sheep breaks, the shepherd never sends his dog after it, for no dog can turn a breaking sheep. It will dash itself into a rushing river or even jump over a precipice that lies in its way sooner than turn, once its line of travel is decided upon.

It is much the same with the red deer. Great artists invariably paint a magnificent stag leading the herd, but generally it is a wise old hind. She knows the deer paths through the mountains, older many of them than the oldest human highways, and when her herd-mates begin to lose their brightness of eye and their lustre of coat, the wise old hind knows what ails them, and it is she who leads them to a distant place where certain herbs grow, or perhaps down to the sea-shore, where they can lick the medicinal brine from the rocks.

Major Radclyffe Dugmore

Major Radclyffe Dugmore

BUFFALO AND HIPPOPOTAMUS HERDS IN THEIR AFRICAN HOMES

To procure the lower photograph it was necessary to ascend a tree, and wait for the buffalo to come—and go. The African buffalo is considered by many hunters to be the most dangerous animal in the world, since it will attack without further provocation than the nearness of a human being, and will wait at the foot of a tree if its intended victim should climb one Above is a scene on a mud-bank in an African river showing just how a herd of hippopotami keep together when resting.

WILDEBEESTE AT A WATER-HOLE IN THE KRUGER NATIONAL PARK

So shy are the wildebeeste or gnus of Africa, that the photographer had to spend fourteen hours up a tree near a water-hole to obtain this view of the wild life of a herd. At one time there were enormous numbers of wildebeeste and the black variety were full of curiosity about any human beings they might see, and used to gallop round hunters' wagons in a playful fashion. But persecution followed the white man's invasion of their territory, and in becoming scarce they also became so very shy that it is now impossible to approach them near enough for photography on the open plains where they live. The bulls, which keep watch, sometimes standing quite still for several hours, are extremely keen-sighted.

E. N. A

WOLF THAT IS SOMETIMES SOLITARY AND SOMETIMES RUNS IN PACKS

In the spring and summer wolves usually run alone or in pairs, but when the winter comes they form a pack for hunting such creatures as they could not deal with singly. The cunning of the pack is amazing, the leader winning the place of honour by its own superiority. A pack of wolves has brought concerted running to such an art that every individual of a pack can pass and leave only one trail—that of the leader. All the rest place their feet exactly in the leader's snow prints and so avoid having to break an individual trail.

As the buffalo once trod the prairies, so even to-day the caribou make their great journeys north and south, across the Barrens of the New World which are equivalent to the tundra of the Old. They stick to their recognized routes, and I myself have seen a caribou path deeply trodden into the earth, and as clearly defined as a human highway. Now and then a city may spring up along one of their lines of travel, and the antlered pilgrims have been known to walk through its avenues, staring wide-eyed at its human dwellers. Great lakes may bar their way, blizzards may hinder their progress, but the caribou have been evolved for these great journeys across the bleak lands they haunt.

Every hair of a caribou's coat is a hollow quill, so that it swims high out of the water, buoyed up by its natural lifebelt, and it can swim for miles. The hoofs, too, are specially designed, for the arrangement of the joints is such that when the animal treads on soft ground or snow, the splay opens enormously, and the whole hoof comes in contact up to the forelock joint, thus preventing its sinking. Moreover, the hoof clicks loudly at every step, and this constant clicking keeps the herds together, just as the twittering of small birds heard high in the heavens at night-time keeps the migrating flocks together. The Indians of the Barren Lands lie in waiting for *la fièvre* of the caribou, and massacre hundreds of them, the meat being cached underground, where it freezes solid and will keep for months. So a long line of caches is built across the Barren Lands, but should the caribou, ever whimsical, pass by a different route, the Barren Lands Indians may find themselves face to face with starvation in a day.

The caribou is not swift; his maximum speed probably does not exceed fifteen miles an hour, but he can keep it up for hours on end, and the herd you startle at daybreak may be a good hundred miles distant by dusk.

AMONG certain creatures which live in herds we find markings which, on the face of things, seem to bear evidence contrary to Darwin's theory, which is that no creature has acquired a marking or an attribute otherwise than what it has evolved for its safety and betterment. Why, then, the white tail of the rabbit, which betrays him every time, and yet is of inestimable value to his fellow colonists in that it spreads the news of danger? The saying that the white tail serves to deceive the eye will not bear close scrutiny, for why catch the eye simply to deceive it? Better far to escape observation.

When a rabbit rises and runs, he unwittingly hands on the warning to those around him, and taking the hint, they steal away, so that the news quickly spreads two fields ahead of the man with the gun. In the dusk of the evening I have shot more rabbits than

Herbert G. Ponting, F.R.P.S., Copyright

PENGUIN COLONY AT CAPE ROYDS IN THE ANTARCTIC

The Adelie penguins may be seen nesting by the thousand in the Antarctic. They each collect a little pile of stones and on this unpromising "nest" lay their eggs. Each pair have to guard vigilantly against their neighbours who are waiting to steal a stone for themselves from someone else's heap. One of the Antarctic expeditions noticed that the penguins used to go about in great parties with no other apparent object than to see the country, considering that they feed entirely in the sea. In parties, too, they used to visit the explorers' camp.

I can remember, owing simply to that white danger flag, but a more impressive example is afforded by the white stern disks of the antelope, which normally lives in herds. Ordinarily, the white disk is hardly noticeable, but immediately an individual antelope becomes alarmed, every hair stands on end, and the disk shines like an aluminium frying-pan, catching the eye not only of the lurking foe, but of every other antelope within the range of visibility. Simultaneously with the erecting of the hair, musk glands in the centres of the disks come into play, so that should the visible warning fail, the scent warning will at least reach those down wind.

Now, could a more elaborate system of self-advertisement be imagined? Could a creature possess any feature more betraying in itself and detrimental to its own individual safety? Yet, to its herd mates, to those dwelling with it, the attribute is of immense value. Evolution cannot, of course, have brought about a destructive feature, but in the case of animals which dwell in herds, the survival of the individual has but one safe foundation, which is the survival of the herd. Thus, we come back to a set of rules governing their protection which are quite different from the rules which govern solitary animals. We come back to the rule of the herd which will dash itself over the edge in pursuit of the leader.

Creatures which live in herds are generally the most sagacious, because the best brain governs the movements of the rest and, as I have said, a pack or a herd generally consists of a family. A pack of timber wolves, for example, consists of the parents and the cubs of that year, and by early spring the parents have the cubs pretty well trained. In Algonquin I have heard wolves ranging for game night after night, and in the morning have seen the signs of their passing, the cleanly picked backbone of a deer with skull intact. We have stood these grim tokens up in the snow to serve as signposts, and, believe me, there is not much that the wolf-pack does not know by mid-November.

They are not swift, and when running a deer timber wolves probably run no faster than a good human sprinter, yet they work so well together that the swiftest of creatures has no chance. With them hunting is a great science, and every trick of the ambush and the relay chase is known to them. On one occasion we fired into a pack in full cry along a blood trail, and owing to the clearness of the

Mortimer Batten

Chas. Barrett

GANNETS IN THEIR NOISY COMMUNITY AT NESTING TIME

In Scotland, Ailsa Craig on the west and the Bass Rock (top) on the east are renowned for the gannet colonies where thousands make their nests annually. During the time the birds are building the nests the din made by the colony is terrific since the pieces of grass or seaweed, out of which the nest is made, are continually being pilfered and fought over. Gannets are more abundant in the Southern than the Northern Hemisphere and our lower photograph was taken on an island in the Bass Strait between Tasmania and Australia.

Natural History, N.Y.

BIRD LIFE IN THE MASS: PELICANS AND SEA GULLS

By first constructing a " hide " and then having the young birds driven towards it the lower photograph was obtained, for the parent birds, though very suspicious, followed their young, every now and then flying away in alarm, but soon returning. The old birds seem to feel the responsibilities of parental care and try to keep their offspring in some sort of shelter from the sun, restraining any efforts to stray by vigorous pecks. In the upper photograph we see a vast cloud of gulls attracted to a meat-packing works by the presence of offal.

Elwin R. Sanborn

AMERICAN BASS KEEPING WARM IN WINTER TIME

ound widely distributed in the rivers and lakes of the United States, the handsome bass are related to the perch of Britain, and provide uch good sport for anglers. These fish have the strange habit of huddling together in winter time with their heads all pointing in the same rection, as we see here. This extraordinary cluster, which seems to hang in the water by means of some invisible suspension, was photographed in the New York Aquarium. The fish, it will be noticed, have very handsomely marked skins.

atmosphere, they looked hardly a hundred yards off, though they must have been fully a mile distant. As the bullets ricochetted and boomed across the ice, casting up white spumes, the wolves turned and streaked in single file for the nearest cover, but going up, we found in the snow the tracks of only one wolf. The others had placed their feet exactly where the leader had trod, so obtaining the easiest going without each one breaking trail for itself.

Such is the wariness and the cunning of timber wolves, such is the denseness of the regions in which they live, that I have known men who have lived the whole of their lives in wolf-infested forests, who have taken scores in their traps or by poisons, and who have heard them almost nightly, yet who have never seen a single wolf alive and free.

Many of the higher animals that dwell in packs are human in the extreme; the old dog baboon will face death unflinchingly to save a "woman" or a "child" of his clan, and those who have visited Gibraltar will have heard almost incredible stories of the social circles and the human reasonings of the monkeys that come down from the Rock from time to time.

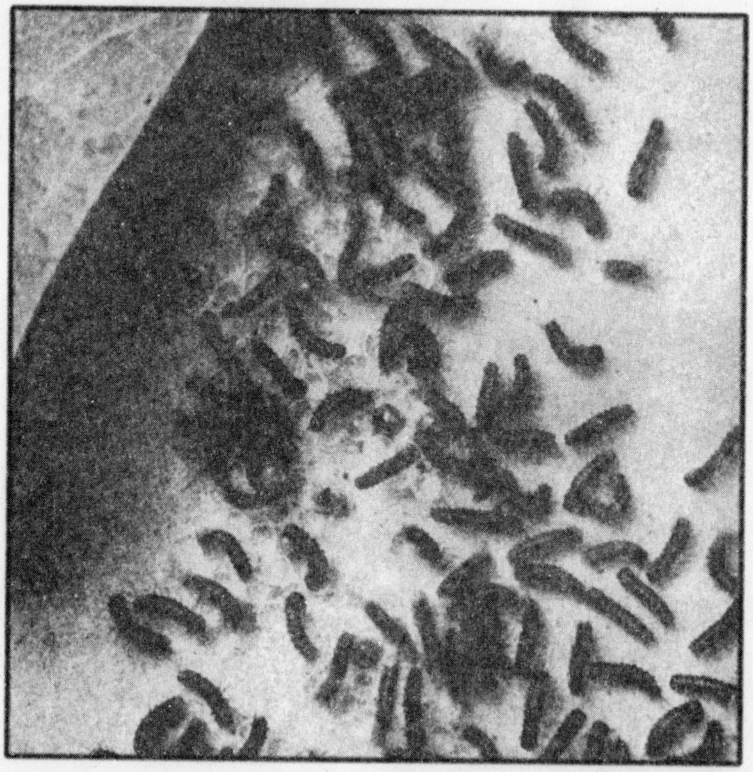

M. H. Crawford

CROWD SCENES IN NATURE; CATERPILLARS AND ANTELOPES

The lower photograph shows a batch of tiger-moth caterpillars just about to begin a life of hard feeding and rapid growth. Above is a herd of antelope coming to the feeding-ground at the Mount Dome antelope refuge in California. The animals have seen the camera, and are huddled together, watching, suspiciously, for danger.

So much, then, for the gipsy folk, but those which dwell in cities are equally interesting. Space does not permit a description of the beaver city with its dams and its canals and its flood gates and its lodges, nor yet of many of the cities of the insect world. Darwin said that but for earthworms, which turn and air the soil, nothing could grow, but he evidently forgot the vast and fertile regions of our great continents which for several months are frozen, and where there are no earthworms. In so far that the earth must be turned, Darwin was right, and where this has not been done by worms, ground-burrowing rodents have taken their place. For example, look at the prairie dog cities of North America. If a dog city be pegged out and watched, it will be found to be constantly creeping one way or another, and ten years hence it may be centred half a mile distant. Thus through the ages burrowing rodents, including the mice millions, have rendered the earth fertile that they themselves may live upon it, just as the squirrel, by burying nuts, then forgetting where he has buried them, extends the forests with the valuable nut-bearing trees on which his race depends.

We speak of the wonders of bird migration; how birds traverse seas and continents, coming and going to the day, but what about the wonders of the migrants of the sea, who cover distances as great, or greater, and that through unfathomable depths where there are no landmarks—the four years' journey of the elver eels from the depths of the Sargasso Sea; or the annual movements of the herring and the mackerel which are more prompt in their migrations than the cuckoo and the swallow.

Chapter LIII

Bird Friends of the Farmer

By H. J. Massingham

Author of "Some Birds of the Countryside"

No subject—thus I would like to begin this article—is so littered with ignorance, prejudice and confusion as that of the economic status and utility of wild birds. Unfortunately, I am unable to think of any other subject concerned with the values, material or spiritual, of life which is not equally clogged with the same importunate interferences. The reasons are not far to seek. Nowadays we—and by "we" I mean those powerful enough to do so—interfere with everything. It is an age of interference, and has been so for a hundred years. At the same time, we are martyrs to certain abstractions—"Progress," "The Conquest of Nature," "Morality," "Science," and a round dozen of others. We are too much in a hurry ever to pause and ask what we mean by these words, and whether all the results we achieve by them are worth while. We pursue these abstractions because they are a means to power, and the acquisition of power, which, of course, implies interference, is the main object of Western civilization. Such questions as the value of power, whether it makes people wiser or happier and what use we are to make of it when we have got it, are pure irrelevancies. The object of life is power; the means to acquire it are institutional or mechanical and the driving-force to achieve power is, of course, the love of power itself.

This is no idle excursion away from our theme. The inter-relationship between birds and vegetation is an exceedingly intricate mechanism which took nature millions of years of experiment and labour before just the right balances and adjustments were in proper working order. Up to the nineteenth century man's dealings with nature did not affect the equilibrium very materially. Changes in the relative abundance of certain species over others, variations in the food-habits of birds living in the neighbourhood of man, were inevitable consequences of the invention of agriculture. But it cannot be said that these changes amounted to a serious dislocation of natural balances. Birds and crops and insects went on playing their respective parts in the complex interplay of natural economy. Then came the nineteenth century, the unprecedented advances of the sciences, the discovery of a new deity "The Conquest of Nature," and the capacity, extended to a large number of people, of taking life very much more expeditiously and comfortably than ever was possible before in the whole history of mankind.

These new powers were not, however, accompanied by any corresponding advance in sanity, wisdom or good feeling. Man in other words was given a new lease of power without any but the dimmest idea of how to use it. Consequently he misused it, as any child will make mischief with a revolver if he gets the chance of handling it. The way that the last century handled its new powers was to make chaos of that infinitely delicate mechanism commonly known as the "Balance of Nature," that is, the mutual interdependence of all forms of life upon each other scaled to that nicety where no one type, genus or species of living thing preponderates to the undue disadvantage or the exclusion of another. The Great Dislocation happened in so many different ways that I shall not even try to give more than a very few cursory examples. In order to enable retired stockbrokers to kill game-birds in large numbers and without too much trouble, the game-keepers made away with the birds of prey, with the result that mice and voles and sparrows exultantly multiplied to such an extent that the farmers began to lose hundreds of tons of crops and roots every year.

YOUNG THRUSH WITH FULL BEAK

For about nine months of the year—the months when our food supplies are growing—the thrush feeds largely on harmful insects and grubs. Here is a young bird with its beak full.

The decline of agriculture, precipitated during the twentieth century, was made the occasion after the War of a concentrated offensive against the very birds who made a livelihood out of their hosts of insect foes. A war of extermination was waged against the birds that frequent orchards because some of the fruit was pecked by some of the birds. It never occurred to the zealous fruit guardians to inquire into the feeding habits of these birds over the rest of the year and so to estimate to what extent the amount of fruit consumed or spoiled by them was

Ralph Chislett

BLUE-HEADED WAGTAIL, AND A RED-BACKED SHRIKE WITH A MOTH

Among the casual visitors to Britain is the blue-headed wagtail (left), distinguished by its blue-grey head and neck. It often makes its nest right in the cornfields, where it feeds on insects and their grubs. It is also very fond of flies and is a friend to the grazing cattle, fluttering to within a foot or two of their muzzles to snatch at the tormenting insects. The red-backed shrike (right) visits England in April or May, and proceeds to capture large quantities of mice and beetles, later on attacking wasps and moths.

compensated for or overborne by their checks to the inconspicuous and far more insidious insect larvae which could only achieve maturity on a fruit diet. Yet it is certain that if the popping of those well-intentioned guns in the orchards had not been at last partially silenced by the passionate efforts of a few intelligent observers, fruit cultivation in this country would have perished with its insectivorous defenders.

SINCE it will be tedious to multiply such instances, I will wind up this census of the Kingdom of the Blind with two very striking illustrations. One concerns the world-famous guano islands off the coast of Peru. These islands were once inhabited by species of gannet, pelican, cormorant, tern, petrel and shearwater in such countless numbers that they passed to and fro between them like scudding clouds before a sou'wester and hid the eternally blue heavens. In the course of centuries such huge deposits of bird-droppings were accumulated that the isles actually rose many feet higher from the sea. The value of the guano deposit as a fertiliser for the barren fields of the mainland plain between the coast and the Andes was greatly enhanced by the aridity of the atmosphere, and it was through these birds that the ancient Incas accomplished such prodigies of making the desert fruitful. Consequently they were very strictly protected by the archaic Children of the Sun.

In the middle of the Victorian period, however, the islands were ceded by a corrupt administration to various British and European firms. A time of cut-throat competition ensued. Coolies, slaves in all but name, were imported in British ships to die by suicide and over-work in such numbers that they became mummified in the guano, the birds nested in their empty skulls and the modern diggers find cartloads of human bones. In the scramble for guano and nothing but guano the birds who supplied it were killed off by the hundred thousand. When a wiser government took over the islands after a fury of carnage and exploitation lasting for nearly fifty years, only about one-tenth of the most economically valuable birds in the whole world remained to scream the good news of the exploits of progress to the new century. And to-day the existence of Peru as a nation practically depends upon the regular supply of guano dug out of the desolate rocks sticking out of the Humboldt Current with its super-abundant wealth of marine life for the birds and sea-lions to feed upon.

The second illustration is like a parable from Hans Andersen. For many years all manner of boards, councils, conferences, associations, committees, assemblages and other black-coated teams have been vociferating to a mighty crescendo that as many a sea-bird lives on fishes, and fishes were obviously created for the sole purpose of entering the stomach of man alone, a holy war must be declared on the fish-eating birds. It was calculated that since an average of twenty-five birds a day was captured by the St. Andrews fishermen among the shoals, these birds must dispose of 26,880,000 fishes per annum. The fact that only a certain proportion of the finny tribes are food-fishes and that even the abandoned gulls, terns, cormorants, puffins, guillemots and razorbills could not be fishing all day long and every

A. H. Willford

W. H. Crawford

J. T Roberts

G. Hearn

THREE OWLS WHICH DEVOUR FARMING PESTS

Although the little owl cannot properly be called a British bird, large numbers have been introduced into the country from time to time. In the lower photographs we see two of these birds which have joined the war against farming pests. One has caught a big mouse (left), while the other is pouncing on a mole. The barn owl (top left), or white owl, is widely distributed over England and Wales. It feeds largely on voles, and rats and mice. The long-eared owl (top right) frequents woods, and devours moths, beetles and mice.

M. H. Crawford

J. T. Roberts

LONG-EARED AND BARN OWLS, DESTROYERS OF VERMIN, DISPLAY THEIR FIERCE DISPOSITIONS

During the autumn the numbers of the long-eared owl (left) are greatly raised by migrations from the Continent. This owl takes possession of an old squirrel's nest or the deserted home of a magpie or crow, and sets out at night in search of rats and mice. The brown owl (right) haunts the woods and often lays its eggs in a hollow, ivy-covered tree. It allows itself a fairly generous diet, including voles and rats and small birds, and will occasionally take a squirrel or even a fish that is swimming near the surface. Moles and insects are also readily eaten by this formidable bird, which has a wing span of about sixteen inches. Strangely enough, this owl seems to be unknown in Ireland, but is common in Great Britain in wooded or rocky localities.

Oliver G. Pike

CURLEW, THE FARMER'S FRIEND WHEN YOUNG, AND THE MOUSE DESTROYING KESTREL

Curlews make a simple nest (left) of grass and leaves on the open moor and the young, when hatched, stay near at hand for a few days, after which they begin to pick up a living in the surrounding country. Insects, spiders and snails are plentifully eaten, but after a time the birds take to the sea-shore and feed on crustaceans and marine animals, when they cease to be of service to man. The kestrel (right) may be distinguished in the air by its habit of flying up into the wind and hovering for a time. It folds its wings and falls like a stone upon its prey, which consists largely of mice, particularly in northern England and Scotland. In the South the kestrel also eats grasshoppers and beetles. It is one of the farmer's very best friends.

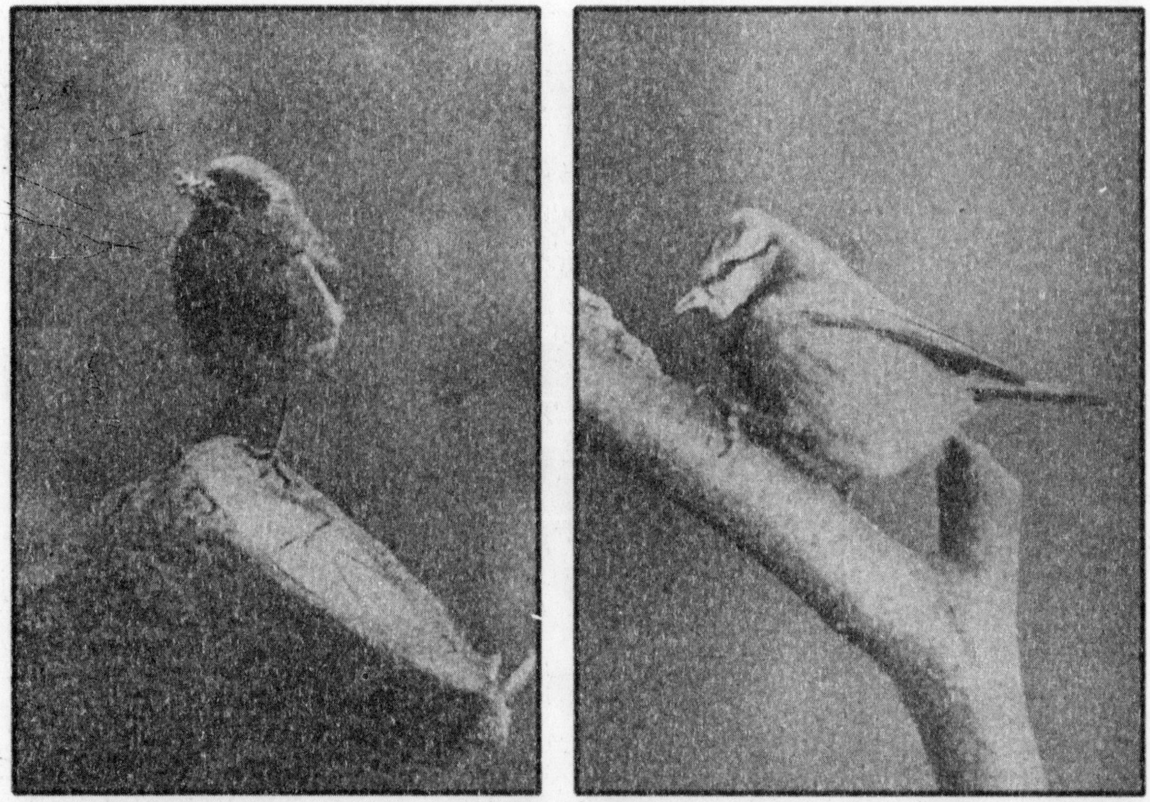

R. Chislett

G. Hearn

INSECT CATCHERS OF FIELD AND GARDEN: TREE SPARROW, STARLING, ROBIN AND BLUE TIT

The tree sparrow (bottom left) hunts the trees for insects and caterpillars, and nests in holes in the trunks or branches. The starling (bottom right) was formerly of good service to farmers since its food ordinarily consists principally of insects, grubs, and slugs. But the number of starlings has now increased alarmingly and the birds have turned their attention to eating seeds and fruits. Above are a robin (top left) with a beak stuffed with insects from a garden, and (top right) a blue tit, a great searcher for grubs

A. H. Willford

RINGED PLOVER ON ITS NEST BESIDE THE SEA-SHORE

The ringed plover is one of those birds which pick up much of their food along the sea-shore but make excursions inland for a change of diet. This particular plover nests, like the Kentish plover, on the shore, often not far from high-water mark, and finds sand-hoppers and shrimps along the beach. It becomes an assistant to the farmer when it goes off to the fields for a meal of insects. This bird is fairly evenly distributed along the coasts of Britain, especially where there are sand dunes or pebble beaches.

day, did not prevent the appalling question being asked—if twenty-five birds can consume this mountain of fish in a year, what of the birds round the entire British coast ?

A similar agitation fermented for years on the East Coast, where it was demanded that, since terns had increased at Blakeney Point, in Norfolk, and the flat fish had decreased, these flying feys must die. Forty-eight were killed and sent up for stomach analysis to Dr. Collinge. Not a bone, not the tiniest fragment of flat fish was discovered in a single one. Yet before protection was accorded to terns and certain other sea-birds on our coasts, the coastal bird-homes resembled a bird-battlefield at the end of last century. Analyses of other fish-eating birds (nineteen species) were made, and it was found that only 45 per cent. of their food was piscine.

But the point of the story is that in 1883 Huxley had declared that all the principal food-fisheries—cod, mackerel, herring and others—were "inexhaustible," while later investigators have corroborated his verdict to the effect that "no action of man or bird can make any appreciable difference to the plenitude of fish," such is the overwhelming fecundity of the ocean. The irony is the more pointed from the fact that it has been the bird-accusers themselves who have been responsible for the excessive wastefulness of the fishing industry in the destruction of millions of useless young plaice by the trawlers. All the sea-bird battues, all the Reports, all the expenditure of money, argument and foolish greeds that made them boiled down to a vanity of nothingness from the simple fact that the sea provides and always will provide more than enough for all, men and birds and porpoises and dolphins and seals and sharks and dog-fishes alike.

It is, indeed, literally impossible to estimate the magnitude of the destruction in wild life, of the impoverishment of nature and of the losses to agriculture for which the acquisitive elements nurtured by the industrial revolution are responsible. It is not a very comforting thought that such losses might have been avoided if we had known nothing about nature at all, but if good feeling had taken the place of lack of knowledge. Injurious species of bird, that is to say, are in so small a minority that had they been protected together with the beneficial species purely out of sentiment, we should to-day have been materially the richer for it. In the light of such a fact it is odd that the illusion should persist that what are commonly called "sentimental considerations" are entirely impractical. On the other hand, the reiterated voices of the few urging us to observe

Oliver G. Pike

the poetic justice of that lack of sympathy which drove us to "conquer" nature at the price of so many disasters are nowadays beginning to be heard. In many different ways, our fatal interference with the slowly-perfected adjustments of nature has produced harmful repercussions. Not the least of them is the wilful creation of a mass of highly complicated problems which never existed before we tipped over the natural balances of wild life.

The life of nature is an interwoven pattern of strands; break one and others come apart, and they in their turn introduce confusion into other sections of the wonderfully constructed fabric.

Various blunderings through it, for instance, have caused a wholly disproportionate increase of that brisk little urchin, the house sparrow. In agricultural districts, 75 per cent. of the sparrow's food is cereals and only five per cent. injurious insects. He gorges on ripe crops; he usurps the nesting sites of more desirable species; he riots among the flowers, and his mobs have the same general effect on bird-life that the standardised herd-mind has upon human society. He depreciates the qualitative currency of bird-life. Yet it is impossible now to shrink his numbers to their natural balance with those of other species by artificial means. Even cats, which, according to the evidence, destroy something like fifty per cent. of our garden birds every year, do not sensibly diminish the sparrow hosts. On the other hand, we reduce birds like the corn-crake, that Samson among the insect cereal-devourers, to such scarcity that the species is near that margin of resistance when it, as it were, loses heart and fades automatically into extinction. Moreover, in order to redress this topsy-turvydom of common and uncommon species, we have elaborated a system of bird protection laws which nobody understands, nobody enforces, and nobody observes. Our birds are far better protected to-day than in those havocking Victorian days, not by the cumbrous machinery of the law, but by the steady growth and widening of a delight in their beauty, animation, and a kind of celestial quality they have about them.

Poetic justice has overtaken our prideful short-sightedness in another direction. The plagues of Egypt are always on the horizon; the rustle of their champing mouths might well drown even the din of our mechanical civilization. It has been estimated that the passerine birds of the eastern half of Nebraska destroy 162,771,000 locusts a day. The average locust weighs fifteen grains, and consumes its own weight of cereals every day. In a year this number would devour 174,397 tons of crops, worth nearly two million dollars. In the Abruzzi, locusts move in such earth-darkening swarms as occasionally to hold up the trains between Rome and Avezzano. An ornithologist has worked out that a pair of gipsy moths, if unchecked, would beget enough offspring in eight years to destroy the entire foliage of the United States. The chinch bug, a potato-glutton and a favourite food of the quail, can accommodate 20,000 of its numbers on

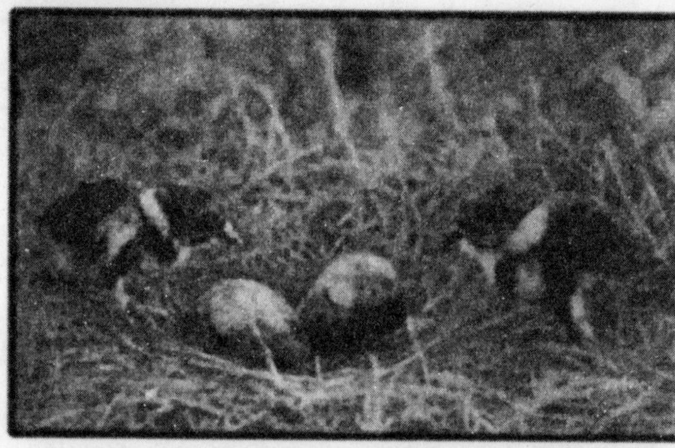

YOUNG LAPWINGS AND THEIR PARENT

Any depression in the turf or on the plough will serve the lapwing for a nest, and the young, on hatching in a ploughed field, find themselves at once in the midst of a plentiful supply of grubs which are destroyers of crops. The lapwing's other name is peewit, in imitation of its cry.

eight inches of grass stalk. Or listen to this. If a hop aphis succeeded in developing thirteen generations in a single year, the brood, if marshalled in line, would extend to a point so remote in space that light, travelling at the rate of 186,000 miles per second, would take 2,500 years to reach the earth from the head of the procession.

It is not surprising, therefore, that the early settlers of Salt Lake City erected a monument to Franklin's Gull for clearing their wheatfields of the crickets that threatened them with starvation. One rookery of Australian straw-necked ibis (*Carphibis spinicollis*) was calculated to have digested 482,000,000 grasshoppers in one year.

M. H. Crawford

CORNCRAKE THAT PREYS ON SNAILS

Reaching England in April from its winter quarters in Africa the corncrake or land-rail likes low-lying meadows, and places its nest in the standing hay or corn. It preys on small snails and slugs and insects. When alarmed it sneaks from cover to cover along the ground, only taking wing in the last resort, when it flies clumsily.

TAKE a few percentages of the insect food some of our more familar birds feed their nestlings on—starling 90 per cent., songthrush 86 per cent., blackbird 60 per cent., great tit 90 per cent., skylark, wren, yellowhammer, blue tit and chaffinch 100 per cent.: add to this the fact that the nestlings are fed at intervals of from a half to a full minute with a beakful from sunrise to sunset, and the statement that if the entire bird-stock of the world were to be annihilated, the earth would become totally barren of vegetation in three years will not appear very extravagant.

Of course, a certain proportion of the insects eaten by birds (the ichneumon fly, for instance) themselves prey upon the noxious members of the insect multitudes, and though it is highly immoral of them, birds do not discriminate between them. Man, too, invents ingenious artificial devices to check the invading hordes. But on an all-round view, a working knowledge of the inter-relations between birds, crops and insects shows that the practice of destroying the former on a large scale is one not of nature-conquerors but of lunatics. A swelling of the insect legions follows upon a diminution of bird-life as all effects follow upon their contingent causes.

Another ill-effect of crashing through the subtle architectural poises of nature is our habit of sticking moral labels on birds as a porter registers trunks to different destinations. We speak of "good" birds and "bad" birds when what we really mean is birds that live on different types of diet.

Actually there is an extremely simple way out of all the artificial complications of economic ornithology. Thanks to the researches of Dr. Collinge ("The Food of some British Wild Birds") and others, we know precisely how birds stand to the farmer and how the farmer should stand to birds. The "volumetric" method, that of averaging the total food of a given species in different districts and all the year round by examination of the crops of various individuals of it, clearly reveals that the great majority of species are beneficial to man. Seventy per cent. of the food eaten by the lapwing, which agriculturists have allowed to become reduced so seriously from its former abundance, consists of the wireworms, leather-jackets, weevils, myriapods and coleoptera which live entirely upon the fruits of the field. The woodpeckers, shot for the damage to trees attributed to them, devour the ash, pine and bark weevils, the longicorns, leopard, clearwing and tortrix moths, which spend their larval stages in riddling timber which the birds themselves never touch except for the purpose of extracting these pests. Seventy-five per cent. of the total woodpecker food consists of these insects.

To this general rule that nearly all our British species do far more good than harm to our agriculture and fruit-growing there are eleven exceptions, which have to be differently graded. The rook and the starling are more injurious than beneficial in certain

G. Hearn

ALLIES IN THE INSECT WAR: THRUSH, SEDGE WARBLER, STARLING AND FLYCATCHER

Though the song thrush (bottom left) is a favourite because of its music, it is also to be commended for the slugs and grubs it consumes. It is nearly always found in cultivated places, such as gardens and orchards, and while it makes some havoc with fruit in the late summer, it more than compensates for the damage by the good work it puts in, ridding the land of pests during the rest of the year. The sedge warbler, which we see here (bottom right) building its nest, is found in marshes and by the banks of rivers, and is very partial to slugs besides the water insects and larvae. The starling (top left), where it is not over abundant, is a good insect destroyer, and the name of the flycatcher (top right) tells of that bird's most constant occupation.

areas, because our interferences with the web of natural life have increased their numbers out of all proportion to their natural rate of reproduction where the checks and balances of the wild are in operation. The house sparrow, the ring, stock and rock doves, and the bullfinch certainly do more harm than good to fruit, cereal and garden cultivation.

But the bullfinch and the rock dove are uncommon birds, and the aggregate harm they do is shrunk to a little measure by the paucity of their numbers. With the bullfinch, beautiful alike in his plumage, so English in its colouring; his music and his devotion to his mate, good feeling and love of beauty should have the last word. The sparrow hawk, blackbird, greenfinch and chaffinch are partially harmful.

THE sparrow hawk accounts for rather too many insectivorous birds, though he reduces the numbers of sparrows and starlings. But he is not really a serious problem, partly because the gamekeepers wage such merciless war against this poor Ishmael, and partly because birds of prey only secure the weaker members of their natural food-birds and so help to preserve the vigour of the stock. The black one of the woodland Pan-pipes with "orange-tawny bill" devotes 25 per cent. of his total dietary to the fruits he is luckless enough to enjoy as much as we do. On the other hand, 22 per cent. of his yearly sum of meals consists of injurious insects. The chaffinch's bill of fare is 56 per cent. of weed seeds, 16 per cent. of injurious insects, 1 per cent. of beneficial insects, 4 per cent. of fruit buds, and 8 per cent. of cereals, so that it is difficult to assess which has the better of it—the cloud or the silver lining.

A. H. Willford

INSECTS BY THE BEAKFUL

Some idea of the number of insects demanded by the average family of long-tailed tits can be gathered by a glance at this photograph. The parents catch their food largely on the wing, and every few minutes one or other of the birds is at the nest.

Oliver G. Pike

WHITETHROAT FEEDING ITS YOUNG

Whitethroats raise two broods each summer, and have to keep a number of widely gaping beaks satisfied. This means hard work and a tremendous toll of insect life. The nests of these small birds are virtually insect-destroying factories.

Hence the reduction of the superabundant species has to be moderately and scientifically undertaken, while those which are not plentiful should be allowed to contribute their glow to the prism of life. To exterminate a species on any account whatever or reduce it to a perilous rarity is a crime unpardonable, and even with the house sparrow and the wood-pigeon, who do vastly more harm than all the other nine species put together and multiplied by ten, we owe it to the creative power of life and evolution (what used to be called "the glory of God") to depress their numbers humanely and courteously. The winter wood-pigeons have to be shot because they are immigrants, but the true method of reducing too abundant species and so restoring balances is to remove their eggs and diminish the available number of nesting sites.

Our legislation, which is usually a hundred years or more behind contemporary enlightenment, should follow suit by repealing all Protection laws at present in pseudo-force and passing a single comprehensive Act protecting the eggs and person of all wild species, excepting (I quote Dr. Collinge) "such as are known to be too numerous or injurious." This "black list" should be strictly subject to local conditions and to constant revision, while the nine, ten or eleven species on it should be safeguarded from indiscriminate, wanton or ill-judged destruction. If we were to carry out this simple measure, we could in time undo an imponderable amount of mischief both to nature and ourselves, enjoy our birds and our crops together, and hear a great deal less of that overdriven expression, "economic ornithology."

E. N. A.

James

BULL AND BEAR WHOSE STRENGTH HAS SO OFTEN BEEN USED FOR "SPORT"

To men the bull has always stood as a symbol of strength, and in the wild state an extra ferocity is added to the power of the great neck which operates the horns. Above is a bull from a herd of the English wild cattle which are still preserved in some parts of Britain. The upper photograph shows two bears, and it will be remembered in this connection that two of the favourite old English sports were bull and bear baiting, where these Samsons of the animal world were goaded by a Philistine crowd who set dogs on to attack these great beasts

Chapter LIV

Samsons of the Animal World

By W. S. Berridge

Author of "Marvels of Natural History"

PHYSICAL fitness plays an important part in the lives of all living creatures, and the old adage that "the weakest go to the wall" is especially applicable to the members of the Animal World, for without health and strength they have little chance in the struggle for existence. The very term wild beast seems to suggest power, vigour, agility, and muscular development, and it is difficult to conceive a C3 grade of animals, to make use of a war-time expression.

But although there is no disputing the fact that some creatures are much stronger than others, such a difference is largely of a relative nature; for the tiny flea and the mighty elephant are both entitled to rank as Nature's Samsons.

Animals characterised by their large size are normally endowed with great strength, for they must necessarily possess large bones, to which are attached powerful muscles. Bulk, however, may to a certain extent be due to obesity, especially among those animals, such as the bears, that hibernate and accumulate a store of fat upon their persons prior to their winter sleep. But such a condition is only temporary, for when the time arrives for the creatures once again to lead an active life, they have absorbed into their systems all their superfluous fat, and come forth from their lairs both lean and very hungry.

The bulkiest of animals, though not the largest, is the hippopotamus, a creature that sometimes attains a length of fifteen feet (inclusive of the short tail), and a weight of four tons. Its barrel-shaped body is supported by stout, short legs, and the massive head is set upon a thick neck. The mouth is enormous, and instances have been recorded of the hippopotamus upsetting and crushing a native canoe between its jaws. It has been known even to ram a river steamer, and one writer mentions an individual that chased and overtook a man on dry land, and then bit him in half.

As a rule, however, the hippopotamus leads a somewhat sedentary life, and spends much time basking and dozing upon the mud-flats; but should it be disturbed, it rushes into deep water, and makes such a splash that one might almost imagine a tidal wave had arisen.

Another animal giant is the elephant. Found in Africa and Asia, an individual from the former Continent has been known to measure eleven feet, eight and a half inches in height, and one from the latter region ten and a half feet. Such measurements, however, are unusual, and a stature of between nine and ten feet may be regarded as the average.

Although the skull of an elephant is very large, it is not so solid as it appears, the interior of the bones being honeycombed with cells separated from one another by thin partitions. The incisor teeth are developed into tusks that may protrude beyond the lips for a considerable distance. It is recorded that a pair of tusks of an African elephant weighed as much as 293 pounds, and measured respectively eleven and a half and eleven feet in length.

BEISA ORYX OF AFRICA

Among the most powerful of antelopes is the beisa oryx, which lives in British East Africa and Abyssinia. The horns are long and only slightly curved and are tremendously formidable, the upward double-pointed thrust being delivered with great power.

Needless to say, the combined weight of the elephant's skull and tusks could only be supported by a short thick neck, and as a short neck would not allow the animal to reach the ground with its mouth for the purpose of picking anything up, Nature has endowed it with a wonderful organ known as the trunk or proboscis—an elongation of the nose, pierced by two tubes or nostrils surrounded by a great mass of muscles.

Elephants will often uproot trees in order to feed upon the foliage of the upper branches; the leaves of the mimosa being regarded as a special dainty. Trees of thirty feet in height

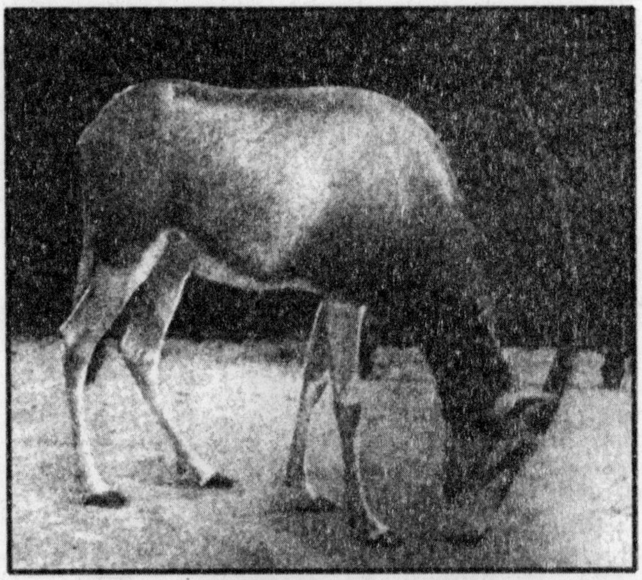

W. S. Berridge

DANGEROUS WEAPONS OF THE ANTELOPES

These horns of the sable antelope (top) are used with the greatest dexterity and, wielded by powerful neck muscles, can deal with several dogs at a time. It has the trick of a sideways jerk of the head which will transfix anything attacking from behind. Below is a sabre-horned antelope.

with stems four and a half feet in circumference, are brought toppling to the ground, several animals sometimes combining in the task, some employing their trunks for pulling, while others will dig at the roots with their tusks.

The great strength of the elephant is made use of to a large extent for lifting and stacking logs in the timber yards of Ceylon and elsewhere, while in the olden days the creatures were employed in warfare, and also for fighting in the Roman arena.

VERY formidable beasts are the rhinoceroses, for in addition to their great bulk, they are armed with one or more upstanding horns, situated upon their snouts. In the Indian rhinoceros, which has been known to measure eight feet in length (exclusive of the tail), only one of these weapons is present, but the common African rhinoceros normally possesses two, and individuals with three have been recorded.

The horns have no connection with the skull, and are merely composed of closely-packed fibrous hair. Moreover, they are slightly mobile, inasmuch as they will yield to pressure. According to an early writer, the foremost horn of the two-horned rhinoceros is plastic and hangs limp like the trunk of an elephant. Only when the beast is enraged does it become erected into an implement of offence. Unfortunately, however, this story is not true.

It has often been stated that the skin of a rhinoceros is bullet-proof, but such is not the case, as the following unhappy incident shows. An Irish soldier, stationed in India, thought he would test his rifle upon a captive rhinoceros. Taking careful aim, he pulled the trigger, and to his astonishment the beast promptly fell down dead. His faith in the toughness of the beast's hide received a rude shock, and the compensation he afterwards had to pay left him a poorer but certainly a wiser man.

In spite of its great bulk, the rhinoceros can run with considerable speed. When charging, the animal rushes blindly forward with head lowered ready to thrust its horns into the body of its foe. Even full-grown elephants have been known to be killed as a result of an encounter with one of these enraged beasts, so dangerous are they even to other powerful creatures.

The possession ot horns s common to other animals, such as oxen, sheep, goats, antelopes, and deer. Those of the latter, rightly called antlers, differ from those of other ungulates, inasmuch as they are solid, and are shed at intervals, instead of being composed of hollow sheaths, supported by a bony core, and retained throughout life.

Major Radclyffe Dugmore

A WRATHFUL SAMSON: RHINOCEROS ABOUT TO CHARGE

Not only is the rhinoceros enormously heavy, but it is also a quick mover when anger or fear is the incentive. Its charge is irresistible for any living thing, for there are several tons of weight behind the drive of the great horns on its snout. This specimen is from Africa, and has two horns, whereas the Indian rhinoceros has only one. Notice the typical attitude that denotes danger, the ears pricked and the tail erect, making a picture of indignation. There is, however, one great safeguard. This Samson is not blind, but he is very short-sighted.

STRENGTH IN REPOSE FACES THE CAMERA

With one blow of its paw a lion can kill an ox, and it is on these terrific blows rather than on its fangs, which usually attract more popular attention that the lion relies. A lion has been known to leap a wall nine feet high while carrying a calf in its mouth, and the possession of the power for such a leap easily constitutes the animal a "Samson." Even when taking its ease the lion gives an impression of self-confident strength, and if the animal yawns and stretches itself the great muscles can be seen moving under the skin.

The largest of the wild oxen is the gaur, a creature that may stand as much as six and a half feet at the shoulder; while of somewhat smaller stature is the Cape buffalo, a beast that has the reputation for being the most dangerous and fiercest of African animals. Both of these Samsons possess very massive horns, those of the latter being extremely broad at the base, and meeting across the forehead so as to form a cuirass that no bullet can penetrate. The strength of these huge cattle can well be judged by stating that some at the London Zoo have bent the thick iron bars of their cages with their horns to such an extent that large pieces of stout timber have had to be clamped crosswise thereto, so as to prevent further damage.

Among the antelopes, certain species stand out as being Samsons of their kind, the beisa oryx, the sabre-horned antelope, the gemsbok, and the sable antelope being notable examples. Endowed with great strength, and possessing long, backward-sweeping horns, they can render a good account of themselves if brought to bay, and instances have been recorded of lions being killed in combat with these courageous and graceful creatures.

Even the normally placid sheep do not always live up to their reputation. Indeed, the Indian fighting sheep or hunia (a domestic breed), is of such a pugnacious disposition that it is reared and kept for the sole purpose of affording sport, two of the animals being pitted against each another in combat. They fight with their heads, rushing at each another from a distance of about ten or twelve yards, and meeting with a crash that would split the skulls of most creatures. Sheep, however, are notoriously thick-skulled, and such blows do not appear to give them even a headache, for no sooner has the first one been delivered than they walk backwards to their stations and prepare for the next round. But even the strength of the mightiest has its limits, and in time the battle must end either in a draw or a "knock-out." On one occasion a fighting-ram was pitted against a tiger, the former attacking with such determination that a well-placed blow in the ribs caused the downfall of the giant cat.

The lion must also be mentioned among the Samsons of the animal world, for has he not earned the title of "the king of beasts"? Endowed with great muscular power, and having jaws armed with a formidable array of teeth, he is a creature that can command respect. He can fell an ox, an antelope, or a zebra with a single blow of his paw, and has even been known to leap over a wall, nine feet high, with a newly killed calf in his mouth.

As a rule, lions do not molest human beings, although occasionally individuals will turn man-eaters. Curiously enough, these are invariably old animals that have become too decrepit to overpower their normal prey, and have learned that an unarmed native falls an easy victim to their attack.

At the Zoo the lions are always sure of having an appreciative audience. But natural history is not always a strong point with visitors, and a man was once heard to exclaim to his companions who were gazing at a very fine specimen, "Fancy him being able to kill a man with a blow from his tail." It is true that a lion's tail has a small thorn-like growth at the extremity, hidden beneath a tuft of hair and that at one time it was supposed that the beast employed this to lash his body and goad himself into a state of fury. These picturesque conceptions, however, are not based upon fact, and the tail can in no way be regarded as a weapon.

As in the case of the elephant, lions were often engaged in the animal fights that the Romans used to organize for the amusement of the public, and we also read that it was an ancient custom in the East for offenders against the law to be cast into a den of these animals.

But the lion is not the only creature that has been employed in the rôle of executioner, for, according to an old account, the gorilla has been utilised for that purpose, the huge ape tearing to pieces the unfortunate malefactors that were thrown to it. It has also been stated that gorillas will carry off natives and overcome the elephant in combat.

"They goe many together," to quote the words of Battel, "and kill many negroes that travaile in the woods. Many times they fall upon elephants which come to feed where they may be, and so beat them

AN ELEPHANT'S GREAT STRENGTH UTILISED TO PUSH A FREIGHT CAR

.. very massive head armed with weighty tusks such as the elephant has must be supported on an enormously powerful neck. The pushing power of such a head and neck with the weight of an elephant's body behind it can be imagined. Here is an elephant being used in the U.S.A. for shunting a heavy freight car. Notice the position of the head and the attitude of the great forelegs, suggesting mighty effort. As for the strength of elephants it may be mentioned that these animals have a short way with a tree whose foliage is out of reach. They uproot it.

RAM'S POWERFUL HEAD ARMED WITH TWICE CURVED HORNS

The name of that once most effective weapon of siege war, the battering-ram, was a compliment to the strength with which the male sheep attacks its foes. One still speaks of warships "ramming" each other, but this form of attack, which is often almost as disastrous to the attacker as the attacked, is undertaken lightly by the animal which will charge and charge again against the equally hard and forceful head of a rival. In addition to the strength of the neck and the hardness of the skull, the ram possesses these twice curved horns

with their clubbed fists and pieces of wood that they will runne roaring away from them. These pongos are never taken alive, because they are so strong that ten men cannot hold one of them."

ALTHOUGH too much reliance must not be placed upon these early stories, the fact remains that the gorilla is one of the most powerful creatures that populate the earth. The great breadth of its chest at once proclaims it to be endowed with exceptional strength, while its arms are of enormous length, and its hands at least a third larger than those possessed by a human being.

Another of the manlike apes famed for its strength is the orang-utan, or mais, as it is called by the natives. With the exception of the crocodile and the python, no creature dare attack this Simian Samson, and even such encounters as may occur may be regarded more as accidents than otherwise, and the reptiles usually pay the penalty with their lives.

When dealing with a crocodile, the orang-utan pulls apart the reptile's jaws with his hands and then rips up its throat with its teeth; while the python, despite its strength, is also seized in the ape's terrible grasp, and then bitten so severely that it quickly succumbs to its injuries.

The great power in the hands and fingers of the orang-utan was revealed by an incident that occurred some years back at the London Zoological Gardens. After the keepers had departed, one of these apes amused itself by picking away at the stout wire-netting in front of its cage. Soon it managed to break a piece in half, and then it was a comparatively simple matter to enlarge the hole thus commenced. The next morning workmen were sent to replace the broken wire, and although the ape had succeeded in bending and breaking it with its fingers alone, the human artizans were unable to make an impression upon the metal without the use of a cold chisel and a heavy hammer.

Of the smaller type of monkeys, the baboons possess great muscular power, as well as canine teeth almost as large as those of a lion. They fight freely amongst themselves, and have been known to attack man. As they congregate in troops, they are unpleasant customers to meet, although it must be stated that nowadays they have learned to realize the significance of firearms. But should an enraged baboon get at close quarters there is little chance of escaping serious injury, for it buries its teeth in its victim, and, without for one moment releasing its grasp, tears right through the flesh.

Although baboons are so powerful, they are by no means untameable if captured young. That they can be taught to perform manual labour was exemplified some time back by a chacma baboon which had been trained by a cripple railwayman who worked on a branch line in Africa. At the word

of command the animal would pull the heavy levers that worked the signals, he would pump up water from a well near by, and even push along the lines the trolley upon which his master travelled to and from his work.

The ugliest, and possibly the most powerful, of all baboons is the mandrill, a creature that always causes merriment to the beholder because of the bright red and blue tints that decorate the face of the males, and more especially so on account of the colour scheme revealed when he stands back to his audience. Found in West Africa, the natives hold the beast in great dread, and state that sometimes it will attempt to carry off women and children. Although such stories are probably much exaggerated, and it is more than doubtful whether the baboon could drag along an adult human being, there is no disputing the fact that it is endowed with comparatively enormous strength.

W. S. Berridge

NEPALESE FIGHTING RAM AND A DUEL OF CYPRIAN SHEEP

Fighting rams have long been kept in India just as fighting cocks and dogs used to be kept in England. From a distance of about ten yards the rams rush at each other with all the gallant fury of two knights at a jousting, and meet with such a crash that one would think no skull could stand. The upper photograph shows a fight between wild sheep from Cyprus.

W. S Berridge

Neville Kingston

POWER OF THE LEGS AND POWER OF THE HEAD

Strength, in the kangaroo's case, lies in the hind limbs, and it is these which the animal chiefly uses in its defence. The most terrible kicks can be inflicted, especially as the feet are armed with formidable toes which are capable of ripping up the body of a foe. Above is an East African buffalo which has a most powerful head and neck and a broad and massive pair of horns.

Of the marine animals renowned for their muscular development, first place must be given to the whales, the largest of which may attain a length of as much as 95 feet. The naturalists of early days classified the whales as fish, and even at the present day there are many people who still consider them as such. But, although fish-like in form, they are mammals, breathing atmospheric air by means of lungs, and the females suckling their young.

Whales propel themselves through the water by lateral movements of their tails, which terminate in horizontally flattened and forked expansions called flukes. When harpooned they rush off at terrific speed, and an instance is recorded of a blue whale, or Sibbald's rorqual, towing a steamer by the harpoon rope for 24 hours on end, notwithstanding the fact that the boat's engines were reversed in an endeavour to stop the leviathan's progress. On another occasion an individual plunged downwards in the sea to a depth of a mile, and then broke its upper jaw by the impact upon the bed of the ocean. Whales have been known to descend nearly five thousand feet below the surface of the sea, and at that depth the water exerts a pressure of about 140 tons on every square foot of their bodies. The greatest depth to which a human diver, equipped with modern appliances, can descend is stated to be about two hundred feet, but such a feat would certainly not be unaccompanied with the risk of paralysis.

Other denizens of the sea that claim our attention are the octopods and squids. Their enormous muscular arms are provided with numerous adhesive disks, and woe betide a victim that should be so unfortunate as to get within their grasp.

The octopus, as implied by its name, possesses eight arms, each of which is furnished with about 120 pairs of suckers, arranged in two rows. When these suckers are applied to an object the interior part is first of all raised, and then retracted, a vacuum of great tenacity thereby being formed. Many very sensational stories have been recorded about the octopus, and enormous individuals have been described that could have existed only in the imaginations of the writers, but it is safe to say that specimens with tentacles six feet in length occur, though such a measurement may be regarded as a maximum.

Some of the squids, however, do attain to an immense size. Mr. A. E. Verril gives a description of a stranded squid in which the body measured ten feet in length, each of its two long tentacles (not possessed by an octopus) 42 feet, and its eight shorter arms, six feet.

Needless to say, one of these giants would be most unpleasant to meet at close quarters, and for a victim to be enfolded in its clinging tentacles and to feel the

G. Hearn

STRENGTH IN THE SWAN'S WHITE WING

Anyone who has seen the deadly battles which swans wage (bottom) will be readily convinced of their great strength. In fact, these are among the most truculent of birds, and the wings can break a man's arm at a blow. These birds often fight to the death and are sometimes very fierce when disturbed (top).

suckers attaching themselves one by one with an unrelaxing grip, must be a terrible experience. The more the captive struggles the more it is encircled within the squid's awful embrace, and slowly the victim is drawn towards its mouth, armed with a parrot-like beak.

Suctorial power is developed to a very high degree in the limpets. They excavate shallow depressions, or "scars" on the face of rocks, always returning thereto, and settling down on their chosen spots after their journeys in search of food. Those of us who have endeavoured to remove one of these molluscs from its citadel will know from experience what force it is necessary to employ before the animal can be induced to release its hold. "So firmly do they adhere," says Dr. Riley, "that it is estimated that they exert a resistance capable of lifting 62 pounds, or about 1,900 times their own weight."

The oyster is another example of a shellfish endowed with great strength, for by contracting certain powerful muscles it can hold together the two valves of its shell with remarkable tenacity.

The giant clam also exhibits its power in a similar manner, but as the largest specimens may weigh as much as two thousand pounds, or nearly a ton, it is of a much more formidable nature. Men wading or diving in search of pearls have lost their lives through accidentally placing a foot between the open valves of this giant shellfish, and once within the clam's grasp there is no escape unless a companion should happen to come to the rescue with some powerful lever with which to prise the shells apart.

Mention must be made of the coconut, or robber, crab, a giant of its kind that often measures a foot in length. According to report it is able to break a man's arm, or crack the shell of a coconut, with a nip from its powerful, pincer-like foreclaws, and Darwin records that a specimen secured in a strong tin box actually made holes right through the metal, and also

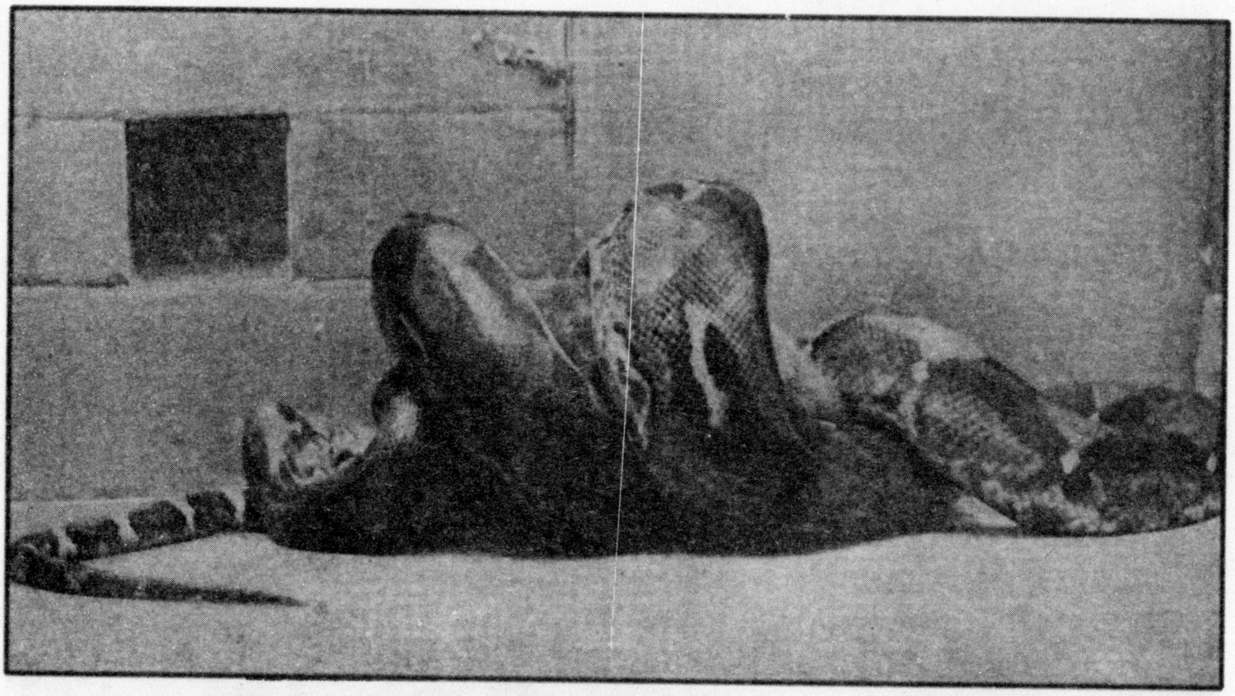

DEADLY STRENGTH OF THE BOA CONSTRICTOR IN OPERATION Neville Kingston

One sudden, deadly contraction of a large boa constrictor's coils can crush a man's ribs in a dozen places, and mammals the size of deer are killed in this way. In addition, the boa can use the strike like a poisonous snake, save that the hammer-like blow of the head takes the place of the poison fangs. A big boa can thus deliver what is probably the most powerful punch in the animal world. Above is one of these creatures engaged in crushing an animal preparatory to swallowing it.

bent down the edges of its prison so that it escaped. One of these crabs exhibited a short time back at the London Zoo would crack the shells of Brazil nuts, a feat that most of us find none too easy to accomplish even with the aid of nutcrackers.

The strength of some animals is displayed in their jumping powers, the kangaroo being a notable example among the higher creatures, and the flea being numbered among the more lowly forms.

MANY of us have probably at some time or other had experience of the elusive nature of the flea. It can leap two hundred times its own length, and it has been stated that if a human being, six feet in height, was endowed with proportional strength, he would be able to jump to a height of two hundred feet, or in four consecutive bounds cover a distance of a mile. One writer likens the performance of a flea to a man leaping from Bow Church, in Cheapside, over the top of St. Paul's Cathedral, and landing at Ludgate Circus, but this is probably an exaggeration. The strength of the insect has been exploited by man in a somewhat curious manner, for troops of performing fleas have been exhibited from time to time, the liliputian actors being harnessed to small wheeled-carts, made of cardboard, which they pulled along in a somewhat jerky fashion.

The kangaroo also rivals the human athlete in its jumping power, the larger species sometimes covering a distance of about ten yards at every bound, and keeping this up for as much as eighteen miles without stopping. If brought to bay the animal proves a very formidable antagonist, striking at its enemies with forward sweeps of its hind feet, and endeavouring to rip up their bodies with its large toes. The forearms are to a lesser extent also employed for offensive purposes, and many instances have been recorded of dogs being seized within their grasp and then held under water until drowned.

Passing to the birds, we find that although the majority are built on somewhat slender lines, and can by no stretch of imagination be regarded as Samsons, certain kinds prove an exception to the rule.

Some birds are endowed with exceptional muscular power of the wings, others demonstrate their strength by the use of their talons, while others are remarkable for the development of their legs. Although the wings are primarily intended as organs of flight, not infrequently they are employed as weapons, and so great is the force delivered by a blow from the wing of a swan that men's arms have been known to be broken thereby. Spurs are present upon the wings of some birds, and also upon the legs, such weapons being capable of inflicting serious wounds. No less formidable are the talons of the eagles and vultures, and some years back an official at the Zoo was badly injured by one of the former birds that suddenly pounced upon him unawares.

But the most powerful of all birds are the ostriches, the cassowaries, the emus and the rheas. These avian giants cannot fly, but they make up for their lack of ability in such respect by running with great speed. They possess very long legs, and their strong toes are utilised as weapons. Not all of these birds

A SAMSON AMONG ANIMALS: THE TIGER IN ITS FIERCE STRENGTH

Neville Kingston

LAND CRAB FROM WEST AFRICA AND ITS HUGE CLAW

As they grow old the male land crabs develop enormous claws powerful enough, it is said, to crack a man's arm. The specimen seen above is from the London Zoological Gardens, and is seen dealing with its dinner. In the upper photograph it has caught a mouse and is holding it up in triumph, while below we see the mouse, limp and dead, being conveyed to the crab's mouth. This particular crab came from Gambia, West Africa, where these creatures are abundant in the coastal parts.

however, attack in the same manner, for the emu delivers its blows in a forward direction, and the others strike out backwards and sideways.

The secretary-bird also uses its feet as weapons, stamping upon the snakes upon which it largely feeds, and reducing their bodies to a pulp. The force that the bird puts into its blows is astonishing, and the foot comes down with a thud that one would imagine would break the bird's leg.

Possibly the most terrible exponents of strength are the large pythons and boas, reptiles that smother their prey with their coils, and by sheer muscular pressure squeeze and crush them to death.

The largest is the South American water-boa, or anaconda as it is more usually

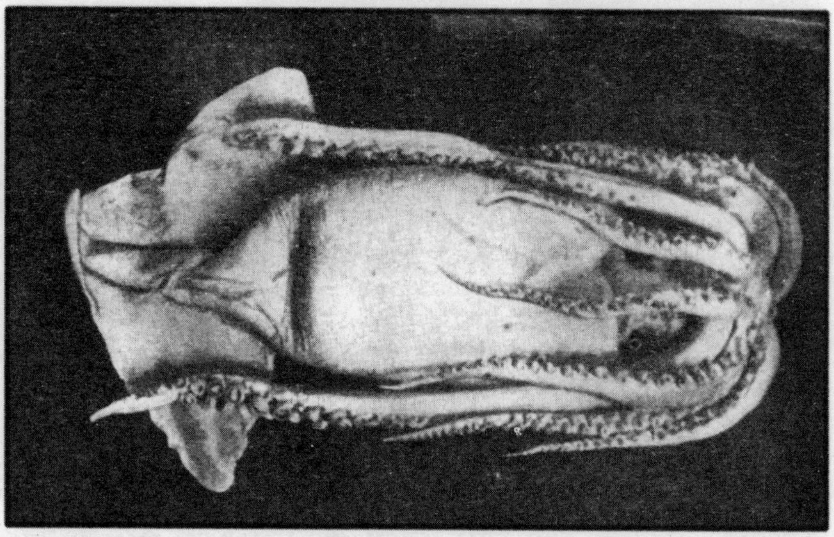

W. S. Berridge

RELENTLESS SUCKING ARMS OF OCTOPUS AND SQUID

These horrors of the sea are Samsons indeed, with their powerful arms covered with suckers which each exert a powerful vacuum. The squid (bottom) has two long arms, and eight shorter ones, and a specimen which possessed these two large tentacles forty-two feet long, has been found and measured. The octopus probably does not grow arms longer than six feet.

Harold Bastin

GIANT TORTOISE AND HERCULES BEETLES

Here (bottom) is one of the giant tortoises of Galapagos weighing 350 pounds with a 3¾ ounce tortoise on its head by way of contrast. Above is the Hercules beetle of tropical America. The male has the remarkable habit of carrying its female about with it between its enormous pincers. The Hercules beetle belongs to the genus Dynastes.

called. By the Spanish settlers it is known as the matatoro, a name meaning "bull killer," and they say that it grows to a length of eighty feet. Such a statement, however, is a gross over-estimate, and competent authorities are agreed that a length of thirty feet may be regarded as the maximum.

The reticulated python of the Malay regions, when full grown, is little inferior in size to the anaconda, and the Indian, or black python does not exceed 25 feet in length; while other large constricting snakes are the Australian diamond python and the South American boa constrictor, the latter seldom exceeding fourteen feet in length.

Numerous stories have been related of the great strength and swallowing capacity of these enormous serpents, but many of them are the outcome of a vivid imagination and are not based upon fact. In one old Natural History book, for instance, an account is given of a fight between a boa constrictor and a buffalo. The snake encircled the quadruped with its coils and, to quote the words of the narrator, "at every twist the bones of the buffalo were heard to crack almost as loud as the report of a gun," while as a fitting sequel to this astonishing yarn we are told that the beast was swallowed whole by the snake.

As a matter of fact constricting snakes do not crush the bones of their prey, and although they can swallow objects of much greater size than the girth of their own bodies, yet such creatures as wild pigs, antelopes or small deer are the bulkiest fare they can negotiate.

Although we have endeavoured in this article to cover as wide a field as possible our subject is one that could well be extended, the strength of the ant, the power of various big fish, the great muscular development of the forelimbs of the ant-eaters and the aard vark, and the wonderful manner in which some creatures will suspend their entire weight by their prehensile tails being a few other illustrations of remarkable physical development attained by animals that might well be included in our survey did space permit. It is clear that there are Samsons in all spheres of animal life.

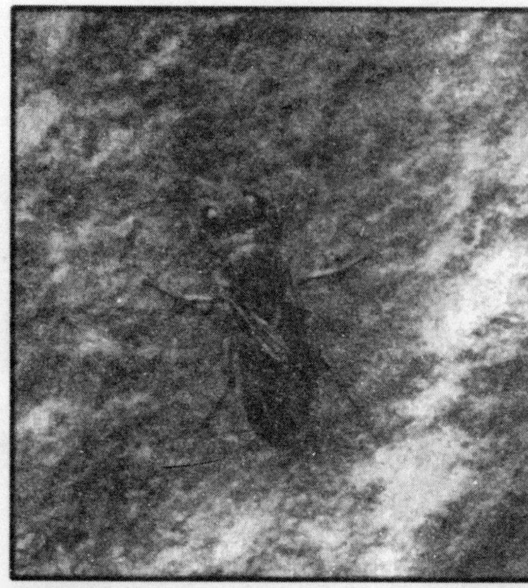

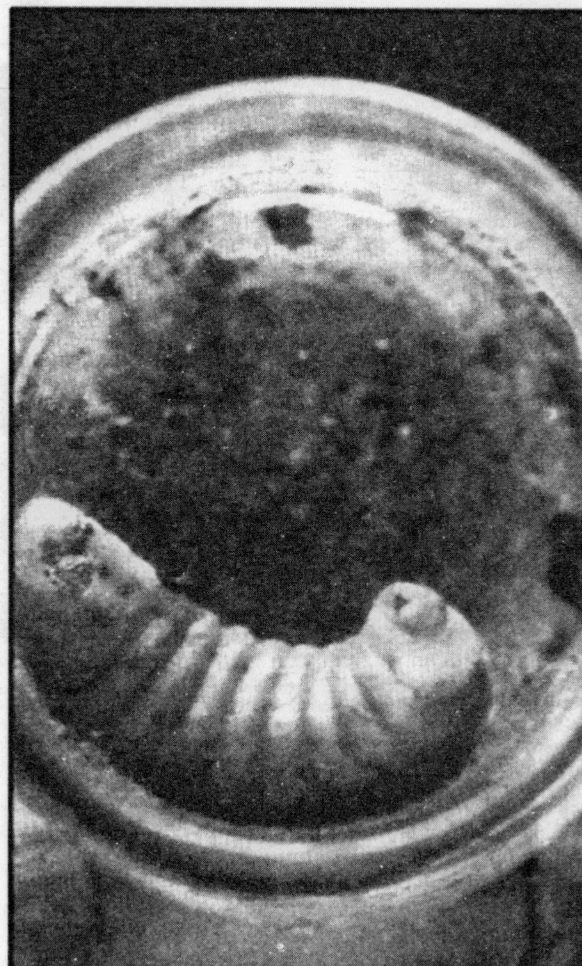

J. J. Ward

INSIDIOUS PARASITE WASP THAT PREYS ON THE MUD WASPS

As an illustration of the law of "eat or be eaten" the case of the so-called cuckoo wasp is striking. This wasp seeks out (top photos) the already built nest of a mud wasp and lays an egg within. The cuckoo grub (bottom left) hatches first, and proceeds to feed on the mud wasp grub. Nine days later (bottom right) it has finished the store of caterpillars as well. But it sometimes happens that ichneumon flies have already laid their eggs in the caterpillars. The ichneumons hatch first, and deal with both wasp and cuckoo grub. The photographs illustrating this chapter were taken over a long period by Mr. J. J. Ward who has made a long and patient study of these solitary wasps and their habits.

Chapter LV

Wonder Ways of the Solitary Wasps

By John J. Ward, F.E.S.

Author of "Insect Biographies"

MANY people begin to study the wasp at the point of its sting; although, on the other side, it may be contended that is the point at which the wasp begins to study us. There are, however, many wasp species that never trouble us with their stings, or ever even annoy us at our picnic parties; indeed, whose whole function is to render valuable service in our gardens, woods, and fields. Such are the solitary wasps—insects scarcely known except to the working entomologist, yet whose life stories are of astonishing and absorbing interest.

These insects, found in most parts of the world, may be divided into two classes: sand wasps, or digger wasps (*Fossores*), and mud wasps (*Odynerus*). There is no social life; each female of the species constructs a nest of her own and stores it with food material for her offspring. In the case of the digger wasps, some species construct a burrow in sandy soil, or amongst sand dunes, while others prefer to bore a wooden post, or a bramble stem. Of the sand-burrowing type *Ammophila sabulosa* is a good example, an insect nearly one inch in length, with black head and foreparts, a long, stalked body, orange red in colour, and terminating in a pear-shaped end, the latter half of which is black. In sandy places this insect is sometimes quite abundant, and its borings may be seen in large numbers. For hours together in the bright sunlight it is occupied in sinking its vertical shaft, throwing out the loose sand, and carrying away in its powerful mandibles bits of gravel and the larger particles of earth; for its mouth weapons are, in this species, the chief excavating tools.

When the burrow is nicely drilled to a depth of about three inches, the mother wasp turns to the heap of excavated bits of gravel she has thrown aside and, carefully selecting a suitable piece, she returns to her tunnel and cleverly fixes it across the entrance. Then, after a rapid run round the mouth of the burrow she takes to her wings. It may be an hour or two before she returns, for she has gone on a hunting expedition to capture the quarry to provision the cell she has just constructed.

In due course our patience is rewarded, for she appears amongst the tufts of grass well astride a huge caterpillar many times her own weight, which she is holding with her powerful mandibles and dragging along with difficulty. As she approaches the burrow she seems a little doubtful as to its exact location and, releasing her capture, she rushes here and there in an excited manner, continually returning to the caterpillar as though it might escape. There is no fear of that, however, for although it is alive, yet it is under the control of a powerful anæsthetic imparted to its nerve-centres by a series of stings administered by the wasp when it effected its capture.

At last she has arrived at the shaft, and with great speed she removes the covering stone, and then rushes back to her quarry. Getting a good grip, she then proceeds direct to the entrance of the burrow, and both wasp and caterpillar disappear into the hole. When, shortly afterwards, she reappears, she rapidly shovels sand into the burrow, occasionally dropping in one or two of the bigger pieces of gravel as the surface is reached. Finally there is another scattering of sand grains, together with a few cut grass blades, the whole strewn about so as to hide the burrow completely from view.

The mother wasp is then free to construct another tube, for she has successfully provided an ample supply of fresh meat food for one of her offspring. If we unearth the caterpillar, on the side of its body a conspicuous white egg will be found, and from that egg will hatch the young wasp grub with its food supply all in readiness. If the caterpillars are of smaller size, there may be two provided. By some marvellous instinctive calculation the wasp is able to anticipate the exact food ration necessary to allow of the full development of the wasp grub until it is able to pupate in the cell in which it was born. When it becomes a wasp the following year there is no difficulty in its emergence from the burrow, for it then possesses mandibles and strong legs well adapted for sand manipulation.

MUD WASP, LIFE SIZE
Here is a wasp that never troubles us with its sting or plagues us at meal times in the summer. It helps to preserve plants by preying on destructive caterpillars.

While the above life story may be taken as typical of the digger wasps, yet there are many variations in the habits of the different species and genera. The members of the genus Pompilus store their cells entirely with stung and paralysed spiders instead of caterpillars. In another group (*Sphecoidea*), of which there are nearly a hundred British species, and which includes the *Ammophila sabulosa* whose life story has here been told, there are not only earth and sand burrowers with caterpillar provender, but also borers into decaying

with a variable number of small caterpillars, and the nests are usually attached to heather stems. Of the genus Odynerus there are sixteen or more British species, most of which build mud nests, although some adopt the digger wasp's method of using bramble stems; but even then sand grains are employed for lining the stems in which the cells are made.

The mud wasp's method of building is extremely interesting. There are two species (*O. parietum* and *O. antilope*) which have evolved a distinct liking for the mortar between the bricks of a well-built house as a building site. The better pointed-up the mortar is, the more likely is the wall to be selected for a row of cells. Since insects more often appreciate old buildings for nesting purposes, it was for a long time somewhat puzzling why these wasps should prefer to associate themselves with new, and especially smooth, well-built walls. One day, however, their secret was revealed, for I espied a common blue tit making occasional jumps from a window-ledge in an effort to reach a row of mud wasp's cells arranged on the window frame. The smooth brick wall does not provide a landing-stage for the tit; but when a window-ledge is near the persistent tit will see to it that no caterpillars remain to serve as mud wasp grub provender.

These pretty little mud wasps are often seen during the month of June, although a second generation may appear in late summer. Sometimes before building the wasp will lay out a building site, bringing little dabs of cement and arranging them more or

DIGGER WASP AND ITS MOUTH PARTS

In the excavating operations in which it engages while making the shafts for its nest the digger wasp uses its mouth parts. In the lower photograph we see, highly magnified, the feelers, and the tongue, the mouth, and the horny toothed mandibles. The upper photograph shows the wasp itself and the **shaft** it has dug for an egg.

wooden posts, old trees, or dry bramble, briar, ash, and other stems, from which they excavate the pith, and in most cases store their cells with two-winged flies of the house-fly type, especially preying upon the black and yellow-banded hover-flies. Some species have specialised so far as to capture exclusively one genus of prey.

It would seem that these wasps are Nature's means of guarding against an excess of some of the insect species on which they prey. On one occasion I found on a sandy track of the Devonshire coast some thousands of the newly-made burrows of *Ammophila sabulosa*, with wasps themselves also in abundance, but not a burrow contained a caterpillar. For a whole month close observation never revealed a caterpillar, and eventually the wasps disappeared, leaving their open burrows. The only explanation I am able to offer is that probably the previous year the wasp species was in excess, as sometimes happens with these insects, and in their search for caterpillars they collected them so effectively as almost to bring about their complete annihilation in that particular area. When the wasp progeny emerged the following spring, with inborn instinct they proceeded to form their burrows, but their search for caterpillars proved fruitless.

LEAVING the fossorial wasps, we may now consider the mud wasps, a more advanced family nearly approaching the social types. But two genera are represented in the British Isles, namely Eumenes and Odynerus. Of the former genus there is but a single British species (*E. coarctata*). This insect forms little globular nests built of mud, or sand grains agglutinated with mucus, which, in common with all the members of the mud wasp family, are stored

J. J. Ward

GRUB, PARASITE, AND NEST OF THE MUD WASP

For the sake of exact observation a wasp grub was removed from its cell and placed, with its store of caterpillars, in a glass tube (bottom left). It is seen sucking the juices from its last caterpillar. The bottom right-hand photograph shows a mud wasp's cell with a grub inside it and, on the grub, a parasite wasp which will deposit its egg on the grub's body. When the egg hatches the parasite larva will feed upon the mud wasp's grub. Above is (left) a nest photographed through a window and (right) the same nest one day later with an extra cell.

DIFFERENT ARRANGEMENT OF MUD WASP CELLS
Sometimes the mud wasp builds her cells in a single row, sometimes, as here (bottom). with one row upon another. In such a case the grubs in the top row hatch first and those in the lower bite their way up into the empty cells above and so escape. The upper photograph shows a row of cells built on a new wall.

less in line for even a yard in length. It then begins to build its cylindrical cells at one end of its selected site. Considering that the wasp will probably not live for more than three weeks, its building project is a very ambitious one. If all goes well, it may build forty or fifty cells, all of which, quite unaided, it stores with caterpillars; not infrequently, after building some eight or ten cells, it changes its site and makes a fresh start, probably to avoid the danger of "putting all its eggs in one basket."

The name "mud wasp" seems to imply that these wasps collect mud for building purposes. Such, however, is not the case. What the wasp does is to select a particular piece of sandstone to which it continually returns, each time scraping it with its mandibles until it has obtained a mouthful of sand grains, which it mixes with saliva to form its cement. Each little mouthful is moulded into a ring and plastered round the mouth of the tubular cell, and can be seen as a moistened layer immediately after it is added; but it dries hard before the next mouthful is brought.

When we remember that the little wasp is working in bright sunlight, it is somewhat astonishing how it is enabled continually to moisten the material from its salivary glands. It may be that it is able to store a supply of water in its body, for at intervals it ceases to visit its nest and its sandstone, and may be away for an hour or more; probably it is then seeking a fresh water supply and feasting at the flowers—for the wasp itself feeds on pollen and nectar. Another curious point is why it should return time after time to the same piece of sandstone, often at some distance from its nest, while other pieces of what are apparently the same kind of stone are close by. That may be purely instinctive behaviour, the wasp having found a suitable supply goes to that source with automatic precision, and has not the reasoning faculty to select a piece nearer to its nest and so save itself much time on its numerous journeys.

When the cell is completed a large sausage-shaped egg is deposited and attached on a delicate stalk to the interior of the cell wall. Then six to twelve stung and paralysed caterpillars are closely packed in like sardines in a box, except that they are placed in a coiled position to fit the cell. The cell being filled the wasp then closes it with a lid of cement, which serves as a floor for the next cell to be made.

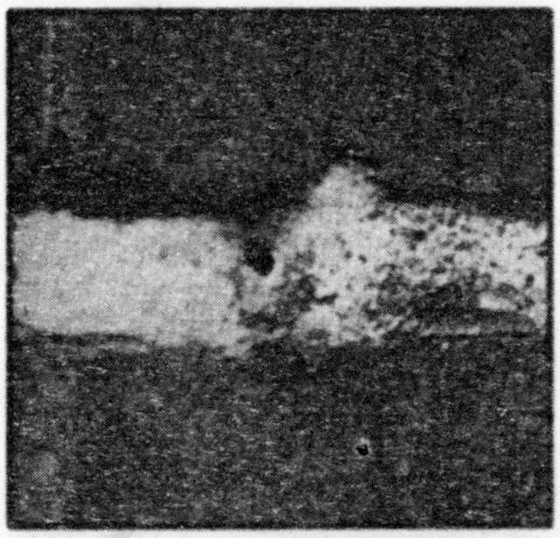

Nest

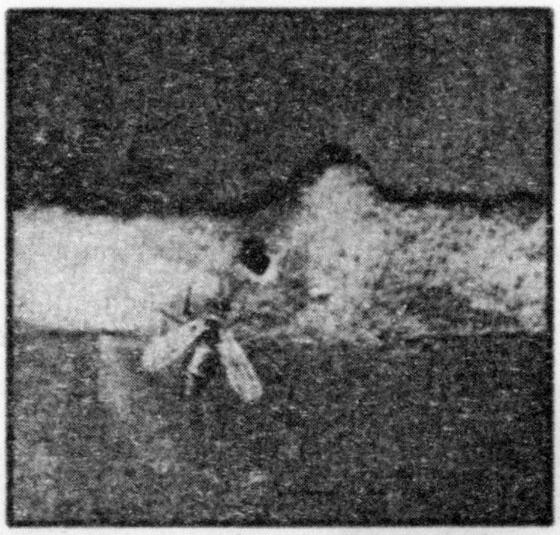

Wasp alighting

About to enter burrow

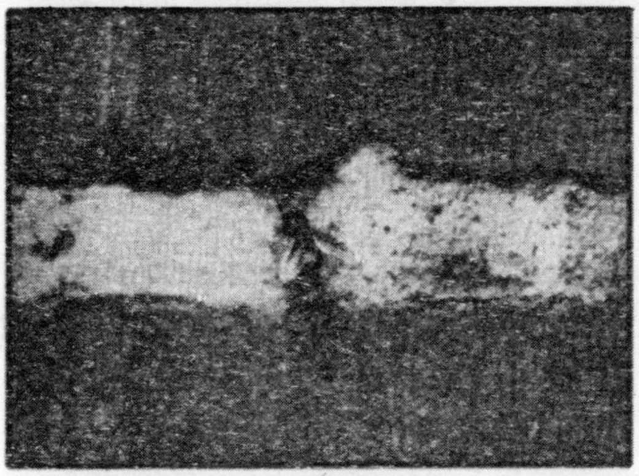

Entering burrow

Inside the burrow

Window frame with mud cells

Wasp cell damaged by blue tit

Cell opened showing wasp egg

ONE OF THE SOLITARY WASPS: ITS NESTS AND ITS ENEMIES

The mud wasp likes to construct its nest on the mortar of a newly-built wall, because such a wall affords no foothold for the blue tit, which is a great raider of mud wasp nests, since the bird knows it will find a free meal of caterpillars, laboriously collected by the mother wasp, inside. The mud wasp does not collect pieces of mud for building purposes, but manufactures its own by scraping a piece of sandstone with its mandibles, and then moistening the grains with its own saliva. The photographs are by J. J. Ward.

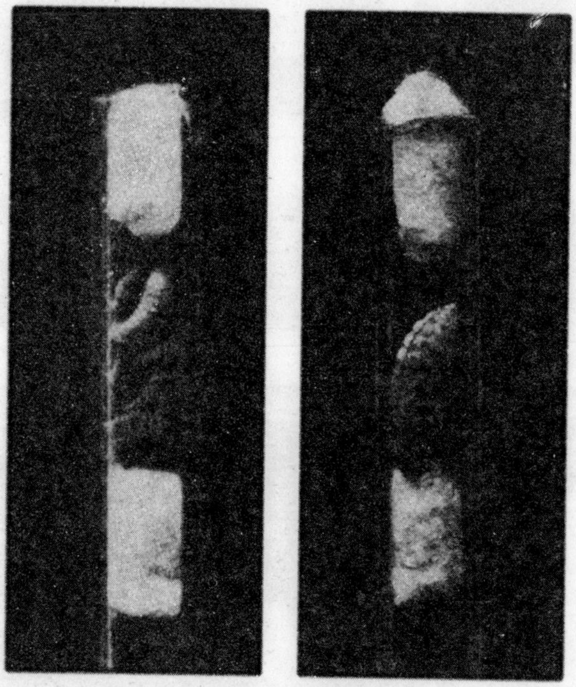

THE CUCKOO IN THE NEST
Here is a three-days' old cuckoo wasp grub (left) photographed in a glass jar for observation. It has the store of caterpillars, alive but paralysed, provided by the mud wasp for her own grub. After eight days (right) they are sucked to nothing.

Sometimes the cells are grouped irregularly instead of being arranged in a single line, in which case the lower ones are buried beneath the upper and last formed. The problem of the escape of the wasps from the lowermost cells is solved by the wasps in the upper and last formed ones emerging first, those beneath them biting their way through their cells into the empty ones above. The grub that appears from the egg, which hatches in about three days, disposes of its caterpillars at the average rate of one per day. It then covers its body with a silken sheet, under which it changes to the pupa stage, remaining in the cell until the following June, when the wasp bites its way out and once more begins the cycle of life which has been described.

THESE mud wasps are up against a formidable foe in the form of another family of solitary wasps (*Chrysididae*), insects gorgeously attired with bodies of glowing ruby-red, while their heads and foreparts glisten with splendid metallic blues and greens. Making no nest of their own, the females of these jewel-like insects search the walls and crevices where mud wasps are building, and just before a cell is closed stealthily enter it and leave there an egg in much the same way as the cuckoo selects and uses the nest of another bird as a home for her egg.

From that egg comes a "cuckoo wasp" grub, whose first business is to seek for the sausage-shaped egg of the mud wasp, and then to suck it. Having in that manner entirely disposed of the mud wasp grub problem, it then proceeds to devour the caterpillars provided by the mother mud wasp for her offspring, and completes its development in the cell instead of the rightful owner.

There are even more insidious foes that attack the mud wasp grub, tiny wasps (*Chalcididae*) so minute that even when two or three abreast they can pass through the eye of a fine needle. These microscopic insects penetrate the mud walls of the cells to deposit their eggs on the body of the wasp grub. But it sometimes happens that both cuckoo wasps and chalcids are frustrated in their parasitic habits, for it may be that the caterpillars captured by the mother mud wasp were already carrying eggs from an ichneumon wasp; in which case those eggs hatch first, and the ichneumon wasp grubs are the winners, devouring all the provender that the cells contain. Many other enemies might be mentioned, for the story of parasitism is a very involved one.

This, then, is the remarkable story of the solitary wasps. Elsewhere in this work there is given some account of the paper-making wasps—those which live in communities and contrive wonderful nests out of wood pulp. They, the pests of summer picnics and the bane of fruit growers, have a life, quite apart from man, which very well repays a little study and attention. The man who goes to destroy a wasps' nest in some grass bank by asphyxiating the inmates; or to annihilate the inhabitants of one of those apparent lumps of mud which are seen hanging from the branches of trees and which are really the nests of tree wasps, is certainly putting an end to a nuisance to human beings. But he is also exterminating a large and organized community of perhaps unguessed interest, as we shall see.

CUCKOO WASP LOOKING FOR A NEST
This is an enlarged photograph of a parasite cuckoo wasp hunting along the top of a wall for the nests of mud wasps, where she may deposit her eggs. This parasite wasp is gorgeously coloured with a ruby-red body and a blue and green head.

Chapter LVI

How Wild Animals are Caught

By G. M. Vevers

Superintendent of the London Zoological Society's Gardens

THE shooting of big game and the more modern method of hunting them with a camera in their native haunts are generally regarded as being two of the most dangerous and thrilling things a man can do, but both these pursuits undoubtedly take a second place when compared with the risks which are run by those who engage in the capture of wild animals alive. There is, however, a lamentable lack of literature upon the subject as those engaged in the trapping of live things for the most part do so for a living and apart from their natural unwillingness to give away trade secrets, they generally have neither the will nor the opportunity to write about their experiences.

In recent years there have been one or two striking exceptions to this rule. Charles Mayer, who for many years was employed by Barnum and Bailey in catching animals for their travelling menageries, has in his book on the trapping of wild animals given an account of many adventures in the jungles of Malaya and elsewhere, before which the thrills of a modern "mystery" novel are as mere episodes, and in a still more recent volume the intrepid explorer and hunter, Ben Burbidge, gives a most enthralling description of encounters with whole families of gorillas and the capture of youngsters for the American zoos.

Charles Mayer's life would appeal to anyone with the schoolboy love of adventure. To begin with, he ran away from home at a tender age to join a circus menagerie which happened to pitch its tent in the square of his native town. Starting at the bottom rung of the ladder, he worked himself up until he became circus manager and the friend of the great Barnum, who gave him his first commission to go to India and buy a "fourteen-foot elephant," an animal which never existed outside the rather vivid imagination of some Bombay dealer.

ALTHOUGH this expedition ended in disappointment, Mayer saw enough to realize that the East held great possibilities for the animal collector, and we next hear of him learning to speak the Malay language and catching a thirty-foot python in Sumatra. This snake had just swallowed a large pig, and was in a more or less torpid condition when Mayer found him and roped him round the neck; before he was boxed, however, he managed to crush one man to death in his coils, and injured several others by knocking them flat with his lashing tail. The capture of the python earned Mayer a great reputation as a hunter of living things, and very soon he was engaged in an elephant drive on behalf of the Sultan of Trengganu—one of the states of the Malay Peninsula—whose rice crops had suffered severe damage by the invasion of a herd of these destructive animals into his territory. The capture of living elephants on a large scale is not a thing to be entered into light-heartedly, for apart from the enormous risk to life and limb in dealing with these monstrous creatures, there are usually weeks of weary toil before the trap or keddah, as it is called, is completed, and very often when this is finished and everything is ready for the drive, the herd has moved on and is a hundred miles away. The work of making an elephant trap is prodigious. This trap is a circular stockade of large trees, each sunk five or six feet into the ground and strengthened outside with other trees to act as buttresses. The diameter of the keddah is usually about a hundred yards and leading up to it is a funnel-shaped stockade with the wings converging to a narrow entrance which can be quickly closed by a strong gate. Surrounding the circular portion of the keddah is a platform upon which the natives climb when the drive is over and from which they select the animals to be tamed and those to be killed. When all is ready, the herd is located and many hundreds of men surround it in a semi-circle and drive the animals little by little towards the entrance of the keddah.

THE final scene is one of indescribable confusion. The ever-closing circle of beaters make a last rush with drums and flaring torches to drive the panic-stricken creatures into the trap. During this last stage, many of the younger animals perish, being trampled underfoot by the larger members of the herd. In some parts of India, the keddah is divided into three portions, with narrow entrances leading from one into the other. The first portion is for the capture of the herd, the second is smaller and generally contains a pool of water, and the third is so small as only to be capable of holding one elephant, and it is in this compartment that the animals are roped one by one before they are led out to be tethered to a tree which is the first stage in their training.

Sometimes the pitfall is used in catching single elephants. A large hole fifteen feet deep is dug in a chosen spot known to be frequented by a herd, and then it is covered in with branches and earth, so as to appear as solid as possible. The unsuspecting animal, crashing through the frail covering of the pit, is a helpless prisoner and entirely at the mercy of his captors. The practice, however, of catching elephants in pitfalls has been discontinued as many were killed by being caught in this manner. A third method of capture is by hunting single bulls with female elephants trained for the purpose. Four or five are employed and the mahouts ride on the head, covered in cloths of the same colour as the elephants, so as to render them as inconspicuous as possible. The tusker is followed about by relays of these ridden elephants for days until it is exhausted and finally is taken by means of ropes when it lies down to sleep.

A BOX FULL OF MONKEYS

While on their way from their native land to captivity in foreign parts these monkeys caused much amusement on the vessel which brought them over the sea. By the end of the voyage the animals had already learned that their warders were givers of good gifts, as we can see by the array of eager arms outstretched through the bars for the food they hope to receive.

into the most inaccessible part of Central Asia, and the task of bringing back the foals and their foster mothers over hundreds of miles of desert, through Russia, until in the end they were liberated in Woburn Park, in Bedfordshire, where their descendants are still to be seen. The journey back to Hamburg took eleven months, and out of fifty foals which had started only twenty-eight survived the hardships of the journey.

Most of the large Carnivora seen in captivity have been caught in the cub stage and reared by hand after the mother has been shot, for it is not an easy matter to capture a full-grown lion or tiger alive, although sometimes it is achieved by the pitfall method and strong nets. Fully grown animals caught in this way are quite untameable, for they never forget the method of their capture and ever after regard man as their bitter enemy. On the other hand, the large cats which have been brought up by man from infancy and treated with kindness are for the most part easily tameable and may be handled with impunity.

The capture of a polar bear alive is an exceedingly perilous undertaking, as it is usually done in small, frail canoes, and the hunter runs the risk of being drowned in icy water in addition to being rough-handled by his formidable and savage prey. Two or even three dug-out canoes are lashed together side by side, and when a bear is sighted in the water these are paddled quickly towards him, and when near enough a coil of rope is thrown over his head. The infuriated animal then swims away harder than ever, towing the canoes behind him. This goes on until the animal is exhausted, when the tables are turned and the canoes are paddled back with the now helpless bear in their wake. Usually there is a large boat in attendance, and when the bear is brought alongside further nooses are made fast round his body and he is hauled up on to the deck and thrust ignominiously into a cage. Seals, walruses, and sea lions may be caught in a similar manner, but as these are exceedingly rapid swimmers and dive to great depths, they are generally caught from time to time in nets. Most of the seals which are caught off the coasts of Great Britain are taken quite accidentally in the wide-spreading nets of fishing boats.

The most sporting and risky form of hunting the elephant alive is by means of a lasso from the back of another elephant, or as it is sometimes done, on foot. It is useless to try to capture young elephants running with their mothers as these animals defend their young with great vigour and the latter cannot generally be captured without first killing the mother. This is not the case with some other animals, such as antelopes and giraffes, where the usual plan is to chase the herd on horseback until the young, which are more easily tired than their parents, can be captured without much trouble.

It was in this way that Carl Hagenbeck's collector, Grieger, captured the famous herd of Mongolian wild horses for the present Duke of Bedford in 1901. In this case the actual capture of the young animals was a simple matter compared with the prolonged preparations necessary for dispatching an expedition

The capture of a full-grown gorilla is well-nigh impossible, and although adult chimpanzees and orang-utans are occasionally taken alive they do not as a rule live long in captivity, and their capture is not a thing to be encouraged, for the methods employed are of such a nature that the spirit of the animals is broken and they lose the will to live. On the other hand anthropoid apes which are captured during the first two years of life take to human beings almost immediately, and may live for years in captivity. Of all the apes gorillas are the most difficult to bring home. They require individual and constant attention and have to be treated in much the same way as human babies, and unless one is prepared to do this it is much kinder to leave them in their natural state. In dealing with the anthropoid apes, more perhaps than in the case of any other kind of animal, a study of their psychology is of the highest importance.

ELEPHANTS TRANSPORTED BY RAIL AND STEAMER

Below is a valuable white elephant just arrived from Asia, being unloaded from the ship to the train at a port of the United States. Above is a young elephant being swung out of the ship's hold in which it has travelled by a derrick at the quay. Notice the elaborate cradle which supports this weighty young creature.

BY THE BANKS OF AN AFRICAN LAKE: ENTICING THE CROCODILE

Crocodiles commonly lie near the banks of the river or lake which they inhabit with just the tip of their snout and their eyes protruding above the water. Thus concealed they wait the coming of man or beast, and then make a rush, and the victim is dragged into the water, held under till drowned and devoured at leisure. Above is a strange scene in Central Africa where a native is luring a crocodile from the waters of a lake by making a tempting offer of food. In the opposite page we see how the attempt succeeded.

Sometimes the word goes out from one of the zoos of the world that a large number of one kind of animal is required to make up a spectacular exhibit or colonise some special enclosure. This was the case when the Baboon Hill at the London Zoo was made. Long before that rocky island was ready the Council of the Zoological Society had commissioned a prominent animal dealer to capture and transport to London at least one hundred sacred baboons from Abyssinia. An experienced man was sent out, who, after four days' journey from the coast into the interior, came upon a large colony of the animals. He had taken with him on camels a number of boxes, each capable of holding four baboons.

NEAR their home he built a little hut with a sliding door to which a string release was attached. Leading up to and inside the hut a quantity of maize was laid down as a bait. Then, retiring behind a neighbouring rock with the string in his hand, he awaited developments. In a short time he made his first capture, the large male leader of the tribe. His difficulties, however, were not over then, for the animal had to be tempted from the hut into a box, and this was done by placing one of the boxes opposite the trap door in the hut and waiting until the captive took it into his head to walk in. All this was done with the other baboons crowding round in a most aggressive manner, wondering what had become of their leader. His disappearance, however, did not dissuade the others from entering the hut, and in the course of a few days no fewer than 107 baboons were captured in this manner and transferred into their travelling boxes. These boxes were then lashed in pairs to the backs of camels and the journey made back to the coast again.

The actual transport of live animals across thousands of miles of sea and land, the feeding of them, protecting them from chill when taken from a tropical to a cooler climate—all these and many other problems have to be overcome by the collector of living things. Special boxes of varying sizes have to be made for each individual animal caught, and these must be carefully padded to prevent the captive creature from injuring itself in its efforts to escape from the box and also from being thrown about in it on board ship during rough weather. Perhaps the most difficult and delicate animal to transport is the giraffe. It is of course useless to attempt to send home a fully-grown specimen, as giraffes attain a height of seventeen or eighteen feet, and a box containing a creature of this size would be too high to pass under the highest railway bridge. The giraffe chosen for export usually does not exceed

Daily M rror

CROCODILE TEMPTED FROM THE WATER BY THE OFFER OF FOOD

In the above photographs and the one on the opposite page we have an interesting series showing the gradual approach and emergence from the water of a crocodile, lured by the bait held out by a native. In the upper illustration on this page we see that as the great beast has cautiously advanced up the shelving bank, the native has retreated until the "croc" is emboldened to get as far as resting its snout on the bank. Below we see the animal receiving its reward when three-quarters of its body are out of the water.

DRAGGING A ROPED CROCODILE ASHORE AFTER A HARD STRUGGLE

Catching crocodiles alive is one of the hardest tasks for the collector of wild animals. These creatures are so shy and sink at once if alarmed, so that it is largely a matter of good fortune if a specimen is obtained. The crocodile seen here is by no means full-grown and yet it takes a considerable number of men to drag it to the bank, and this is only accomplished after a terrific tug-of-war. Even when hampered with the ropes the animal makes a good fight for liberty and, once on the bank, brings its dangerous tail into play. One of the natives has seized this active weapon and is hanging on at all costs while the rest try to make sure of their capture.

F. W. Bond

BIG INDIAN PYTHON BEING UNLOADED AT THE LONDON ZOO

Pythons are only to be captured with any degree of safety after they have fed. These great snakes make enormous meals—a pig or a deer at a time—at long intervals, and spend many hours in a state of torpor while the process of digestion is taking place. Thus a specimen such as the one seen here, can, when once safely in its box, be sent on its journey in a quiescent mood, and requires little attention till it reaches its destination. Then, as we can see, it may take seven or more men to hold it.

ten feet in height, and even a box large enough to contain a creature of this size is an unwieldy thing to handle in the absence of a lifting crane.

NOWADAYS the conditions under which live animals are taken from place to place are very much better than those which prevailed in the past, and the mortality among newly imported animals has decreased enormously. Recently a select committee of specialists under the auspices of the Zoological Society of London has drawn up a set of rules for the guidance of those engaged in the transport of animals. Special attention is called to the shape and construction of boxes, overcrowding of specimens, and the general management of various kinds of creatures on road, train and ship-board. Before shipment it is usual to keep animals for some time in captivity so that they may become accustomed to human beings and to the kind of food that can be supplied to them on the voyage which may by necessity differ from the fresh food which forms their natural diet. It is of the utmost importance that animals should be shipped in good condition and very young creatures and pregnant females should not be exported. As a rule, animals should not be transported from the Tropics to a cold climate during the winter months. Sometimes great ingenuity is required to find a suitable food substitute for certain creatures such as anteaters, which normally live on white ants or termites. a supply of which naturally cannot be taken on board ship in order to accommodate these insectivorous epicures. Condensed milk has been found to be a great standby in all such cases, and even some of the smaller birds and reptiles learn to take it.

The advent of the motor-car has made the transport of animals a very much easier matter than it was in the old days. In the capture of giraffes, for instance, the animals are no longer marched for miles to the rail-head after being caught but are lifted into motor lorries, fitted with caterpillar wheels, which carry them from the actual site of capture to the nearest railway station or even to the port from which they are to be shipped.

Taken as a whole, birds are very much more difficult to catch and bring into captivity than mammals, while reptiles are perhaps the easiest of all to deal with. The large flightless birds, such as ostriches, emus and cassowaries are generally hunted down on horseback and lassoed with ropes. In South America, the rhea or so-called South American ostrich is captured by means of bolas which consist of two round pebbles joined together by a long thong. The horseman chases the bird until he is alongside, then throws his bolas, which entangle the creature's legs and bring it to the ground. A vivid account of the use of the bolas is given by Darwin in his "Voyage of the Beagle." This practice seems to have been handed down from time immemorial as

E. N. A.

LASSOING WILD GIRAFFES IN THE EAST AFRICAN BUSH

Armed with nothing more lethal than a length of hemp rope, men now pursue the tall giraffe for capture and transference to a zoological garden or for photography, where once they hunted to kill. The upper photograph shows us a giraffe just after being lassoed in the East African Bush The break in the mane along the back of the neck shows where the noose is holding. Great care has to be taken when "roping" a giraffe as a fall might mean a broken limb. When once lassoed, giraffes often seem too bewildered to struggle (bottom).

TRUCK-LOAD OF GIRAFFES AND A FEMALE DECOY FOR A MALE

Only young giraffes can be transported, for a full-grown specimen may stand seventeen or eighteen feet tall, and the height of the ordinary bridge above a railway would prevent a box tall enough to house such a creature from being carried by train. In the lower photograph we see a truck-load of five young giraffes on their way from East Africa to the Berlin Zoo, while above, one method of capturing a male giraffe is illustrated. A female is caught and put in a cage on a lorry. She acts as a decoy for the males, and when one arrives it is quietly roped.

employed by the natives of New Guinea and the neighbouring islands in the catching of the many varieties of Birds of Paradise which abound in this part of the world.

The capture of some species which spend their lives in the tree-tops is not unattended by great risk to life and limb. Recently two specimens of a very beautiful bird known as the cinnamon roller were brought from Portuguese East Africa to the London Zoo by Mr. C. S. Webb, the well-known bird collector, who had spent several weeks in observing these birds through field-glasses as they hawked for insects at the very top of a group of high trees. Marking down the boughs they used most frequently, he climbed up the tree until he was able to reach the branches he had located and smear them with bird-lime. He then descended and went away for some hours to await results. On coming back he was overjoyed to see four birds fluttering helplessly. Once again he made his perilous ascent and succeeded in securing all four specimens alive. His difficulties, however, had only just begun,

bola stones have been found on several occasions in strata of undoubted Paleolithic age.

Once caught the easiest way of dealing with an ostrich is to put a sock over its head so that it cannot see, when it can easily be led about by two men—one walking on each side grasping a wing.

The ways of capturing flying birds, both large and small, are legion. The larger kinds such as sea birds and birds of prey are generally taken as nestlings and brought up by hand. The smaller birds may be trapped, netted or caught by bird-lime used in various ways. The bird collector usually relies on native help to a large extent to aid him in the capture of the rarer species. Blow pipe darts and blunt arrows smeared with bird-lime are favourite weapons

HOW GIRAFFES TRAVEL FROM THE WILD TO THE ZOO

An important factor in the capturing and carrying of wild animals is getting them accustomed to human company before and during their journey. By the time they reach that journey's end the animals are often tame enough to feed from the hand, as we see here (bottom). Above is a giraffe having its first view of London as it is swung off the boat at Tilbury.

E.N.A.

CAPTURED WILD ANIMALS BEING HAND-FED IN THEIR EARLY DAYS

Food is a great problem when the task of keeping a young wild animal in captivity is undertaken. When at the Zoo the right food, or an efficient substitute, is probably quickly available but, when first caught, and particularly during the journey, the question of diet is all important, and the mortality among captured animals before they even reach their ultimate cages is always high. This young hippo (bottom) took readily to a diet of barley-corn while it was being looked after by a native servant, while a baby rhino (top) had to be bottle-fed.

E.N.A.

MAN'S STRENGTH PITTED AGAINST THE BEAST'S

At the best of times the hippopotamus is one of the hardest animals to approach as, not only is its sense of smell extraordinarily acute, but upon alarm it instantly sinks into the depths of the water. In the lower photograph some African natives have succeeded in the feat of capturing a young hippo alive among the reeds of a lake. They are contriving to keep the dangerous jaws which, in an adult can bite through a canoe, open. Above is a young rhinoceros being captured in Tanganyika.

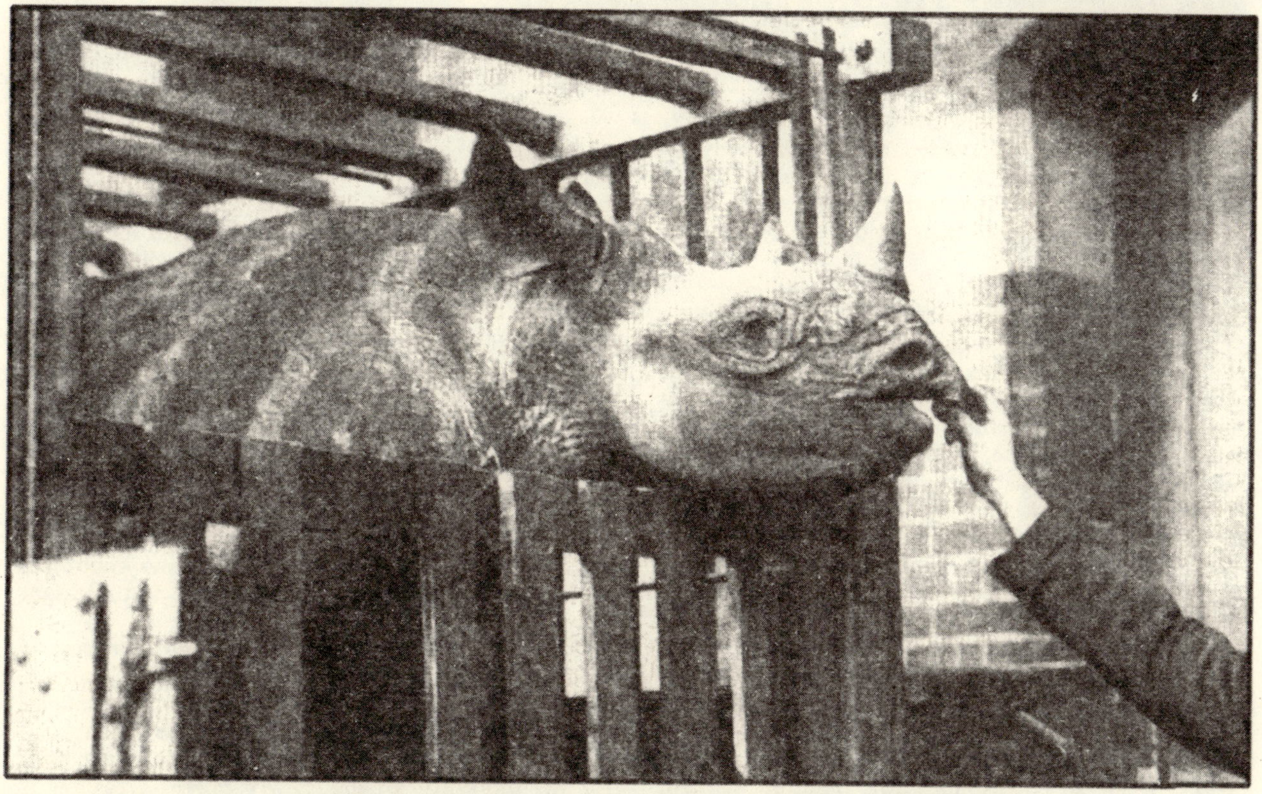

F. W. Bond

ON ARRIVAL AT THE ZOO: TIGER AND RHINOCEROS

Just as a new Zoo tiger began to creep stealthily out of its travelling box and enter the cage in which it was to pass the rest of its days, the top photograph was taken. This is a remarkable view of a new arrival, full of nervous wonder as it surveys for the first time its strange new abode from which there is no escape. A rhinoceros in a crate is an unusual sight, but here (bottom) is one, consigned to the London Zoo and just arrived after many weeks of travel and strange conditions.

E. N. A.

THE NEW CAPTURE: GETTING A LION CUB USED TO HUMAN HANDS

As long as an animal, even so fierce a one as a lion, is caught sufficiently early in its life, while it is still in the helpless stage, it can be kept tame and even affectionate until it is adult: then, the large carnivora are unreliable at the best of times. Nevertheless, if an animal has been always used to human company and has received kind usage all this is likely to make the full-grown creature the more tractable in captivity. Here we see a lion cub becoming accustomed to taking food from a human being. Notice that the cub is spotted.

for he found after cleaning them that they refused to eat every kind of food offered and it was only by forcibly feeding them twice a day for many weeks that he was able at last to bring two of them home to the Zoo, the first of their kind ever to be seen alive in captivity.

Reptiles, with the exception of a few poisonous species, and the large constrictors, are perhaps the easiest of all animals to capture and send home alive. Although it is popularly supposed that lizards are poisonous, there is only one genus that is really so. This is the family of Heloderms or Gila monsters which inhabit the deserts of Texas and Arizona. Although the other lizards can bite and scratch and some make use of their tails to inflict severe blows, they can usually be caught fairly easily and handled with impunity. After capture one good meal will last for many days and these and other reptiles are very easily sent home in boxes packed with moss which must be moistened occasionally with clean, fresh water. Large constrictor snakes such as pythons and boas are usually taken during the period of torpor which follows a large meal. Even so, many men are required to deal with anything over twelve feet if it is warm and in good condition. After being boxed, they can be shipped right away and do not need any more looking after until they arrive at their destination. The poisonous snakes, on the other hand, require more care in their capture. Various devices are used, the forked stick being the most common of all. This method of capture is not to be encouraged as very often the snake lashes about and injures its cervical vertebrae. A useful form of snake catcher and one which is less liable to injure the neck is now in almost daily use at the London Zoo. It consists of a leather loop working against a soft pad in the place of the forked stick, and the loop is capable of being adjusted to fit any size of neck. When in use, the loop is slipped over the snake's head and, being drawn tight, is held in one hand so that the other is free to deal with the body and tail. Poisonous snakes are usually boxed for transport in boxes which have an inner lid of wire gauze so that they can be observed with safety. It is important to see there are no knot holes in the wood as venomous reptiles are not pleasant travelling companions.

Taken as a whole, the collecting and transport of wild animals calls for a marked degree of courage, an enormous amount of endurance and an infinite capacity for taking pains. The risks are many and the failures almost as numerous as the successes, for the mortality among newly caught creatures is very high. Briefly, success in bringing animals into captivity can be measured in the terms of the amount of personal supervision and sympathetic treatment which is bestowed upon them after capture.

CARE IN HANDLING THE NEWLY CAPTURED: CHAMOIS IN A STRETCHER

This is a good example of the careful handling required to deal with a highly nervous animal like the chamois. This animal, which is placed by scientists between the goat and the antelope, is an inhabitant of the Alps and other mountain regions of Europe, and has suffered much from persecution. To this its extreme shyness is due, and in these photographs it can be seen what caution is necessary to prevent the creature from injuring itself in its naturally violent efforts to escape. The stretcher is padded with brushwood.

TRAVELLING BY MEANS OF THE TAIL: HANDSOME POLLACK OF THE NORTH ATLANTIC

Fish, in the majority of cases, swim by means of rapid movements of the tail from side to side. The tail does not consist merely of the hind fin as many people suppose, but a considerable portion of the body as well. The other fins help in turning and in rising and sinking. The pollack has three fins on its back, the foremost being sharply pointed. In colour it is a dark green along the back, and this colour lightens down the sides, which are embellished with golden markings, until the underside is almost white. The pollack is a valuable food fish, and is caught in considerable numbers off the Devonshire and Cornish coasts, and also occurs in Norwegian and North American waters. Its usual length is a little under two feet.

The photographs by F. Schensky in this page and page 611 are reproduced by permission of Dr. Werner Klinkhardt, Leipzig, from Animal and Plant Life in the North Sea, published by the Biological Station, Heligoland

Chapter LVII

Travelling Without Legs or Wings

By W. P. Pycraft

Author of "The Courtship of Animals"

FORCE of habit has made us think always of animal locomotion in terms of legs or wings, so much so that we are apt to forget that many creatures contrive to travel, and often swiftly, without any such aid. The means adopted to achieve this are surprisingly varied.

Directly we begin to ponder over the matter we ask ourselves how did legs and wings come into being. Though there can be no completely accurate solution of such a problem we can come very near it.

Let us begin our survey of this theme with the lowly amoeba, which can be obtained, for the microscope, from the mud of ponds. A mere speck of jelly without definite shape, for it is always changing, it moves along by virtue of an inherent "irritability" of its substance. It progresses by "flowing" movements. The direction in which it is travelling is indicated by a sort of thrusting forward of a part of its outline, a kind of blunt "finger" grows out from the body, which presently flows forward, as it were, to merge with its tip, and presently another "finger" will appear from another area of its circumference, and so it travels in an apparently aimless way by means of these extraordinary "pseudopodia," or "false-feet" as they are called.

An advance on this is made by other protozoa when the substance of the body throws out permanent, excessively delicate, thread-like processes which are actively vibratile. Their rapid side-to-side movements draw the body along as the propeller of an aeroplane draws the 'plane along. Such threads are known as cilia.

THE minute rotifers, creatures much higher in the scale, travel with great speed by means of such cilia which, placed around the mouth, serve the double purpose of organs of locomotion and whisks to whirl particles of food into the mouth. Some, like the wheel animalcule, can also "walk," somewhat after the fashion of a looper caterpillar. Taking a grip of the ground with a pair of short "legs" at the end of the body, it bends forward and gets another hold with its head, then, releasing the legs, doubles the body up so as to bring the legs up to the mouth, and then takes a fresh hold by the head.

Leeches "walk" in a similar way, but when they are in a hurry they swim by undulatory movements of their long, lithe bodies.

The earth-worm crawls up and down its burrow, and over the ground, by means of short, stiff bristles, which run down almost the whole length of the body, while in many of the marine worms these bristles become flattened out to form swimming paddles.

Those repellent creatures which we call "maggots" and the fishermen call "gentles"—the larvae of the blow-fly—contrive to crawl, and with no small speed, aided by nothing more than tiny hooks which they use by alternate contraction and expansion of the body. Similar rhythmical contractions obtain in the snail, where the underside of the body, or "foot," during locomotion is thrown into a series of wave-like movements which carry the body forward. The slime-tract which they leave behind them doubtless helps, but no such tract is left by water-snails, which crawl by the same movements of the foot.

Among the higher animals which crawl without the aid of legs the snake is the most familiar example. "Upon thy belly shalt thou go all the days of thy life." But the implication that the serpent lost his legs suddenly is not borne out by fact. The under surface of the body of a python will show, on each side of the vent, a pair of conical horny spikes, the last vestiges of a once functional pair of hind legs. All trace of the fore-legs has vanished. How then does the snake crawl?

WITH the gradual dwindling of the legs there has followed a corresponding lengthening of the body by the addition of vertebrae to the spine, each vertebra bearing a pair of ribs. There may be as many as two hundred pairs and they function much like the legs of a centipede—but inside the body. Here is another problem. How does the snake, having his legs—the ribs—inside the body, contrive to "walk"? If the belly of a python be examined it will be found to be marked by a number of broad, transverse plates or scales: and to the inner surface of each end the free end of a rib is fixed. As a consequence, as each pair of ribs moves forwards it sets the hinder edge of the scale on end, sufficiently to enable it to get a grip of the ground, and so, as the ribs' next move is backward, the body is thrust forward.

The sea-anemones are generally regarded as creatures which are "fixtures." But this is by no means true. They can, and do, shift from one place to another by movements of the "foot," akin to those of the snail. There are some which go much further than this. There is a Madeiran species, for example, which can crawl with speed, and furthermore detach itself and swim head-downwards at the surface of the sea. There are several species of the southern oceans which have improved on this method of travel, the base of the "foot" having been transformed into a gas-filled bladder. Needless to say they have altogether abandoned a fixed life on the sea-floor.

One more of these "creeping things" remains to be mentioned. This is the beautiful polyzoan *Cristatella*. This animal lives in colonies, and one wonders what is the controlling force which secures common consent from all the individuals of the colony to travel in one and the same direction.

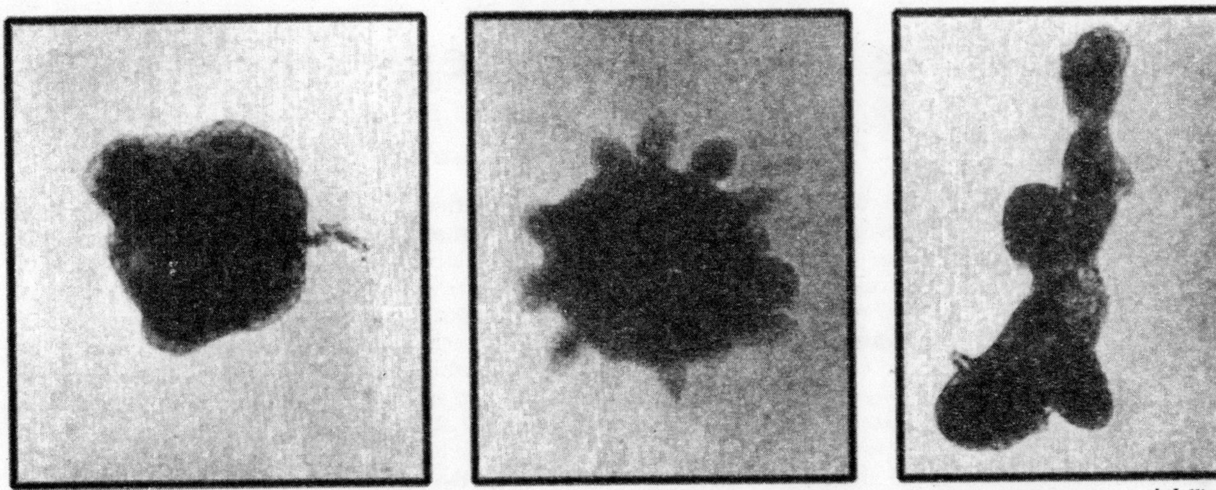

J. J. Ward

HOW THE LOWLY AMOEBA PROGRESSES BY MERELY "FLOWING"

Through the microscope one can watch the amoeba, which is a speck of jelly without any definite form, and can be obtained in most ponds. Its method of progression, as illustrated above, is (left) to extend a part of its substance and to continue the process (centre) until it gradually attenuates its mass in one direction (right). Then the rest of its body flows into the extremity of the extension and the process is repeated in an apparently aimless way. This is how one of the lowliest of living things travels

We are accustomed to think of "shell-fish" as peculiarly helpless creatures, yet we find the cockles buried deep in the sand at low water, and jumping joyously to meet the incoming tide! They rise from the dead as it were without any tell-tale sign, springing out of the ground by the action of the foot. The beautiful pecten with its glorious vermilion red foot swims gaily by rapidly opening and closing the shell-valves: using them with a flapping movement as though they were wings. Some of the mollusca have taken entirely to a "life on the ocean wave."

These are the pteropods. The shell is either wanting or extremely reduced, and swimming is effected by means of expansions of the foot to form a pair of "wings," which in this action recall those of a butterfly. Save when driven by currents they never come near land, and for the most part come to the surface of the sea only by night. When they wish to sink they fold their "wings" and drop slowly downwards. Their numbers are as the sand of the sea-shore: in their chosen waters in the great oceans, even in the icy Arctic waters, they exist in such vast myriads as to colour the sea for miles. They formed the chief item in the diet of the once abundant Greenland whale. These "snails of the open sea," as we might well call them, have but little power of control, but must drift with the current.

Very different is the case with the squids and cuttlefish, the most highly developed of all the mollusca, some of which attain to a gigantic size, rivalling even that of whales.

Not the least remarkable thing to be said of these singular creatures concerns their method of defeating their enemies. They do not fight, but run, and

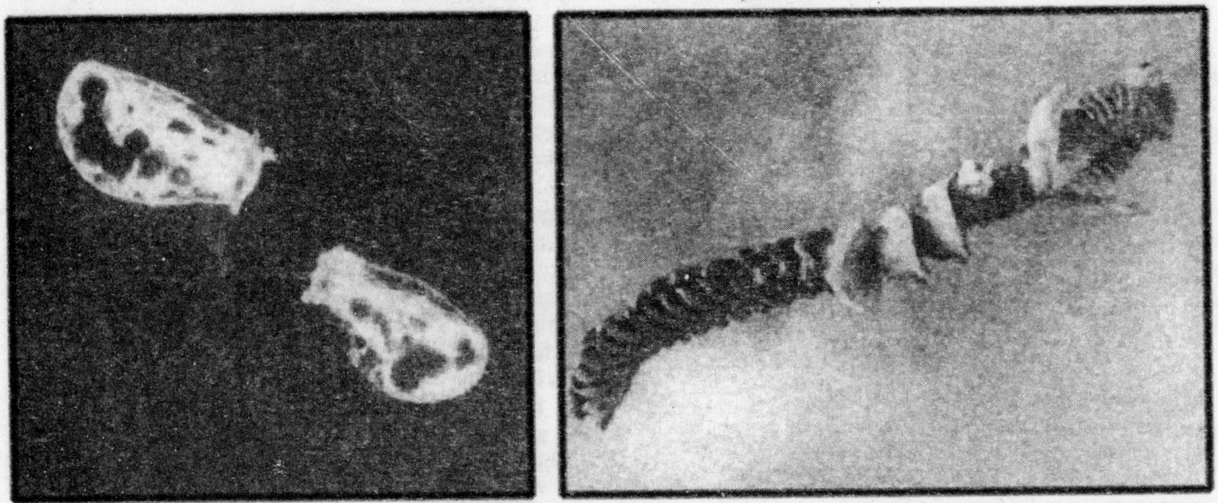

Martin Duncan

ROTIFERS AND A TUBE WORM AS THEY MOVE IN THE WATER

With the rotifers (left), which are considerably higher up the ladder of life's development than the amoeba, definite organs of propulsion have been developed. These are very delicate and threadlike, and are placed round the mouth. Not only do these organs, which are called cilia, serve to propel the rotifers, but also to whirl particles of food into the mouth. On the right is a parchment tube-worm. It leaves its tube home at night and glides along the floor of the sea, where it lives, by means of growths at the sides of its body.

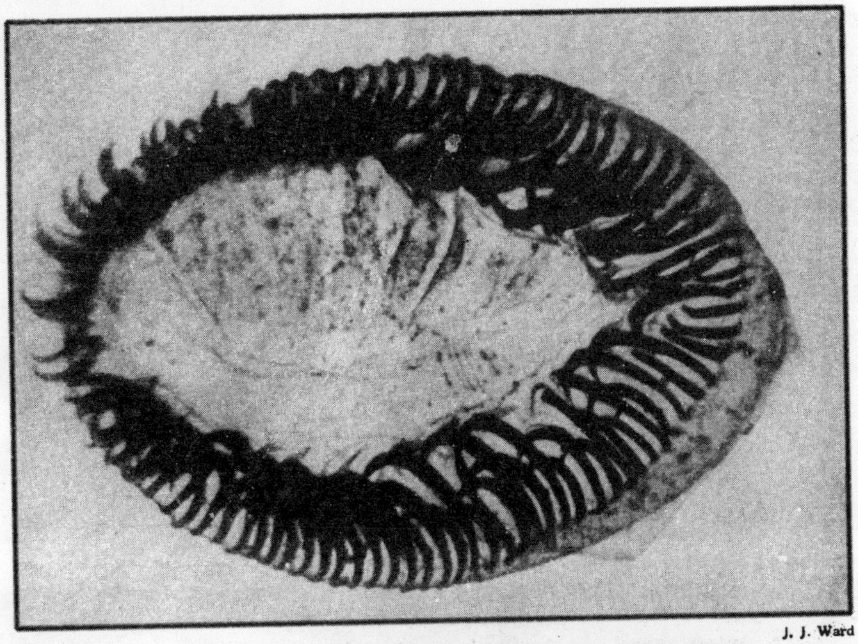

J. J. Ward

CATERPILLARS AND THEIR MEANS OF MOVEMENT

Some caterpillars move by making a loop of their bodies and so moving the claspers or "feet" on the hinder end of their bodies up towards where the fore claspers are, and then, while clinging with the hind claspers, move the fore part onward. Others move by undulating like the Cynthia given above. The lower photograph shows the clasper or pro-leg of a goat-moth caterpillar.

they run backwards! But how, in avoiding the danger which faces them, they avoid the unseen dangers behind them towards which they are rushing, is a mystery. This feat of "running" backwards is accomplished by drawing water into the spacious and closed mantle-cavity, and forcing it out again by expelling it through a narrow tube known as the siphon. The thrust of the column of water is so great as to send the body backwards at a surprising speed. Some of the Crustacea can emulate this feat, but by a totally different mechanism.

THE "swimming" of the jelly-fish is accomplished by the rapid and convulsive expansion and contraction of the disk-like body, which in its shape recalls that of an open umbrella. It is doubtful, however, whether we should attribute its progress to "swimming" since it is really borne along by currents and has no power of controlling its direction. The movements of the umbrella simply serve to keep it afloat. The beautiful Cydippe, looking like a crystal gooseberry, swims after a totally different fashion. Here the elongated body is beset with long bands of cilia, minute, "hair-like" structures, whose incessant movements keep the body at any desired level in the water, while long trailing tentacles serve at one and the same time for the capture of food and as balancers. The fact that one so often sees sandy beaches strewn with these frail bodies bears witness to the fact that they are all absolutely at the mercy of the currents.

Surely one of the most remarkable modes ot swimming is that of the small crustacean, Phoronis—it has no name in common speech—which, with a little poetic licence, may be said to drive itself about in a barrel-shaped saloon car, made of the clearest crystal! The car is provided by one of the "tunicata" or sea-squirts.

Phoronis instals itself within it, and by the movements of its "swimmerets" draws in a stream of water at one end and drives it out at the other, thus forcing itself and its strange carriage along!

The whale tribe have long since continued to do without legs as organs of locomotion—for the "flippers" answering to the fore-legs once used for walking, are mere balancers—yet they are amongst

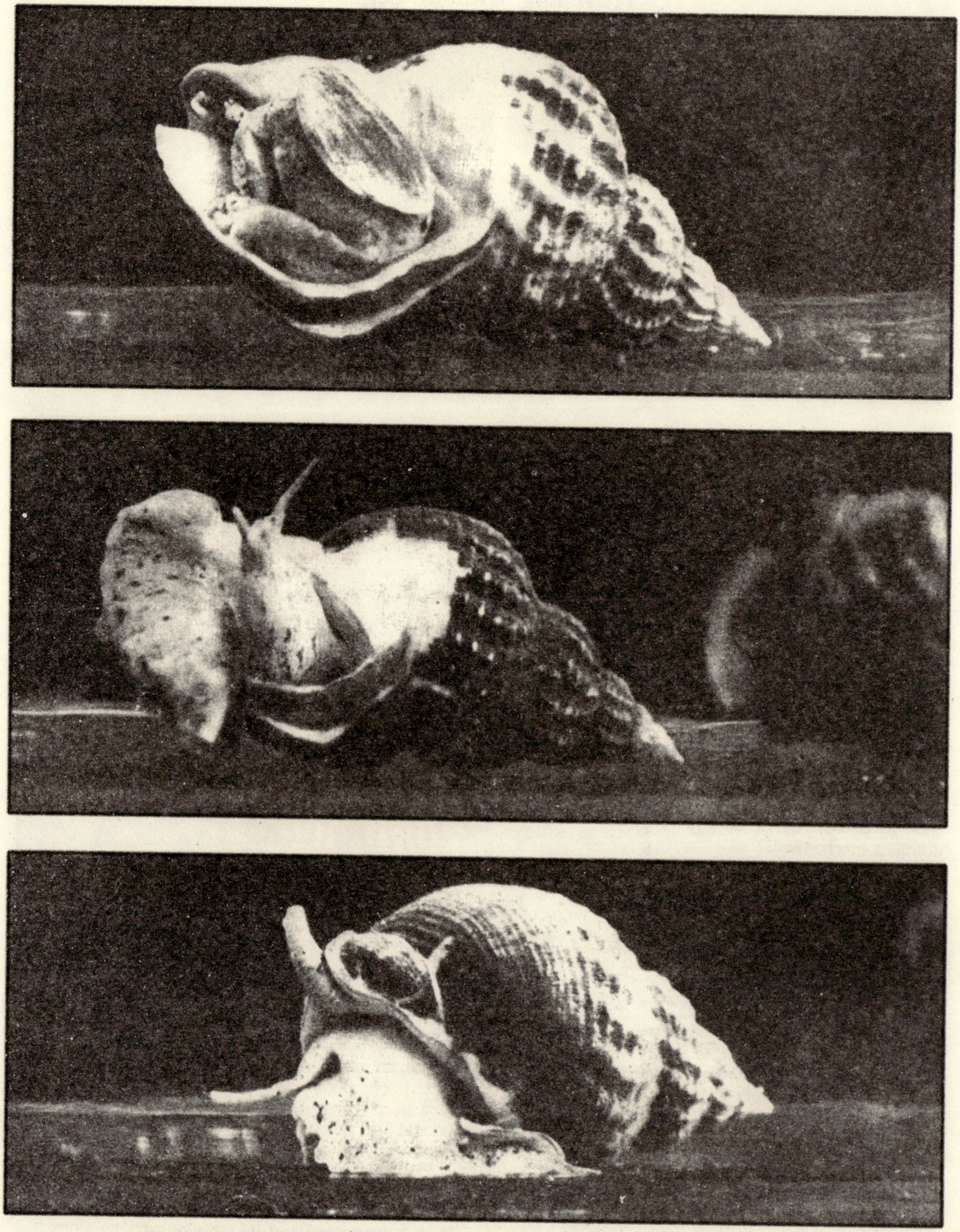

HOW THE WHELK GRADUALLY COMES OUT OF ITS SHELL TO WALK—

When inside its thick protective shell the whelk guards itself from attack through the opening in the shell by closing that opening by means of a horny lid or operculum. When the whelk desires to emerge for the sake of shifting its position and the search for food, it opens the lid (top). Then the beginnings of the " foot " appear (centre) and begin to expand (bottom). The whelk, which is really a sea snail, is carnivorous in habit and preys on other molluscs by boring through their shells and then devouring the soft bodies inside.

Martin Duncan

—THE UNFOLDING AND USE OF A VERY REMARKABLE KIND OF FOOT

These are the further and final stages of the whelk's emergence. The top photograph shows the broad foot with its edges still serrated because the unfolding is still only half complete, and the siphon breathing tube raised. The " foot " is then extended a little more (centre) and the breathing tube is now erect. Finally (bottom) the " foot " is fully expanded, and the wave-like motions are commenced which cause the whelk to move forward. Notice the operculum on the hinder end of the " foot." Like the snail the whelk has two horns.

J. J. Ward

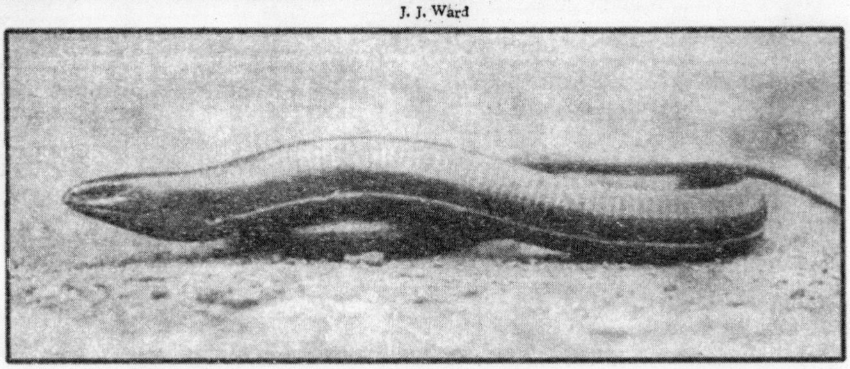

W. S. Berridge

GLASS SNAKE AND SLOW-WORM, LEGLESS LIZARDS

In Russia, Hungary and in Southern Asia and North America there is a certain legless lizard called, erroneously, the glass snake. The legs are absent or very rudimentary, locomotion being achieved by means of the scales with which the body is covered. The slow-worm (top) also moves by the action of its scales, which are themselves actuated by the ribs.

the most powerful swimmers in the sea. To this end the whole body has become profoundly modified so as to offer the least possible resistance to the water, while the tail has developed a pair of enormous flukes spreading out, one on each side in a horizontal plane, therein differing, be it noted, from the tail of the fish, which is always set vertically. There is a reason for this.

THE whale, being a lung-breather, must come to the surface to breathe. The horizontal plane of the tail fin makes this easy, for its function is to thrust the body forwards and upwards for air, or downwards for food, with the greatest possible speed. The fish, being a gill-breather, has no special need to come to the surface ; its tail being vertical drives it straight forwards. But this is not the whole explanation of the matter, for it must be noted that the method of using the tail is quite different in the two types. In the whale tribe the hinder region of the spine has to be moved upwards and downwards, instead of, as in the fish, from side to side.

But the whales have had to conform still further to the demands of their fish-like life ; at least, most of them have, by developing a back-fin to serve to steady them when going full-speed ahead. This fin, like the flukes of the tail, is formed only of fibrous tissue, and has no bony skeletal support as the fishes have. But such as swim in leisurely fashion have no dorsal fin. Now we have a parallel to the whales—the manatees and dugongs, which also have developed whale-like, horizontal tail-flukes, but have no dorsal fin. They are, we know, very slow-moving. A further point of interest about them is that the river-haunting species have a great lobe-shaped tail-fin, while in the marine species this lobe has been produced outwards to form pointed flukes after the fashion of the whales. Whether these differences are due to the purely mechanical stresses and strains of the up-and-down movements or to a reaction to the different specific gravity of sea-water is a problem that is well worth investigating.

It is a very curious thing, but we constantly find that Nature, having, so to speak, gone to the trouble of fashioning bodies to " fit " some particular form of physical environment, is sure to remodel some of that type so as to attain the same general end by a different means.

Fishes, we have noted, swim by means of side to side movements of the tail, the end of which bears a fin, which alone, to most people, is regarded as the tail. But the sea-horse and the pipe-fish swim by a sort of wave-like or undulatory movement of the back-fin. There are, indeed, many species which swim after this fashion, and the most remarkable of all is the tropical Amphisile, which propels itself along by its dorsal fin, and head downwards !

Let us turn, now, from the water to the air. Bats, birds, the old fossil pterodactyls, or flying-dragons, and insects of many kinds have fashioned themselves for long voyages in mid-air by means of wings,

THE ANGEL FISH SWIMS WITH FINS LIKE SILVER PINIONS

Barred with ebony and silver the iridescent sides of the angel fish glint among the seaweeds illumined by the blaze of the sun through the clear water of the tropic seas in which it lives. These silver fins, shaped like the wings that old painters used to give the angels in their pictures, are very fragile and liable to be damaged at the least contact with a rock or the sea-floor. Therefore, the fish is equipped with long bony appendages which warn it when this delicate lower fin is in danger of touching some hard substance.

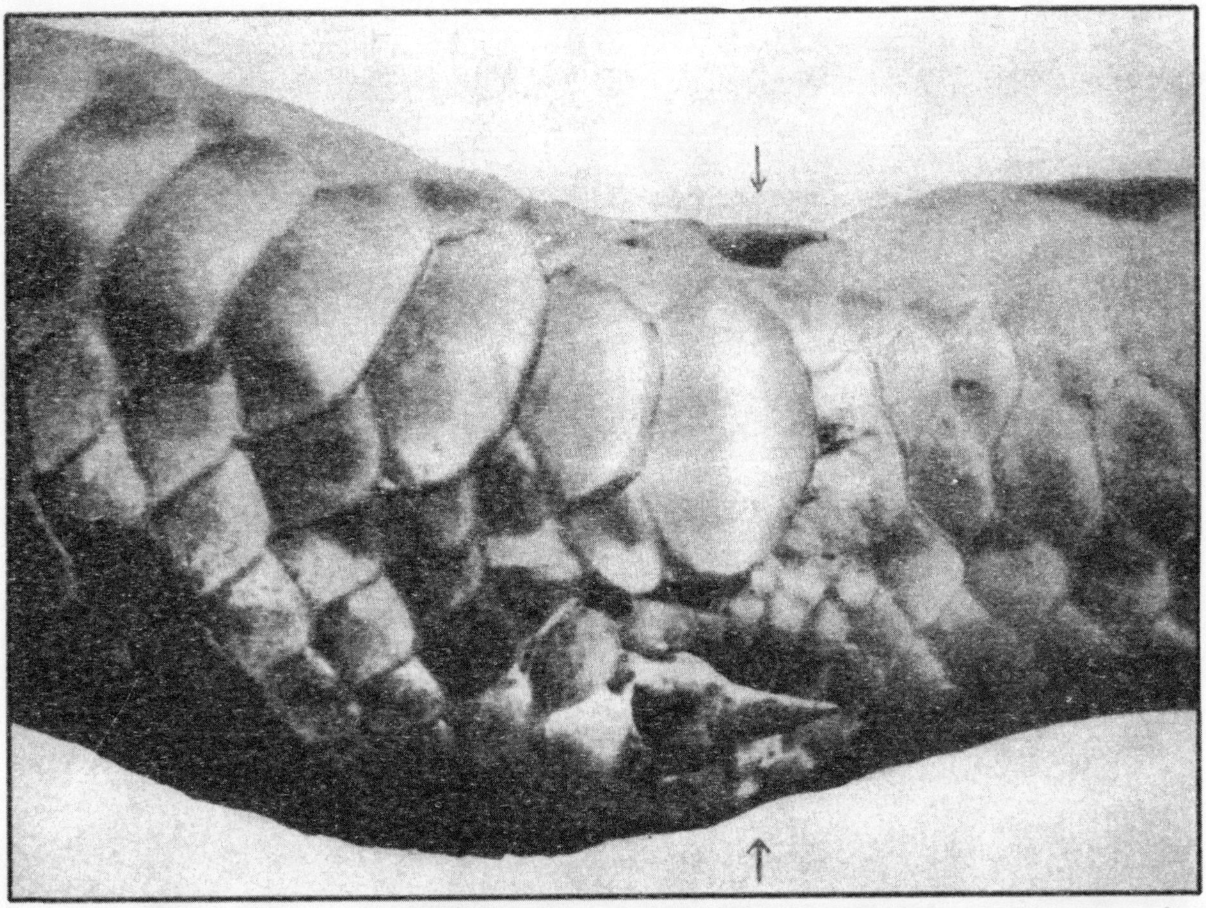

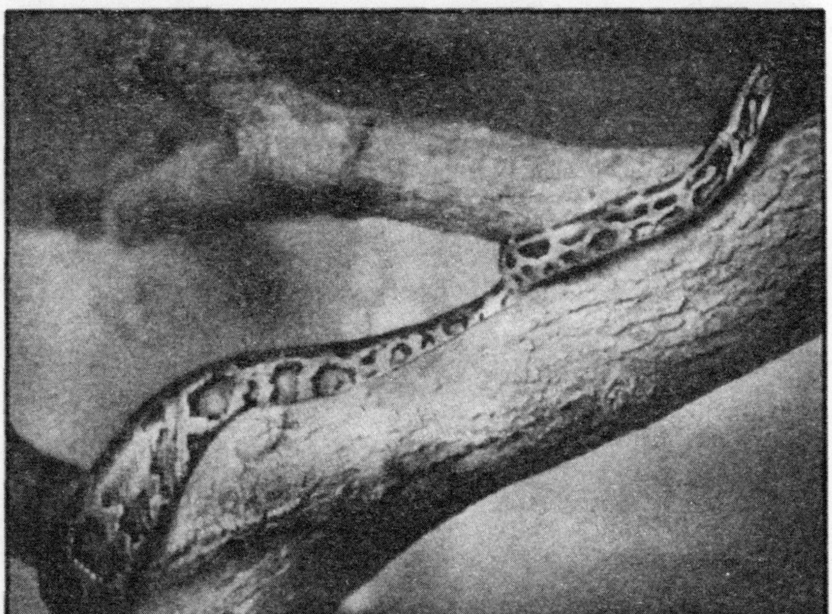

W. S. Berridge

PYTHON AND THE HOOKS THAT ARE REMNANTS OF LEGS

With the gradual dwindling of the legs which has accompanied the evolution of the snake, the body has correspondingly lengthened so that the spine has accumulated more vertebrae and each vertebra possesses a pair of ribs. These ribs function like the legs of a centipede but inside the skin. The skin of a python (bottom) possesses two hooks (top), remains of legs

though each type has achieved this end by a different method. Nature, however, has found the task, so to speak, of devising different means of traversing the upper air more difficult than locomotion on land or in the water. At any rate flying types are less numerous than running, leaping, climbing, and swimming types. But while some are remarkably efficient, others, it is to be noted, scarcely come within the category of flying-bodies: they might almost be called "Nature's experiments" so far as concerns flight.

We speak of "flying fishes," for example. But here the flight is attained by an impetus gained from the water sufficient to carry the body well above the surface, when, by expanding a pair of enormously enlarged breast fins a temporary journey in mid-air is

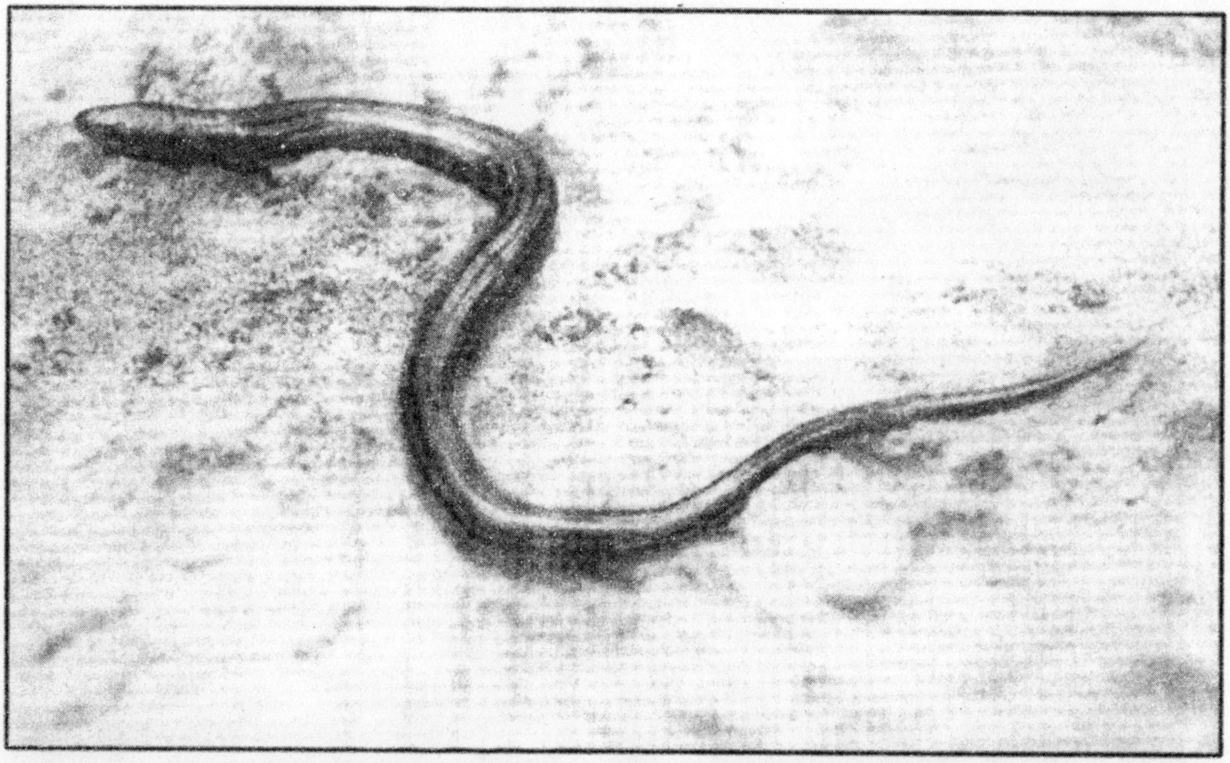

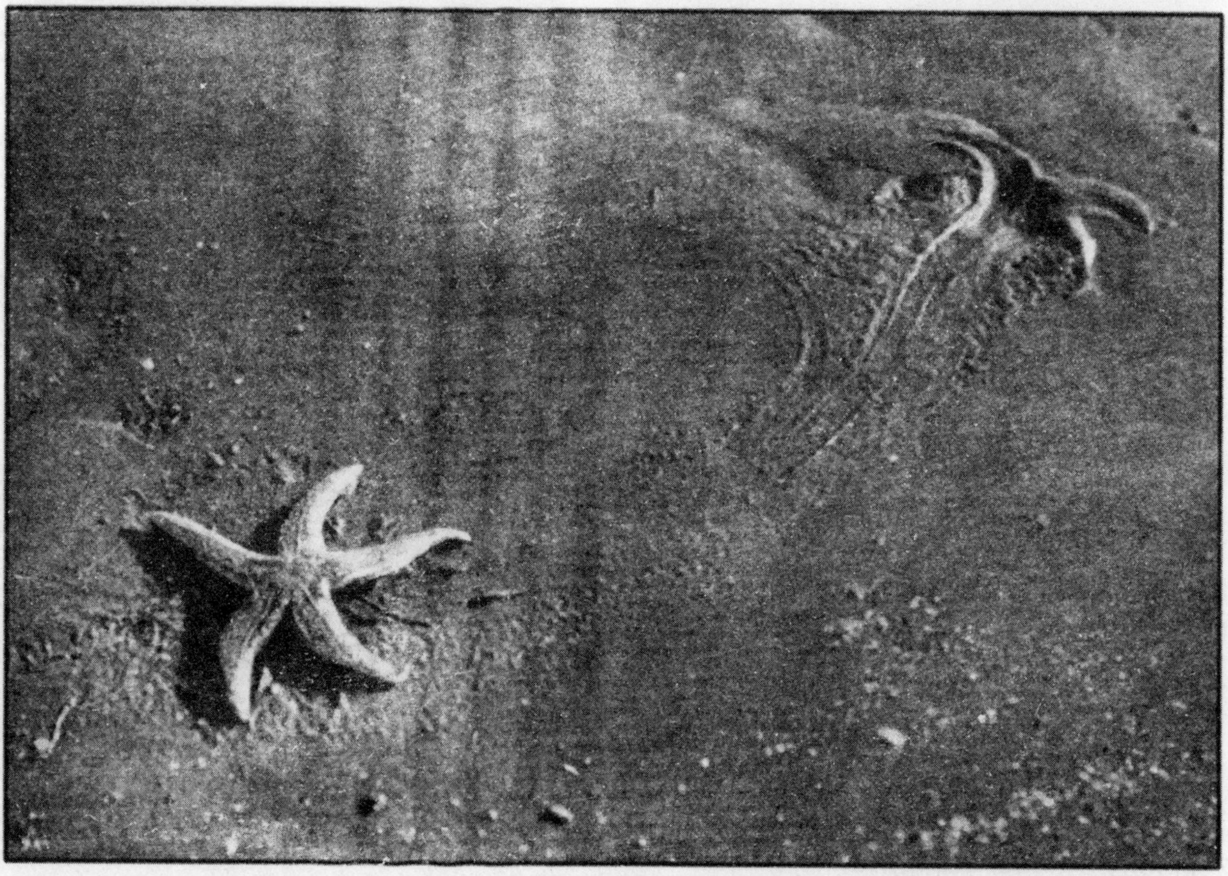

TRAIL OF A MOVING STARFISH IN THE SAND AND THE STRANGE SKINK

The rays or "arms" of the starfish are in no sense limbs but are merely incidental to one or other of the various shapes of body which the different species possess. These rays are covered on their underside with a great array of tiny organs which look to the naked eye like little columns of jelly. These may be seen to move, and they are, indeed, the sucker "feet" by means of which the starfish moves. Below is the track of a starfish and above is a skink which has no hind limbs and only rudimentary fore-limbs.

Shensky

WOLF FISH AND SLIME FISH, TRAVELLERS OF THE NORTH SEA

During the winter the wolf fish (bottom) comes into shallow water to spawn, and has been known to attack people wading with its sharp teeth which, in front, are conical and sharp-cutting and behind are adapted for crushing shell-fish. The slime fish (top) is one of the blennies, and with some other species is found along the British coasts. The photograph shows three females and two males, the latter distinguished by the forward part of their dorsal fins. The heads are furnished with tentacle-like growths and several rows of pointed warts.

W. S. Berridge

A PAGEANT OF ANGEL FISH: TINTED SWIMMERS OF THE CORAL REEFS

In the clear, green-blue waters where they swim, illuminated by the tropical sunshine, the angel fish match or rival the hues of the surrounding coral reefs which are their home. The fins of this species are formed like the wings of a bird, and from the undersides of the body, near the lower jaw, project long, bony structures. These apparently serve the purpose of warning the fish when it is getting near the bottom or any projecting rock which might damage its brittle pectoral fin. These long, bony streamers that hang down far below the fin, are extremely susceptible to touch sensations. The angel fish's movement through the water has a beauty of its own unlike any flying or running in the animal kingdom.

possible; the "wings" serving as planes over a course describing an arc of varying length, depending on the initial impetus of the body and the force of the wind. Three quite different genera of fishes have attained to this interesting means of travel.

The so-called "flying-squirrels" do not really fly, but simply "plane" down from a height, descending in a long curve which may, for a short distance, become an ascending curve. Once launched in the air, however, no augmentation of the velocity derived from the initial jump and the force of gravity is possible to them.

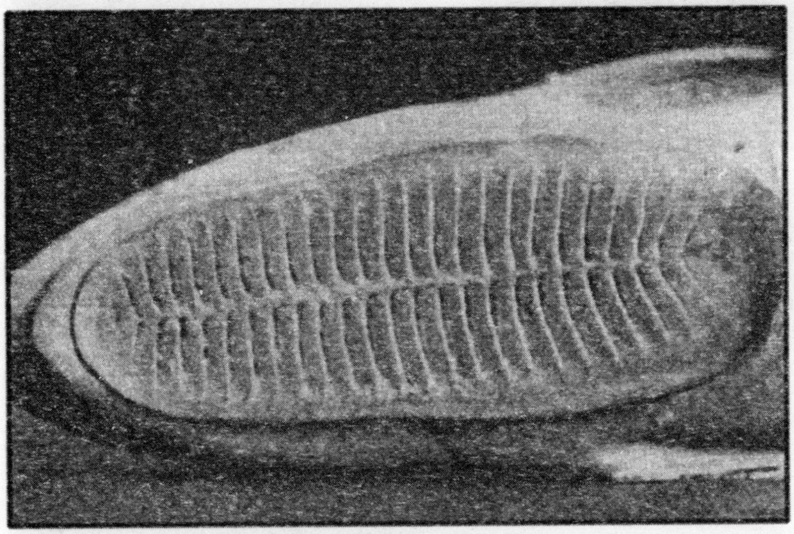

SUCKER FISH WHICH TAKES FREE RIDES ON SHARKS

Sucker fish have evolved, out of what in other fishes would be a spiny dorsal fin, a series of transverse plates, each plate being really an adapted spine of the fin. When the sucker fish wishes to visit another neighbourhood it swims up to a shark, presses its disk against the skin and raises the plates, thus forming a series of vacuum chambers by which it adheres.

In these animals a broad fold of skin extends along each side of the body to embrace the fore and hind limbs, so that when the legs are spread out in mid-air this fold stands out on either side, supporting the body after the fashion of a parachute. But one of the African flying-squirrels (*Anomalurus*) has effected an improvement, greatly increasing the area of the planing surface by means of a long, bony rod attached to the elbow. This, running through the skin-fold, extends it considerably beyond the wrist-joint, while at the hinder end this membrane is attached to the thigh between which and the tail an additional skin-fold is stretched, adding still further to the efficiency of the device.

The Australian "flying-phalangers" have developed a precisely similar device. Having regard to the fact that they are not even remotely related to the flying-squirrels this similarity is noteworthy. All these "planing" creatures it will be noted are tree-dwellers, like our common squirrel. That some should have developed this ready means of passing easily from one distant tree to another without descending to the ground is perhaps to be explained by a difference in feeding habits. For the ordinary arboreal squirrels feed largely upon nuts, most of which probably are picked up from the ground as they fall, hence, though they can leap from one tree to another when they are growing close together, they are not tempted to add to these leaping powers because the intermediate ground between two trees is always a potential feeding ground. Intensive effort always produces structural changes in the parts affected, as witness the tongue of the woodpecker and the whales. Birds probably inherited the potentiality for developing wings from some arboreal reptile-like ancestor which similarly, whenever possible, evaded a descent to the dangerous ground.

It is at any rate always, and only, in tree-dwelling types that we meet these "experiments of Nature" in the evolution of wings. Some curious examples are furnished by the reptiles. There are certain Bornean tree-snakes which take flying leaps from tree to tree, supporting themselves in mid-air by drawing up the belly till it nearly touches the backbone, thus the body, held stiff when taking its arrow-like flight, resembles a split bamboo. The channel thus formed apparently affords a "grip" of the air which gives a steadying action, and helps to maintain the direction of the flight.

Martin Duncan

THE RAY SWIMS BY UNDULATING MOVEMENTS ALONG THE SEA FLOOR

The ray is a fish, yet it hardly uses its tail for propulsion. Its family is an offshoot from that of the shark, and in the course of its adaptation to a life on the bottom of the ocean it has modified its pectoral fins so as to form a fringe round its body. The ray swims by a series of undulations which involve the whole body, but are most marked at its edges, where the fins have a positive rippling motion. The lower photograph shows the whitish underside and the upper the swimming movement.

Neville Kingston

AMERICAN BOWFIN AND ITS STRANGE WAY OF SWIMMING

The bowfin is the only representative of its order now in existence and it lives in the Great Lakes of America and also in the lakes of the Missisippi Valley. The dorsal fin is very elongated and low, and the fish moves by undulating this specialised fin. It is a sluggish creature and has little need of any great speed such as those fish have which swim with the tail. The movement of the fin, rippling gently over all its flexible length is very fascinating to watch through the glass of a zoo aquarium.

Some of the geckoes have a fringe of skin down each side of the body recalling that of the flying-squirrels, but it does not extend on to the limbs. Some authorities regard this fold as a sort of "flying-membrane," others hold that it serves merely to obliterate the animal when clinging to a tree-trunk, by blending the contour of the body with that of the tree. But be that as it may, we have a clear case of a "flying-membrane" in the Malayan "flying-dragon" (*Draco volans*), and this of a very singular type. For in this creature a great fold of skin is extended on each side of the body by means of the hindmost ribs, which are here produced into long, slender rods sweeping outwards for a considerable distance. As the creature takes its plunge into space the ribs are thrust outwards and forwards, spreading out in great and gorgeously coloured wing-membranes. But when at rest the ribs fold backwards, and the body assumes a singularly "starved" appearance.

Borneo has a frog which "flies"! And here again it is a tree-frog. The toes, both of the fore and hind feet, are unusually long, and connected by a web. By spreading these when in mid-air a very considerable surface of resistance is offered to sustain the body till its goal is reached.

Let me turn now to one of the strangest modes of aerial travel in Nature. This is furnished by the spiders, which contrive to make most extensive travels in mid-air without undergoing the slightest modification of their bodily structure to do so.

On calm summer mornings, either of early summer or late autumn, the grass, railings and bushes may be found covered with a delicate carpet of silk, revealed by the dew. And moving about among this maze of threads you may have the good fortune to see what looks like a race-congress of spiders which, for once, have thrown aside their cannibalistic moods for the attainment of a common end. All sorts and conditions are here—wolf-spiders, crab-spiders, jumping-spiders, and the tiny black Therdiid spiders. But they are all small, some being adults, while some are the young of the larger species.

With great good fortune you may see what the gathering means; for you may see one of this crowd holding fast by the silken threads, raising up the forepart of the body, then turning the abdomen skywards. Presently the spinnerets eject liquid silk, which is caught by the gentle breeze and borne upwards. More and more of this silk rope is "paid out" till at last the spinner begins to feel the pull of the rope. He then releases his hold and is promptly borne upwards to a distance of sixty, perhaps a hundred, feet, and away he goes on his travels. If he desires to end his journey he hauls in the rope with the hind legs, rolls it into a ball, and carries it near the mouth.

THIS is the phenomenon known as "gossamer" which so puzzled Chaucer and Spenser, Quarles and Thomson, to whom these filmy floating threads were a mystery. Martin Lister, so long ago as 1670, was the first to solve the riddle. He observed the wonderful flight from the highest point of York Minster, whence he could discern these little travellers "exceeding high" above him. Darwin found them at sea, during the voyage of the Beagle, sixty miles from land! Gilbert White describes a "shower" of these little aeronauts descending from their travels. It extended over an area eight miles in length. In this way not only is overcrowding effectually evaded, but the range of the species is also hereby extended

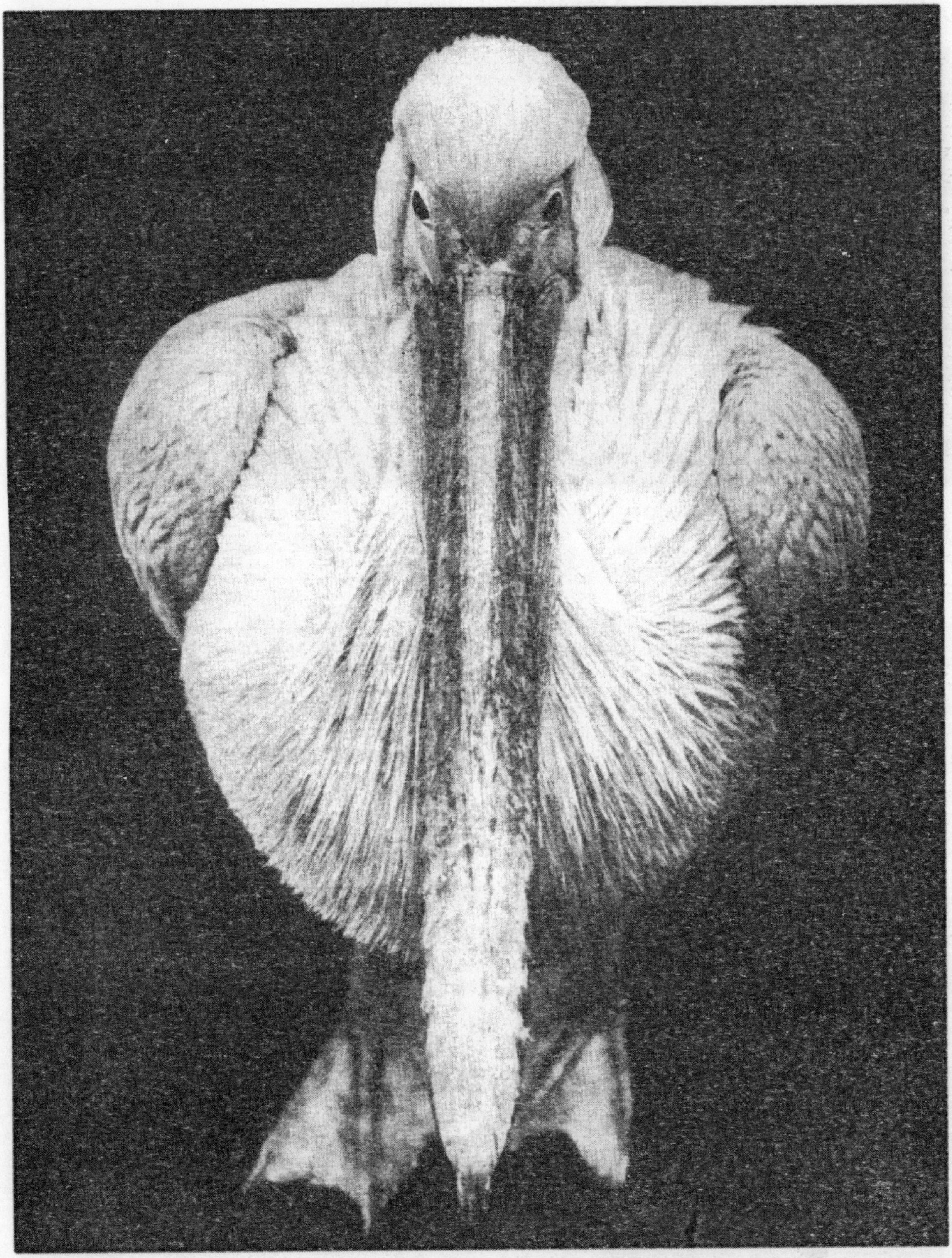

THE RESTING PELICAN: AN EXAMPLE OF NATURAL SYMMETRY

"Stream-lining" has been developed in Nature to a fine point as may be seen by studying the body of a fish or bird which is designed to offer the least possible resistance to the medium—water or air—through which movement has to be made. This utilitarian construction of shape gives us also a design of artistic excellence. Notice in this pelican how wing balances wing and how, with the head feathers which, as a whole, resemble a lawyer's wig, one side balances the other; and yet none of these features possesses an exact measured equality.

Chapter LVIII

Form and Design in the Animal Kingdom

By Stanley T. Burfield

Lecturer in Zoology, Liverpool University

When we speak of beauty in an animal we are more often than not referring to its colour or to the distribution of this. Sometimes movement or general form is spoken of as beautiful, as when we admire the litheness of a cat or the gracefulness of a swan. It is to be noted, moreover, that it is in the higher types of animal life that the average man finds beauty. This is natural, because these higher types are those which most often come within general knowledge. Geometric form and design are not so obvious in these, though closer study often shows beautiful adaptation of form to habits.

More regular geometric form is found principally among the lower and less well-known kinds of animals. Why is this ? There are various reasons. Such regular form is often to be seen among very small animals whose bodies are composed of soft semi-fluid living matter, and the shape of these is more easily directly controlled or influenced by purely physical factors acting in a symmetrical manner. In some larger types of animals, however, a geometrical form is developed by a peculiar manner of growth, as in many shellfish.

All animals grow during some period of their lives, but the general manner of growth is different from that seen in inorganic material such as a crystal. The latter may increase in size, and this is brought about by the addition of further material to the surfaces of the original crystal. The animal, on the other hand, grows by the adding of further living matter within the original body. The result of the first method is often perfect geometrical form with sharp edges and plane surfaces. The latter way of growing, however, tends, with the semi-fluid consistency of living matter, to result in curved surfaces, and straight edges and plane surfaces only appear in connexion with some of the solid dead material produced by the continued activity of the living substance.

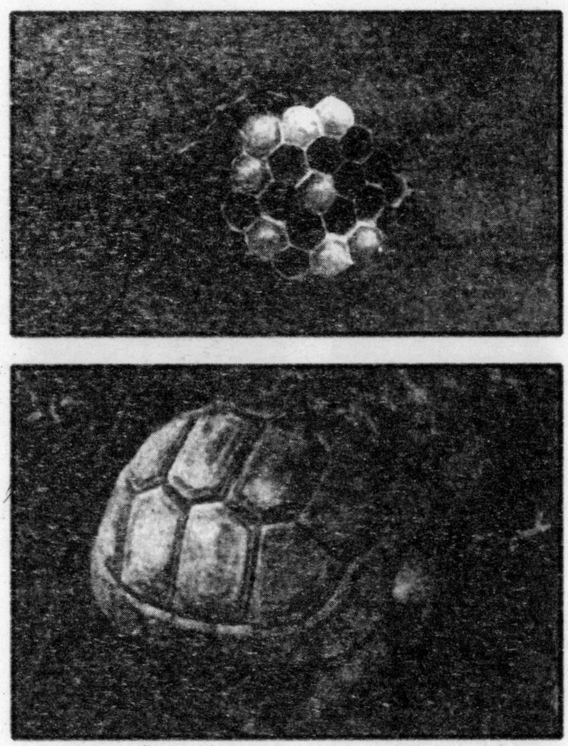

Hugh Main

THE HEXAGON IN NATURE

An explanation of the constant appearance of a hexagon or six-sided figure in Nature is that this figure or shape is due to uniform deformation under pressure. Here we have a tortoise's shell (bottom) and the cell of a wasp (top).

Animals being solid bodies, their form would have to be described strictly in terms of solid geometry, and we should perhaps have cone, sphere, tetrahedron, cylinder and so on. In surface view, however, there would often be recognized plane figures such as circle and hexagon. It must therefore be remembered that if such terms as the latter are used only a surface view is being described.

Many of the most regular and beautiful geometrical forms are found among the smallest known animals, the protozoa. The bodies of these are made of a small mass of semi-fluid living material, protoplasm. An important physical phenomenon which has a profound effect on their bodily form is "surface tension." This is a property of liquids, and is that force which is shown at the surface where the liquid is in contact with another liquid, solid or gas. It is the force by which we can explain the shape of a drop or bubble and of a number of other forms of a similar nature. Whilst this surface tension is an extremely important factor in the moulding of form in the case of the simplest organisms, the final shape also depends on various other phenomena such as gravity and mechanical pressure. For a liquid film in equilibrium surface tension results in a tendency for the surface area to be reduced to a minimum. Where a small portion of liquid is subject only to the forces of its own particles, this tendency accounts for the assumption of a spherical form, as in the case of a raindrop or the body of many simple organisms, because the sphere, of all solids, has the smallest surface for a given volume.

Thus the protozoa belonging to the sub-divisions radiolaria and heliozoa are very often in the form of perfect minute spheres. In other cases there has been some form of pressure or restraint during the development which results in a modification of the simple spherical form. This restraint is most constantly found in the partial or complete solidification of the cell wall. Even among the protozoa, then, there is a great variety of form.

Mountain zebra

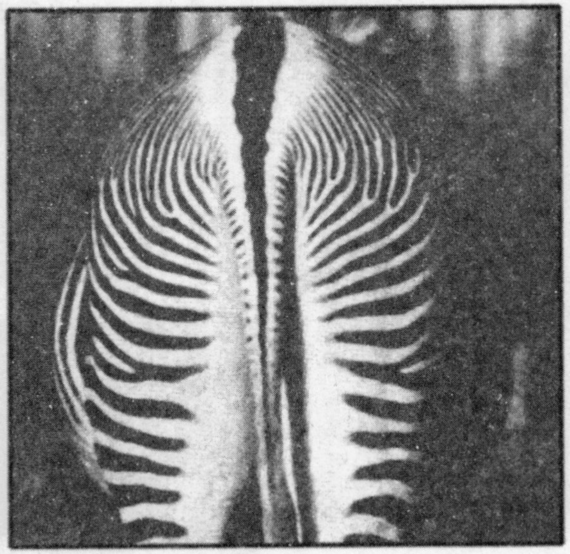

Grevy's zebra

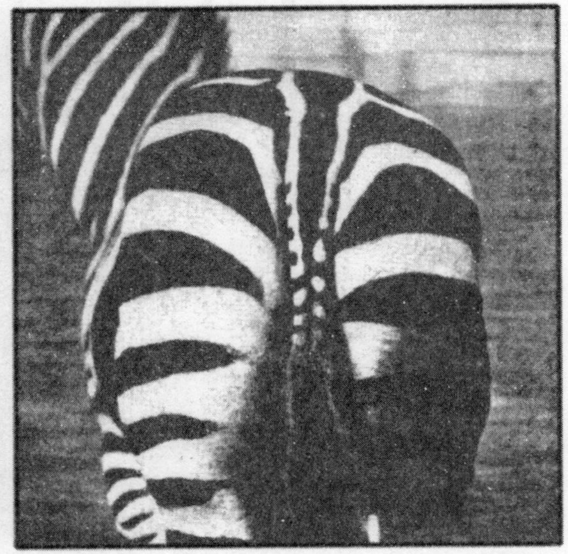

Crawshay's zebra

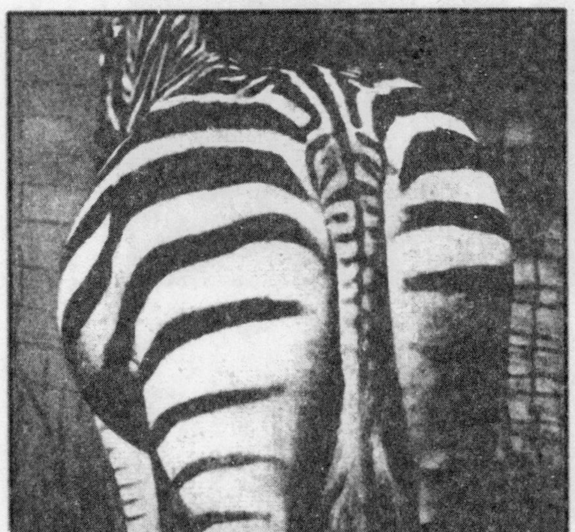

Chapman-Burchell zebra

Shadow stripes on a Chapman-Burchell zebra

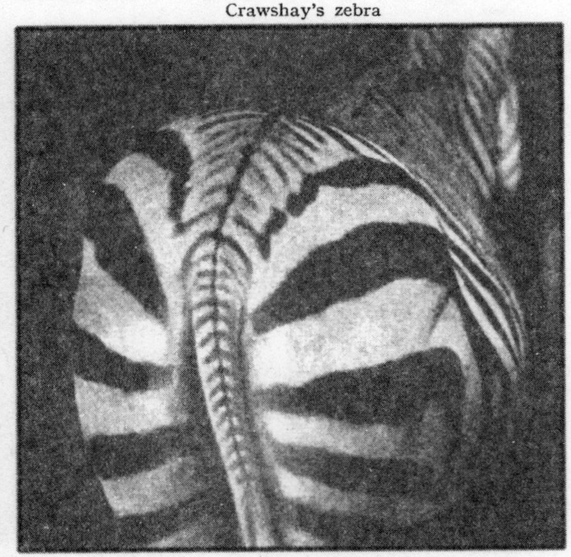

Hartman's zebra

WONDERFUL VARIATION OF STRIPES AND BARS IN THE HIDE OF THE ZEBRA

While a cursory glance might suggest that one kind of zebra was much like another, yet a closer inspection will reveal that this, so far as markings are concerned, is far from the case. The variations in arrangement of the bars of black, and stripes of tawny-white are considerable and intricate. Compare the markings of the true or mountain zebra (top left) with those of the Grevy's zebra (top centre). The former comes from South Africa where it was formerly almost extinct but is now increasing under protection. Grevy's is the largest of the zebras and stands as high as a horse. The hind quarters of a Chapman-Burchell zebra (bottom centre) are, again, quite distinctly marked. The photographs are by Elwin R. Sanborn.

HANDSOME HEADS AND FOREQUARTERS OF THE ZEBRA — Elwin R. Sanborn

Zebras seem to prefer thinly wooded and open country to forest or dense bush, and are specially adapted for a life among rocks and arid plains. But they keep within a few hours' travelling of water. The markings vary greatly, not only with different species but also with individuals. Not even the tiger can outdo some of the zebras in the magnificence of stripes which seem, so far as investigation has gone, to be an inheritance from some remote ancestor of both horse and zebra.

The amoeba is quite an irregularly shaped mass of semi-fluid protoplasm, and its shape as a whole certainly does not conform to one of the types known as surfaces of minimal area. The surface is not, however, an equilibrium surface at all, and the living cell is not itself in any stable equilibrium, but each portion of the surface is constantly changing its form. Those unicellular organisms which rest in stable equilibrium have a shape which either conforms to the conditions imposed by surface tension alone or is the result of some kind of restraint imposed upon the ordinary surface tension.

Among the infusoria some are distinctly spherical, as in the small flagellate monads, but even here they are usually only truly spherical whilst in a "resting" or encysted condition. When a flagellum is developed, we have signs of an unequal tension of the outer membrane, and the end of the cell is drawn out into a tapering point.

A large number of infusoria represent "surfaces of minimal area" in their form. The cups of various vorticellas are a beautiful series of such surfaces. We find every gradation from a form all but cylindrical through a series of unduloids or partial unduloids to an almost perfect sphere. The cylinder, unduloid and sphere are all surfaces of minimal area. In other cases, such as in the various species of tintinnus among the ciliata, we find a similar series of shapes exhibited by a membranous cup which is separate from the animal but was originally moulded upon its semi-fluid living surface. A curious little ciliate called trichodina has a most peculiar shape. It may be compared roughly to a short dice-box, the lower surface being plane and the upper one may be either plane or slightly concave. When the upper surface is plane the equatorial groove forms a surface of minimal area called a catenoid; when the upper surface is depressed the groove tends to assume the form of another minimal area surface, the nodoid.

Among the foraminifera there are great varieties of form which are capable of explanation in the light of surface tension and the principle of minimal area. Many of these protozoa are composite structures formed by the development of a series of calcareous-walled chambers. Some of these are complicated, and we shall glance at a few of the single-chambered and simplest composite varieties.

In orbulina we have a perfectly symmetrical sphere. Most of the single-chambered calcareous foraminifera belong to the genus lagena. These

African whip scorpion

Central American chafer

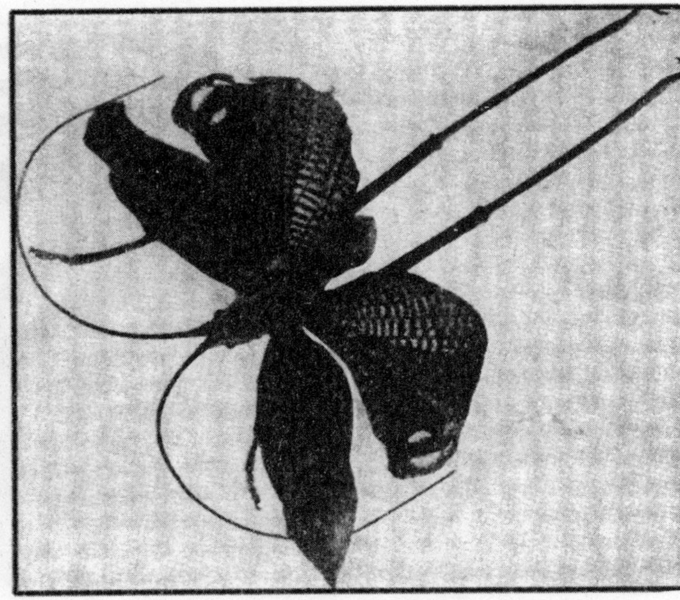

Brazilian leaf grasshopper

Syrian neuroptera

Large dragon-fly

Butterfly of Assam

SHAPES AND STRUCTURES BEAUTIFUL AND GROTESQUE OF NATURE'S FASHIONING

Nature usually makes her creatures beautiful or repulsive or terrifying not only in detail, but also in general design. The African whip scorpion (top left), for instance, seems made to be shunned. The shape of its legs and of the angular pedipalps which serve much the same purpose as the claws of the lobster, and the formation of the rough-looking body, are all designed apparently to make man and beast turn away. On the other hand, the creative power seems to have gone as far in the opposite direction when evolving the form of the winged beauty seen in the lower left-hand photograph, or in the butterfly from the forests of Assam (bottom right). These photographs are by Martin Duncan and H. Bastin.

are beautiful flask-shaped forms whose surface is simply an unduloid or an unduloid combined with a portion of a sphere. These shapes suggest hanging drops drawn out into slender necks by their own weight. Many of the lagenidae have a beautiful reticulated or ridged pattern on the shell, which is probably developed by local shrinkage and changes of surface tension in the outer layers of the protoplasm before the hard shell has fully developed.

ANOTHER series of foraminifera composed of a number of chambers is seen in the species of nodosaria and others. In some of these, rheoplax, for example, with a sand grain covering, we have cases of segmenting or partially segmenting cylinders. Under surface tension forces it can be shown that a cylinder is only a surface of complete equilibrium when its length is not greater than its circumference. If a liquid film in the form of a cylinder be drawn out, it is found that when the length becomes greater than its diameter it changes its shape, passes into an unduloid form and ultimately breaks into two spheres. In other cases we can see by examining the interior of the shell that it has been formed in successive stages. First a simple unduloid "lagena," and then about the neck of this, after solidification, another drop of protoplasm has accumulated and in turn has taken on the unduloid shape.

Neville Kingston

LOVELY MOON MOTH OF AMERICA

Here we have an example of one of Nature's most exquisite designs where the form as much as the colour gives the creature its beauty. This is an American moon moth, and we see it here newly emerged from its cocoon into the sunlight, which is slowly drying the pale green wings. The long "tails" hang down like delicate draperies to bedeck an already lovely creature.

The hexagon is to be found frequently among the lower forms of animal life. We can explain the appearance of this polygon in many cases fairly easily. If we imagine a system of equal cylinders or spheres in contact with one another in a plane, they will be represented in section by equal and touching circles. Now simple geometry tells us that each circle will be in contact with six surrounding circles. If we now imagine the system of spheres or cylinders to come under some uniform pressure the points of contact between the circles will be extended into lines of contact and the equal circles will become regular and equal hexagons.

These considerations will hold true not only for individual cells in the body tissues, but for any closely packed bodies of uniform size and originally circular outline in section which are of such a consistency as to be capable of uniform deformation under pressure. Thus a hexagonal pattern is of very common occurrence and is to be noticed under very varying circumstances.

The corals show us various examples wherever the coral animals or polyps are packed close together. The originally cylindrical soft-bodied polyps become squeezed into hexagonal prisms and the secretion of the chalky outer skeleton over the side walls of the prisms takes the hexagonal form which therefore becomes permanent.

PERHAPS the best known of hexagonal structures connected with animal life are the cells in the comb of the honey bee. These cells are in two layers, the cells of each layer being placed end to end. An inspection of either surface shows at once the hexagonal outline of each cell. The explanation which we have already given of the hexagonal form assumed by closely packed cylinders doubtless holds here.

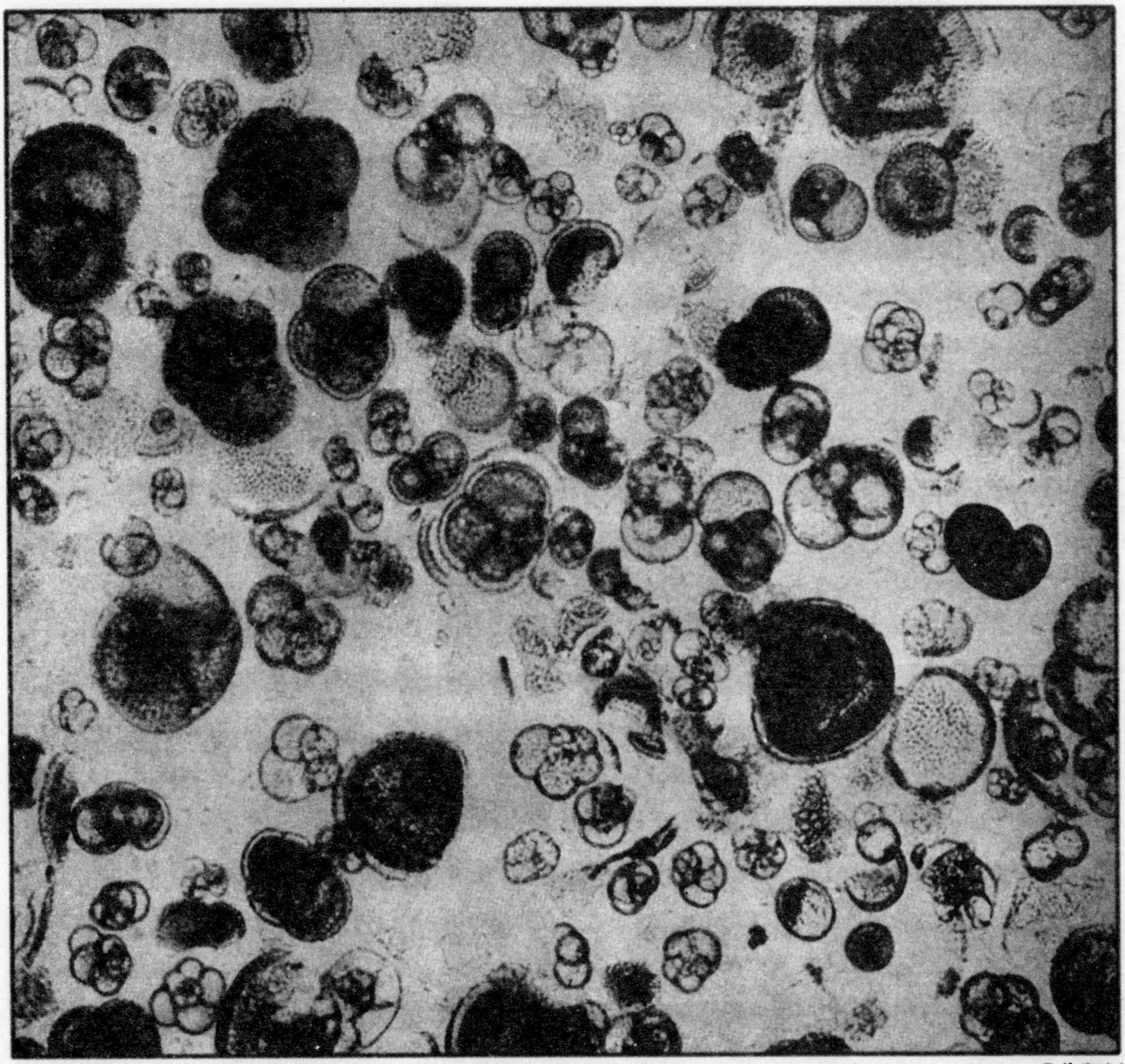

E. H. Botting

SHELLS OF GLOBIGERINA FROM THE DEEP SEA OOZE

These shells which serve to protect the minute creatures called globigerina (that belong to the division Perforata in the order Foraminifera) are found in great numbers in the ooze covering much of the sea floor. They have gone in their accumulated millions to form part of the chalk deposits which, once at the bottom of the sea, now form the subsoil of the cliffs of many miles of English and French territory. So thick is the deposit of this particular kind of shell in some parts of the ocean bed that it is called "Globigerina ooze."

The wax when first produced by the bee in the warm hive is in a semi-fluid condition. The bee fashions a cylinder and packs it as close as possible to the cells already made. The efforts of the bee in close packing are probably not sufficient to produce the even smooth-sided hexagons which finally result, but it is more than likely that the wax being at first in the form of a thin semi-fluid film, surface tension comes into play between adjacent films, and these symmetrical tensions result in the regular form assumed by the gradually hardening cell walls. It is to be noted that the portions of the queen cells which project freely above the level of the others and are therefore not under lateral pressures or tensions are of a cylindrical form. [The Editor would draw attention to the fact that on this point of the formation of hexagonal cells the Rev. Tickner Edwardes in his chapter on "The Wonderful Commonwealth of the Bee" suggests another explanation. See Volume I, page 257.]

THE explanation given is sufficient to cover the hexagonal form as seen at the open ends of the cells of the comb, but the whole cell is more complicated in shape. The point of further interest is the form of the closed ends where the two layers of cells are in contact. Under surface tension forces, a fluid cylinder in equilibrium has a symmetrical end in the form of a portion of a sphere. Now if we can manage to make an imaginary picture of these

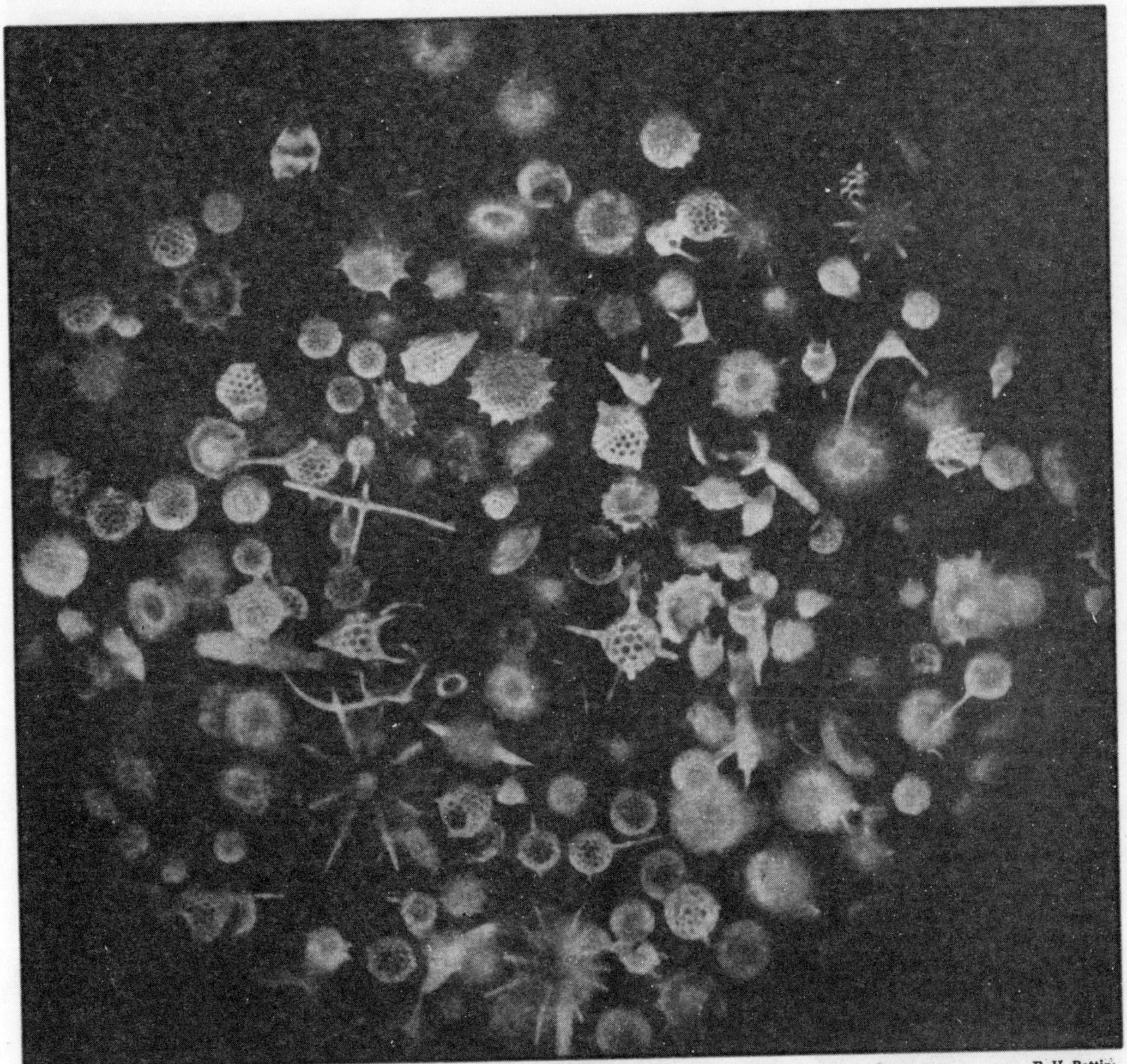

E. H. Bottin

WONDERFULLY FASHIONED SKELETONS OF THE RADIOLARIA

The hard skeletons of the animalcules known as radiolaria are built up into the most amazing complications of shape and design. While alive some of them float on the surface of the sea, their jelly-like bodies aglow with yellow, crimson and blue, while others live at varying depths, and, when dead, their beautiful skeletons sink down through the dark fathoms to rest on the bottom of the sea already thickly covered with the " bones " of their brethren. The shells above came from Barbados where large deposits of radiolaria are found.

inner partially spherical ends of the two layers of cells fitting close against one another, we shall see that each will fit in between three others. By mutual symmetrical pressures the spherical end of any one cell will be pressed by its three neighbours so that the end will take the form of a solid trihedral angle with three meeting edges. This three-surfaced end is fitted on to the six-edged hexagonal prism by planing off every other angle of the prism regularly. Thus the closed ends of the prisms are tapered off to a point and all fit together without intervening space. This is found to be the shape of the closed end of a bee's cell. If both ends of the prismatic cells were closed in this way we should have the regular twelve-sided solid called the rhombic dodecahedron.

When we consider the general body shape among the more advanced types of animal life simple geometric form becomes much less frequent. The reason for this has already been indicated. The larger and more complex bodies are not so directly under the control of the simpler external physical forces. The play of these forces, such as surface tension, is, however, still to be seen in the form of the cells in various tissues of such a large animal, and also in the whole animal in its earliest embryonic stages in which it consists of comparatively few cells.

In the adult form of the higher animals the general shape of the whole is closely adapted to the life of the particular animal, but this shape is the result of the general growth of the animal which is taking

Triceratum

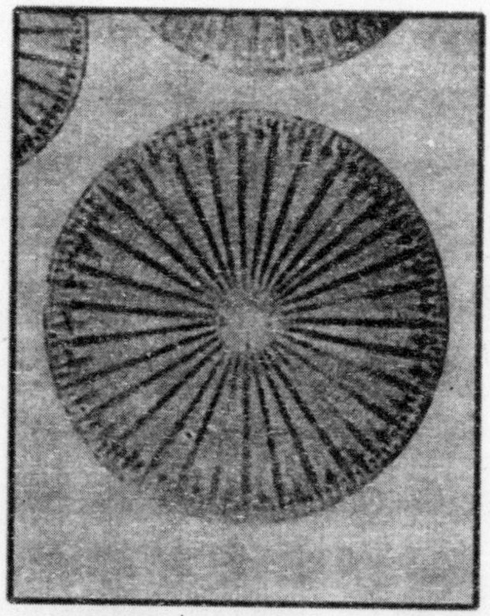

Aulacodiscus

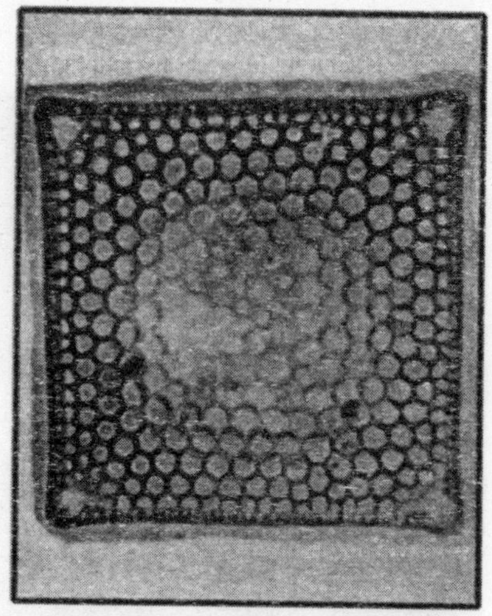

Triceratum

Triceratum

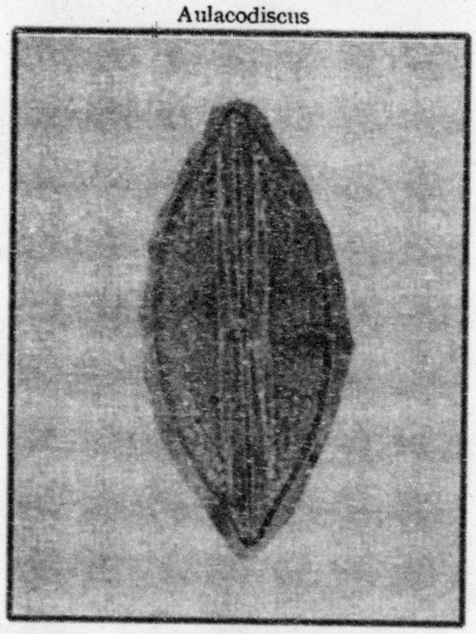

Navicula

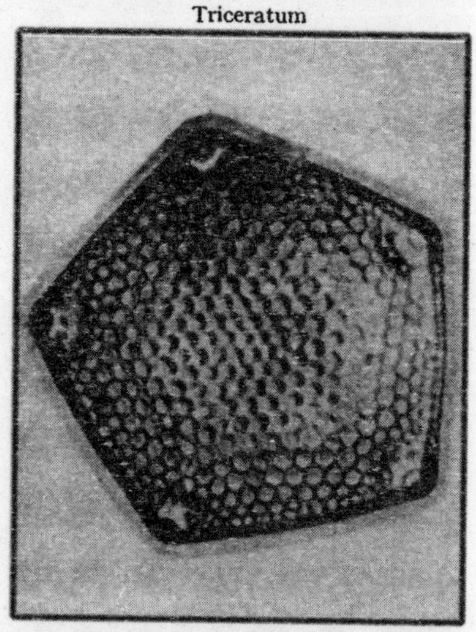

Triceratum

Aulacodiscus

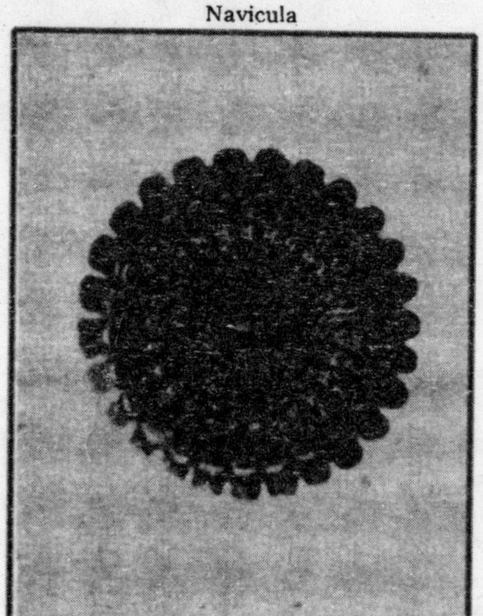

Echinus

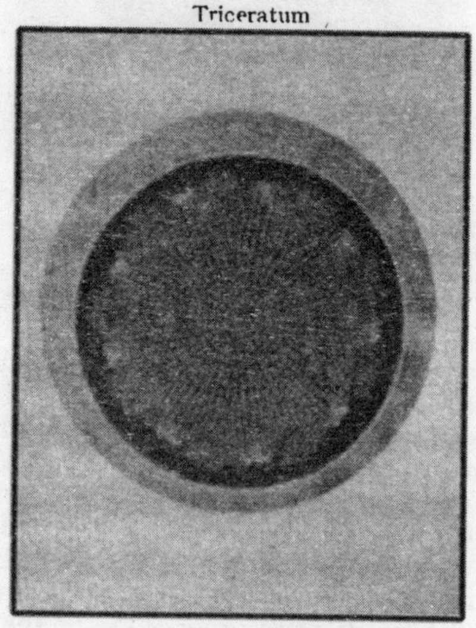

Aulacodiscus

LOWLY ANIMAL FORMS OF INTRICATE DESIGN

Triangular and circular shapes, patterns of the most extreme delicacy and as intricate as anything any Chinese craftsman ever spent a lifetime in producing, the skeletons of the radiolaria are one of Nature's greatest wonders. The skeleton of a mammoth is a simple piece of construction but the framework of these tiny creatures is so intricate that we can only observe and wonder. Above we have eight examples of these pieces of Nature's craftsmanship showing the amazing variety. The echinus is a sea-urchin. These photographs are by H. S. Cheavin.

F. Schensky

Neville Kingston

HANDSOME MARKINGS OF THE CICHLIDS AND THE MACKEREL

In certain of the African lakes such as Tanganyika and Nyassa, and in some rivers of tropical America, some representatives of the perch family are found called cichlids (bottom). Like so many of the perches they have handsome designs on their skins. The mackerel (top) is one of the most handsome of sea fish both in form and markings. The dark blue pattern along the top of the back contrasts at close quarters with green-blue, though, when seen moving in the water, these dark and light colours make a kind of camouflage.

Common Carp

Perch

Bream

Rainbow Trout

VARIEGATED FISH SKINS

In the water the fish of river or lake wishes to be as inconspicuous as possible, whether it is playing the part of hunter or hunted. The markings then, though striking seen out of water, are all designed to blend with a background. Photographs by S. C. Johnson

place in different ways and at different rates in various parts of the body and is often due to the differential growth of a considerable number of tissue masses at the different places. The whole animal becomes more independent of the simpler physical forces of its environment which, as we have seen, tend to result in geometrical forms.

A number of animals exhibit something of a regular star shape. This is perhaps best seen in the starfishes. This is an expression of what is called radial symmetry. It may be considered as correlated with a fixed or sessile habit of life. It is obviously an advantage for an animal fixed to one spot to be able to deal immediately with changes in the environment coming from any quarter of the compass by having such structures as food-catching arms or tentacles, sensory organs and so on placed all around the central body after the manner of spokes radiating from the hub of a wheel. Some of the near allies of the starfishes, the sea lilies, are actually fixed in one spot by a stalk and have this radial symmetry also, and this is found to be general among the whole group of echinodermata. In the free-moving forms the symmetry is probably an inherited form of body, the ancestral type of the group having been sessile. A similar radial symmetry is seen in the little fresh-water hydra and the marine sea anemones.

A BURROWING habit is also reflected in bodily form among animals belonging to various groups. The form of body best adapted to this kind of life is a cylindrical one with little in the way of projections. This we see in various worms, such as the common earthworm, and among the higher animals in the eel among the fishes, in some amphibia, such as typhlonectes, and in snakes among the reptiles.

Some of the most beautifully adapted shapes of body are to be seen in the fishes and birds. In both cases we find a body with an evenly curved outline. The general form is built on what the engineer would call stream-lines. He fashions the torpedo, the ship's hull, and the aeroplane hull in such a form. The curved sides of the body are such as to offer the least possible resistance to rapid movement through a liquid (water) or gas (air). The shape of a mackerel or the body of almost any bird shows this form to perfection. The fish is shaped like a sharp wedge in front, swells out very gradually and evenly along the sides, and becomes flattened again towards the hinder propulsive tail end. Looking a mackerel straight in the face is a revelation as regards form. Fishes which tend to lie on the bottom lose this form and become flattened as in the skate or plaice. On the other hand, some fishes float almost passively in the water, and have a more spherical shape, such as the globe fishes.

The eggs of various animals, especially those of birds and some insects, exhibit beautiful regular form and have excited curiosity and admiration from the earliest times. Amongst birds' eggs the majority are either nearly spherical, ellipsoidal, or else ovoid, with one end more pointed than the other. The differences between the eggs of different birds are

BEAUTEOUS DESIGN IN BLACK AND WHITE OF THE ZEBRA'S HIDE

Of Nature's patterns, as displayed by the animals, the zebra's is the most striking. The hide seems as though the graceful markings—varying subtly with each individual—had been painted in delicately with a brush. The beautiful pattern on the head, like so much stencil work, is particularly noteworthy in the example seen above. On the neck the stripes are continued up into the mane.

principally those of colour and markings. The shape of the egg appears to be due to various pressures on the egg in the stage before the shell substance has hardened. The oviduct down which the egg passes on its way to the exterior has muscular walls, and waves of contraction passing down this tube not only serve to force the egg along but also mould it into the shape it retains after the deposition of the hard shell. We may suppose that in those birds which lay a spherical egg, such as the penguin, the pressures on the egg are not great, the oviduct being large compared with the size of the egg. Thus the fluid portions of the egg, the white covered only by a membrane, take on the spherical form to be expected under these conditions, and the shell is formed on the surface of the membrane enclosing the white. In those cases in which the egg is large compared with the size of the oviduct the pressures on the egg are greater and the various ellipsoidal and ovoid forms result. The colour and markings on the egg shell are due to pigments, largely derived from the blood, being mixed with the shell-forming material.

The eggs of many insects, especially those of butterflies and moths, often exhibit extraordinary shapes and beautiful regular sculpturings on the surface. Here the differences between eggs of various insects are mainly those of shape and not of colour. These eggs are also moulded in an oviduct, and the final form is due not only to muscular pressure, but also to the shape of the part of the oviduct in which they lie whilst the outer shell is being formed. This shell is soft at first, and is stamped with the various regular sculpturings so often seen in these eggs. The hexagonal pattern on the surface, for instance, is apparently due to an imprint of the cells forming the lining of the lower part of the oviduct.

BEFORE concluding this chapter we must deal briefly with what is, perhaps, the most beautiful geometrical form to be found in nature, namely the spiral. Apart from a number of curves which are true spirals having certain mathematical properties, there is also one which is often confused with these—the simple screw or cylindrical helix. Such a curve as this does not begin from any definite point, nor does it vary its curvature as it proceeds. A true spiral does both of these. Among animals beautiful cases of the screw are to be seen in some protozoa, such as the spirochaetes and in parts of others. The stalk of the little vorticella, when contracted, assumes an extremely beautiful helical form.

There are many instances among animals of truly spiral formations. Many of the hoofed mammals have horns curved or twisted into beautiful spirals. Many varieties of sheep, goats and antelopes exhibit this well. The tusks of the mammoth and of the pig-like babirusa are other instances.

Among those animals whose whole body is spirally curved the most familiar cases are those illustrated by the shells of the mollusc and foraminifera. Here we have numerous cases of a remarkable curve called the logarithmic spiral. One of the properties of this

Markhor

Snail

Trochus

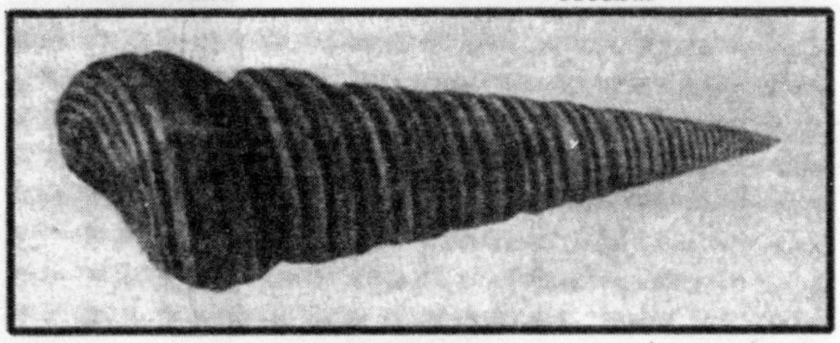

Cingulata

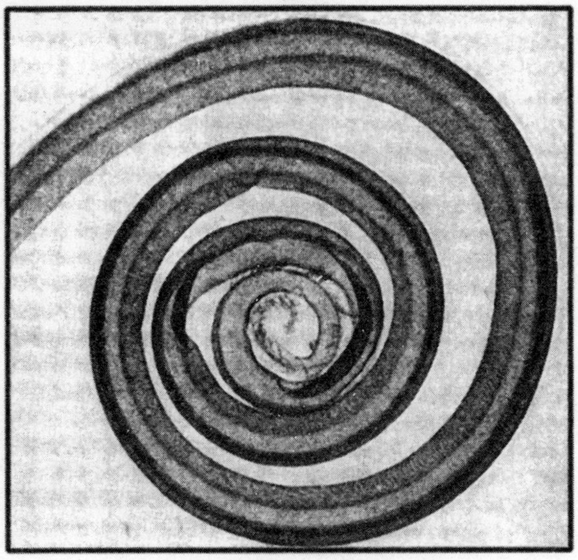

Butterfly's tongue

SPIRALS IN NATURE

Nature employs the spiral continually, and in many surprising ways. In things so diverse as the tongue of the butterfly, the snail's shell, and the handsome horns of the markhor, a wild goat of Afghanistan, we find this graceful design.

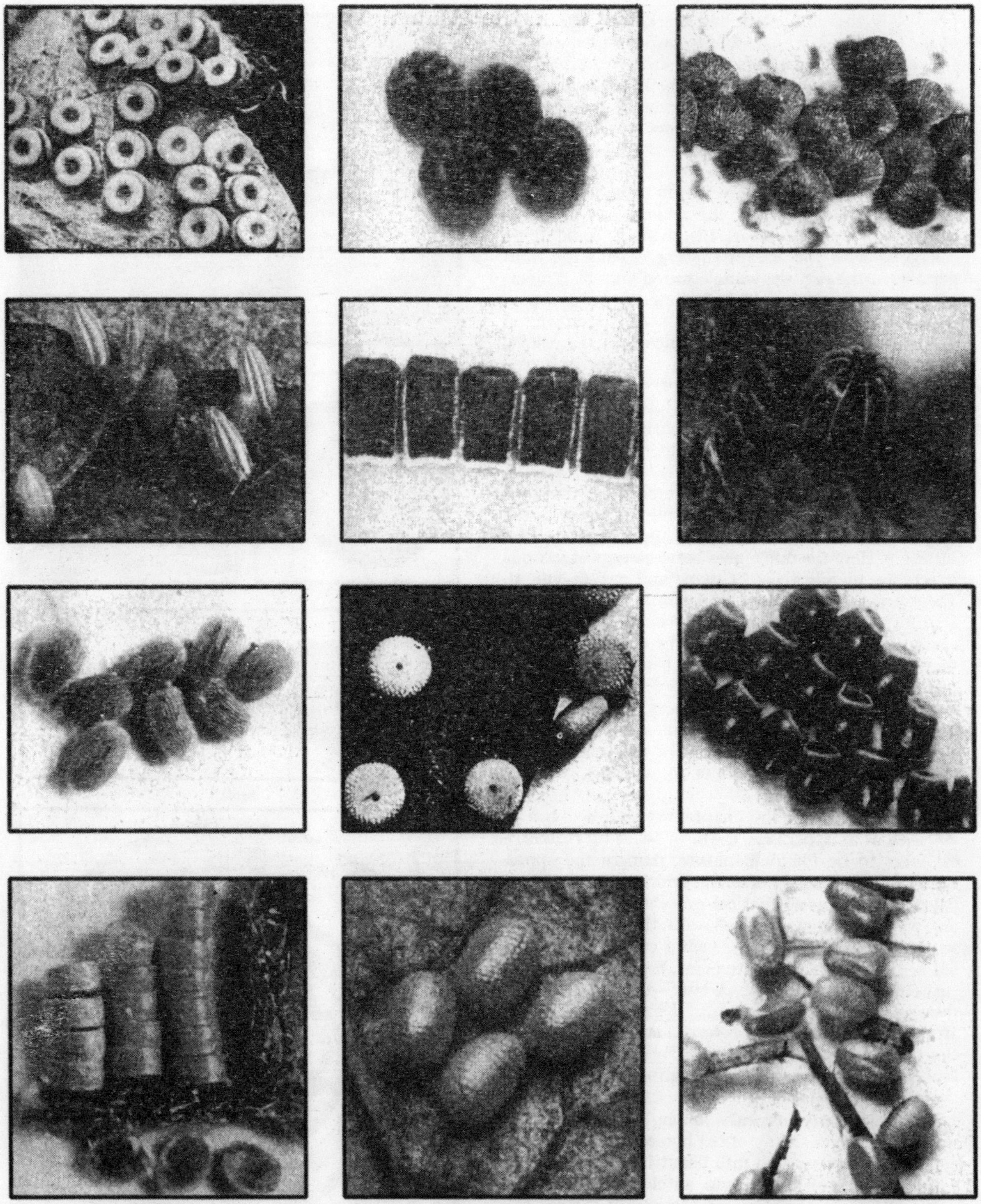

Small emerald moth Magpie moth Scorched carpet moth

WONDERFUL FORMS TAKEN BY BUTTERFLY AND MOTH EGGS

To the naked eye the eggs of butterflies and moths are so many minute particles seemingly no larger than the head of an ordinary pin. But the closer and more intimate inspection that the power of the microscope affords reveals some surprising facts. The eggs are, in many cases, not in the least egg-shaped; and the variety of marking and colour shows an equally extensive range. The eggs of the grey knot moth are, for instance, white with red markings, and those of the Quaker moth like sea urchins. Photographs by M. H. Crawford and A. E. Tonge.

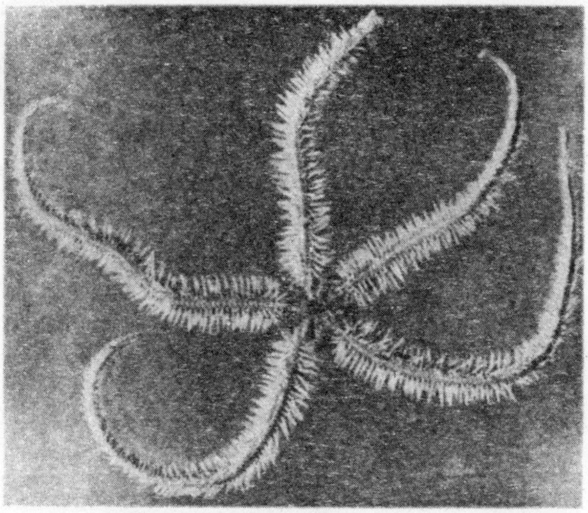

Brittle star

Butthorn starfish

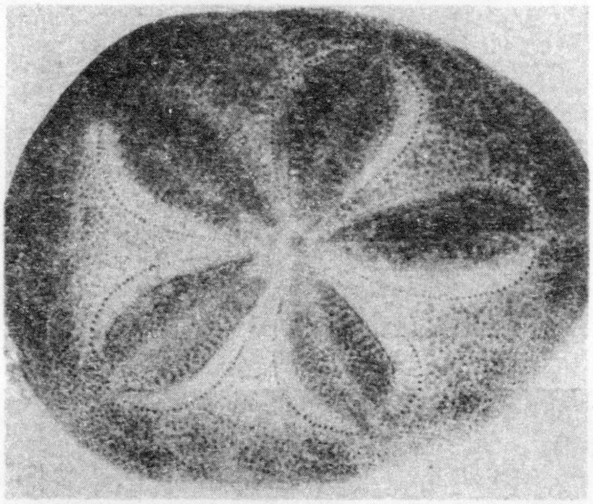

Sea urchin

Rosy-feather starfish

Cushion starfish

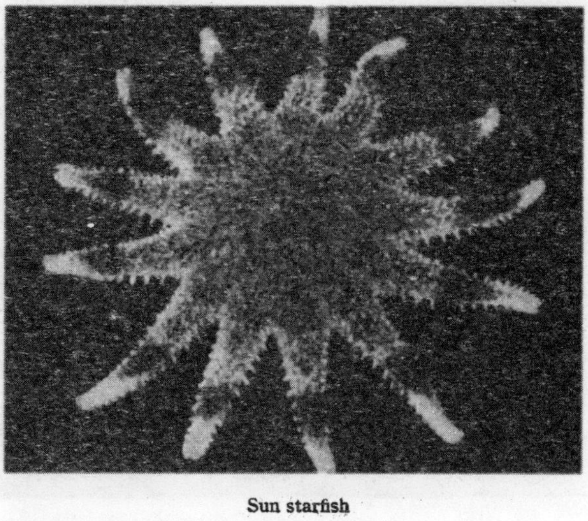

Sun starfish

VARIATIONS OF THE STAR DESIGN IN CREATURES OF THE SEA

Just as a composer may take some simple musical theme and, having expressed it, then elaborate it, and yet that original theme is still the basis and inspiration of each variation, in the same way we find Nature starting with some simple design like the star and adapting it in all sorts of ways. In the starfish alone there is a number of different designs. Compare the cushion starfish with its thickened form and bright mottling with the sun variety or the rosy-feather starfish. Photographs by Martin Duncan.

Cross-bearing spider

Death's-head moth

Pearly nautilus shell and section

Yellow-spotted salamander

Plume-like cirri of the adult barnacle

NATURE'S CRAFTSMANSHIP IN FORM AND COLOUR SCHEME

The pearly nautilus, valued by collectors of shells for its beautiful pearly whiteness when dead, is a dweller in the Indian Ocean. The shell when cut in half is seen to have a design reminiscent of the interior of a turbine. Each of these divisions marks a stage in the creature's growth, the nautilus occupying the outer chamber only. On the outside this shell is beautifully marked. The bottom photograph is of the cirri or tendrils by means of which the barnacle feeds. Photographs by Duncan, Bastin, Main, and Ward.

curve is that however much we lengthen it by extending its free end, the whole always retains the same shape.

A shell likewise, such as a snail shell, does not alter its shape as it grows larger. The whole at any period in the life of the animal is similar in shape to what was the whole at an earlier period. It is doubtless the property of continued similarity which is connected with the logarithmic spiral being so often associated with such structures as shells. The remarkable point to notice is that the shells retain the same form in spite of the fact that they grow at one end only, that is, at the open mouth of the shell. It is this property of retaining form whilst increasing by terminal growth which is characteristic of the logarithmic spiral.

Numerous examples of spiral shells might be given. Perhaps the simplest are those in which the spirals lie in one plane. The fresh-water shells planorbis and many foraminifera, such as discorbina, planorbulina, cornuspira, exhibit this. The most perfect form of this plane logarithmic spiral is, however, to be seen in the truly beautiful shell of the nautilus.

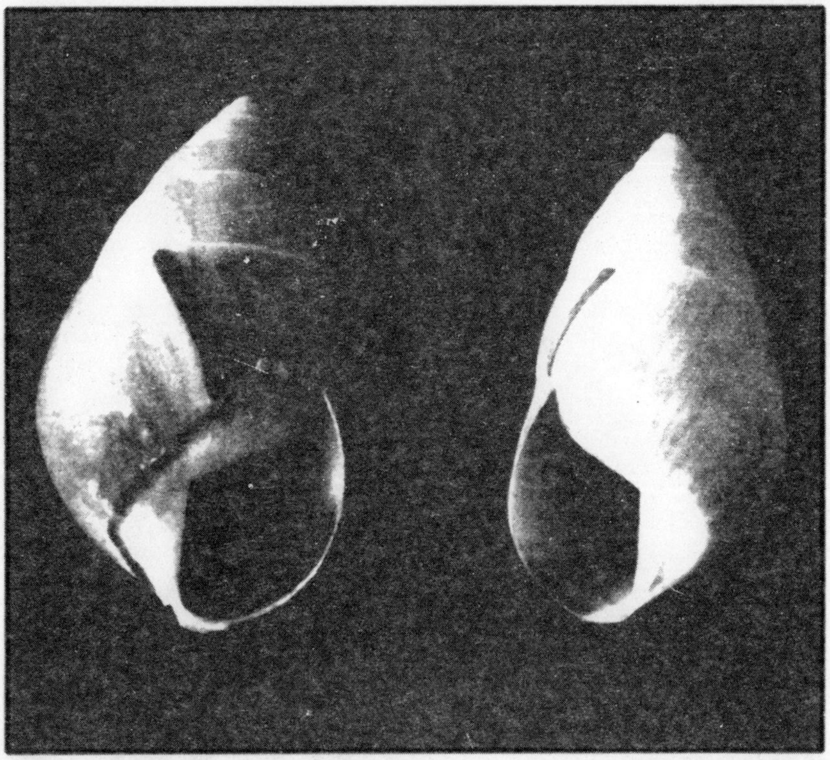

Martin Duncan

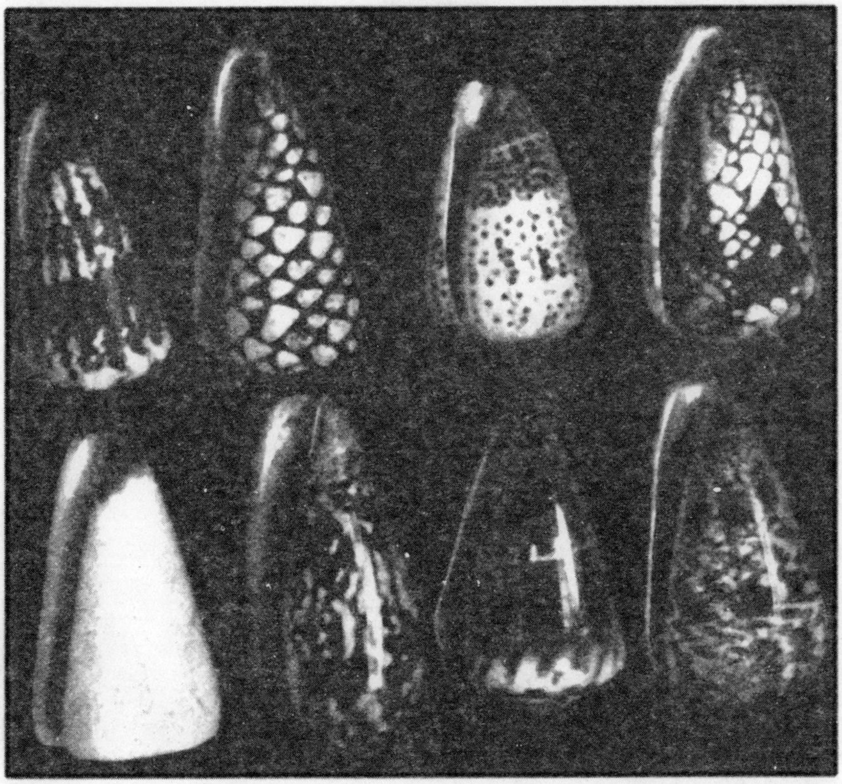

J. J. Ward

GEOMETRICAL SHELLS OF SEA AND LAND

Below is a group of six cone shells from the Tropics, with their markings which are developed more or less on geometrical lines. Above are two snails. The rule with these snails is that the spiral shall go in a clockwise direction from the apex. Only one in a million is counter-clockwise, and a normal shell is given here together with one of the rare exceptions.

In most spiral molluscan shells the curve is drawn out along an imaginary axis and does not lie in one plane. These are called "turbinate" forms. All the snail-like shells exhibit this to varying extents. As examples, we have helix, turritella, trochus, haliotis, and many others. The various riblike markings seen on many of these shells are witnesses of the method of growth. For instance, ribs running across the whorls of the spiral represent the successive positions of the mouth of the shell as the whole grows larger.

Sphere, ellipse, star and spiral, every form and design is some expression of Nature's laws working towards wonderful ends.

VULTURES USE A DEAD TREE AS AN OBSERVATORY

In French Guinea it is quite common, especially near the villages, to find a tree which has been selected by vultures as an observation point where they may perch, waiting for something to turn up. A dead rather than a living tree is chosen, since the view from the former is not obstructed by leaves. These repulsive looking birds play a very useful part in the life of hot climates, since they remove the nuisance of putrescent bodies decomposing very rapidly in the sun. They observe the carcases from very great distances.

Chapter LIX

Animal Scavengers and Undertakers

By W. S. Berridge

Author of "Marvels of Natural History"

Although we are inclined to regard the occupation of a scavenger as a lowly calling, nevertheless it is one of considerable importance, for if decaying matter be left exposed for any length of time it is liable to prove a source of danger to humanity, spreading disease and pestilence.

In the cities, towns, and villages throughout the world mankind has to a greater or lesser degree organized a system for the removal of garbage, but elsewhere the work of scavenging is often entirely neglected, and is only carried out by those creatures that Nature has ordained shall exist either partially or wholly upon carrion.

It is perhaps difficult to realize in this country to what extent man is indebted to animals for the removal of offal. A visit to tropical climes, however, would clearly demonstrate their value, for in such regions not only does the care bestowed upon sanitary matters appear to diminish more and more as climatic conditions become hotter and hotter, but this lack of attention also coincides with the fact that under the influence of a scorching sun the carcases of dead animals and other decaying substances quickly reach the stage commonly designated in polite language as "high."

The most notorious scavengers of the animal world are the vultures, of which numerous species are found in both the New and the Old World. Soaring to great heights, and silhouetted against the blue sky, they wheel around in large circles on the look-out for some creature that has fallen by the wayside. Should one of them espy the carcase of a zebra, camel, sheep, horse or some other animal, it quickly glides down to the ground, its actions at once being observed by others who follow its example, until the body is soon surrounded by vultures that have suddenly appeared from all directions.

Rending the flesh to pieces with their sharp, hooked beaks, and quarrelling with one another in their eagerness to make the most of their opportunities, the birds will quickly finish their repast, leaving behind nothing but the bones. Often they will gorge themselves to such an extent that they are unable to fly, or even stand; but as long as anything remains to be consumed, they will continue to eat whilst lying on their sides, rather than acknowledge they have arrived at the stage of repletion.

But a vulture's life is not one continual feast, for sometimes the bird is forced to abstain from food for days on end, a fact that may well be considered as a blessing in disguise.

Although the various kinds of vultures differ from one another in size and colouring, most of them are characterised by having the head and the greater part of the neck almost, if not entirely, devoid of feathers. This peculiarity imparts a very repulsive appearance to the birds, but it is a wise provision of Nature that allows them to wallow in their food without their plumage becoming unduly soiled and clogged.

The largest of the vultures is the American condor, which may have a wing-spread of nine feet or more; while little inferior in size are the griffons, one species of which has been placed on the list of British birds because an individual was once captured in Ireland.

The eared vultures are curious on account of the fleshy lappets that depend from their rosy-red heads, and another brightly-hued species is the American king vulture, its head and nasal caruncle ranging in colour from vermilion to orange. The latter bird receives its name from the ascendancy it holds over other vultures, which are forced to stand on one side and wait while his feathered majesty feeds.

Some vultures have been given rather quaint names. The black vulture, for instance, is often called the "carrion crow"; the turkey vulture is spoken of as "John Crow"; and the Egyptian vulture is familiarly known as "Pharaoh's chicken." The last-mentioned, which is one of the smallest species, has the reputation of being the most foul-feeding bird that exists, no substance being of too disgusting a nature for it to consume. Its habits, however, render it of great utility to mankind, so much so, indeed, that the bird is protected by special laws.

The marabou stork is another bird that receives the benefit of protection. Taking advantage of its freedom from molestation, it roams about the towns and villages in India, picking up and swallowing all kinds of offal, and even devouring such unappetising items as dead cats. Ungainly looking, bald-headed, and possessing an enormous beak and a large, pendulous pouch upon the lower part of the neck, the bird yields the soft "marabou" feathers that were formerly employed to a great extent in the manufacture of ladies' boas or neck-wraps.

South America is the home of some birds called caracaras or carrion hawks. Although offal eaters, they will also slay living animals. They will sometimes hunt their prey in packs, like wild dogs, and Mr. W. H. Hudson tells us that "they are the unfailing attendants of all flesh-hunters, human or feline, and also furiously pursue and persecute all eagles and true vultures that venture on the pampas."

One species, found in the Falkland Islands, and known as the chimango, is of such a bold disposition that it habitually resorts to the neighbourhood of human habitations on the look-out for any offal that may be cast on one side. Several of the birds will often co-operate and overpower living prey, and it is recorded that they will stand at the entrance of a rabbit burrow, ready to pounce on the inmates.

Familiar avian scavengers to be met with in Britain and elsewhere are the seagulls, countless numbers of which frequent the coasts and add a picturesque touch to the landscape. They congregate in harbours, searching the mudflats for anything of an edible nature that may be left behind by the receding tide, and picking up in their beaks, whilst in full flight, any tit-bits floating upon the surface of the water. On the arrival of the fishing-smacks at the ports the gulls will gather and hover around until the catch is unloaded and

With the kea parrot of New Zealand we come to a bird with a very strange history. Although normally feeding upon fruit, seeds, berries, nuts, roots and grubs, in those localities where the carcases of sheep are dealt with for exportation it has acquired a liking for offal. But not being content with dead mutton, it has also turned its attention to living sheep, settling upon their woolly backs, boring through their flesh with its sharp beak, and feeding upon the kidney-fat of its victims, so that they die as a result of the wounds thus inflicted. Parties of keas have been known to cause the death of a number of sheep during the course of a night, and sheep farms have been abandoned owing to their depredations.

Although the birds have been given a very bad character, it is only just to state that many people consider they are not such villains as they are reputed to be. Some individuals are certainly guilty of the crime attributed to them, and the New Zealand Government pays a reward for every one killed, but the amount of injury suffered by the flock-masters has probably been greatly exaggerated, and of the millions of sheep on the New Zealand pastures but an infinitesimal proportion succumb through the kea's unwelcome attentions.

E.N.A.

VULTURES SEEKING THEIR LOATHLY FOOD

The lower photograph shows a group of palms outside the town of Vera Cruz, Mexico. The great fronds are well suited for the purpose of the vultures we see settled on them, for the birds get a clear view. Above are some more Mexican vultures grovelling for filth in the bed of a creek used to carry off the sewage from a country town.

cleaned ready for dispatching to the inland markets, pouncing upon and swallowing any offal that may be cast on one side. At one Cornish seaport it is the custom to dispose of the refuse from the fish-market by putting it in a small boat and throwing it into the sea about half a mile or more from the shore. The gulls assemble every day at the harbour mouth, and when the man in charge of the boat commences to shovel the offal overboard into the water, they surge around the feast in such numbers that the craft and its occupant is almost lost to view amidst a swirl of snow-white wings. But after an interval of about five minutes not a particle of edible matter remains uneaten, and the shrieking birds one by one make their way to some rocky prominence where they may rest and digest their repast at leisure.

We may well bestow our blessing upon the seagulls, for of all refuse that from a fish-market is probably the most vile and offensive to the human olfactory organs.

W. S. Berridge

DESTROYERS OF REFUSE: EGYPTIAN AND TURKEY VULTURES

Known familiarly as "Pharaoh's chicken," the Egyptian vulture (top) is said to be the filthiest feeder on the world's surface, for nothing is too vile for its taste. The bird is therefore very useful in a hot climate where sanitation and hygiene are not everywhere of a high standard. The lower photograph shows a turkey vulture, in the London Zoo, with a fine wing span.

Many dwellers within the sea and rivers are scavengers, the eels, the hag-fish, the cod, lobsters, crayfish, prawns, shrimps and crabs all feeding to a greater or lesser extent upon dead animal matter.

The common hag-fish, an elongated and slender creature measuring about a foot in length, feeds mainly upon dead fish or those that have been hooked on the lines laid by the fishermen. It burrows into the bodies of its victims through their eyes or gill-covers, feeding upon their flesh until only skin and bone remain. Instances have been recorded of sharks being thus devoured by the voracious hag-fish, but as a rule it is the members of the cod tribe that are the chief sufferers from these attacks.

The cod itself is a most omnivorous feeder, and assists

E.N.A.

VULTURES GORGED AND RESTING AFTER A MEAL

There is always competition for the vultures, for they not only scan the country for dead or dying creatures, but keep an eye on each other. If one bird swoops down there is another within sight who will notice the movement and make for the same quarry. Then the food is bolted until the bird can hardly stand (bottom). It then digests on some perch (top).

in the work of ridding the sea of refuse. Although normally subsisting upon such fare as small fish, crustaceans, worms, etc., it will swallow almost anything of an edible nature, and not infrequently that which is otherwise. Mr. J. R. Norman tells us that keys, pieces of tallow candle, a partridge, and a black guillemot are to be numbered among the strange items of diet found in the stomachs of cods; while one even went so far as to swallow a small book.

Both the common eel and the conger eel are great scavengers, the latter being also addicted to cannibalism and feeding upon its smaller brethren should a favourable opportunity arise.

Crabs are indefatigable in their quest for all sorts of offal, consuming quantities of decaying matter that would soon foul the water if left to accumulate.

The starfish is yet another scavenger of the sea, for, besides preying upon living oysters, it will feed upon dead bivalves and other animal refuse; while among the fresh-water creatures that do not disdain to consume offal is the crayfish, a crustacean resembling a lobster in appearance, though much smaller.

But to return once again to terrestrial creatures, let us consider those mammals that follow the occupation of a scavenger.

Among these are to be numbered the hairy armadillo or peludo, a creature that is omnivorous in diet, such items as ground-nesting birds, insects, worms, vegetable substances, and putrid flesh all being regarded as acceptable fare. It will burrow beneath the

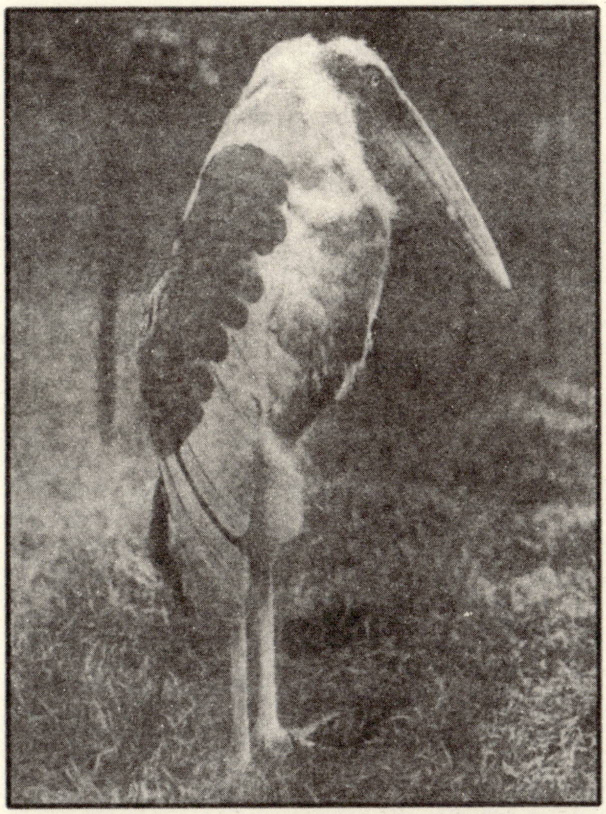

W. S. Berridge

Autotype

MARABOU AND ADJUTANT STORKS, SCAVENGERS OF INDIA

Both the marabou (bottom and top right) and the adjutant storks (top left), which belong to the same family, are thought much of by the natives of the lands where they dwell—India and Africa. This is on account of their usefulness as removers of refuse, the marabou being quite equal to a dead cat or dog. These birds are free from persecution and wander through the villages undisturbed. The adjutant seems to have got its name because its impressive pacing has a resemblance to the movements of one of the more dignified military officials.

W. S. Berridge

E.N.A

SEA GULLS, VULTURE AND CALIFORNIAN CONDOR

While gulls hunt their food to some extent they are also confirmed scavengers, as anyone will know who has watched the screaming confusion round any large dead fish which is floating on the surface and has been noticed by the gulls. Our lower photograph, taken by the harbour at Plymouth, shows two birds fighting for the possession of a dead fish. Above are a Pondicherry eared vulture (top left) and a Californian condor (top right). The condor is the largest of the vultures and may have a wing span of nine feet.

W. S. Berridge

EATERS OF OFFAL AND CARRION FROM NEW ZEALAND AND AMERICA

In New Zealand, where there are factories which deal with the carcases of sheep slaughtered for the chilled meat trade, the kea (bottom left) a kind of parrot, has forsaken its normal parrot's diet of fruit and seeds and taken to eating offal. From this it has gone on to pecking the fat round the kidneys of living sheep. The other birds seen here are from America. There are a Brazilian carrion hawk (bottom right), a Mexican buzzard (top left), so tame owing to universal protection that it lets the photographer approach to within close range; and an American king vulture.

James

thigh-bone of an ox, so as to obtain the marrow, and their digestive powers are so great that they can swallow whole a knuckle-bone without fear of suffering any ill results.

Many fabulous stories have been related in regard to the hyenas, not the least remarkable being that they changed their sex every year. Should their shadow fall upon domestic dogs, the latter would become dumb; while they have even been credited with the power of imitating the voices of men, and even of calling them by their names.

Bears must also be included under our heading, for some of them will consume offal. The body of a dead whale is much appreciated by the polar bear, and it does not object to feast

carcass of a dead sheep, horse or cow, as the case may be, returning night after night to feed upon the flesh.

The peba armadillo also feeds largely upon carrion. Often it will carry some of the flesh to its burrow, where it is stored in readiness for future consumption, the repast doubtless improving in flavour by being kept in this manner.

MANY members of the dog family will eat refuse. Wolves, for instance, will consume almost anything of an edible nature when hungry; in Eastern countries jackals prowl about the outskirts of the towns and villages, picking up any offal they may discover; while the common fox is another creature that will feed upon similar fare.

But the most notorious of mammalian scavengers are the hyenas. They will visit the Eastern villages at night and feed upon carrion; while skeletons that have been picked clean by other creatures are not disdained by these ungainly-looking beasts. With one crunch of their powerful jaws they will break in half the

James

RED RIVER-HOG AND WILD SWINE OF ARABIA

Swine, both wild and domestic, are notorious for their foul feeding, although when domesticated this depends on those who look after them. One of the most interesting of the wild pigs is the red river-hog (bottom) which stands only about two feet high at the shoulder and is a bright red-brown. This is set off by patches of white on the cheeks, while the eyes have white markings round them. The legs are black. Above is a wild swine from Arabia.

W. S. Berridge

ARMADILLOS WITH A LIKING FOR HIGH MEAT

The peludo, or hairy armadillo (bottom) has a novel way of dealing with the carcase of any sheep or horse which it may find. It burrows right underneath its intended meal and will return night after night till there is nothing left. The peba armadillo (top) is also a carrion eater but prefers to take its food home and keep it for a time.

upon the flesh when in a putrid condition. The American brown bear will eat decaying fish, as well as the carcases of dead animals; while the black bear often becomes quite tame and visits the neighbourhood of the hotels in the "up country" holiday resorts, searching among the garbage-heaps for any toothsome morsels that take its fancy.

Both wild and domestic swine are scavengers, and in tropical countries they are especially beneficial to mankind. Domestic pigs, however, are not normally such foul-feeding and dirty creatures as they are reputed to be. When kept in sties they can but subsist upon such fare as is provided for them, and the state of their cleanliness is entirely governed by the conditions under which they are kept. In the Highlands, domestic pigs are often allowed to roam over the moors, and in coastal districts they will visit the sea-shore to feed upon dead fish and molluscs, their flesh thereby acquiring a fishy flavour.

The house rat, or Old English black rat, and the common or brown rat, are feeders upon all kinds of offal, but the value of the service they thereby render is greatly discounted owing to their being bearers of the plague, or "Black Death," as it was formerly called. At intervals this terrible scourge becomes epidemic amongst these rodents, and the fleas that infest their persons leave the dying creatures and search for new hosts. Should the parasites be unable to find another rat upon which to bestow their unwelcome attentions, they may settle upon man, and by their bite infect his blood with the terrible plague bacillus.

As implied by its name, the house rat often takes up its residence in human habitations, but the common rat frequents sewers, drains and waterways, although not infrequently residing in the cellars and basements of buildings. Owing to its greater size and hardier constitution the common rat has almost exterminated the house rat, but from time to time new colonies of the latter become established, the rodents arriving as stowaways on ships.

Among the lower forms of animal life, there are a number of beetles and flies that are accustomed to feed upon decaying matter.

Familiar examples of the former are the carrion, burying, or sexton beetles, seven kinds of which are by no means uncommon in the British Isles. Most

E.N.A.

W. S. Berridge

HYENA AND THE PARIAH DOGS OF OXIA ISLAND

Even skeletons already picked bare by other animals are welcome to the hyena (bottom), which can snap the thigh-bone of an ox for the marrow inside. The island of Oxia (top), in the sea of Marmora, is the home of the descendants of the pariah dogs of Constantinople which were cleared out of the city and marooned here in 1910.

of them are black in colour, decorated with broad, orange bands. Endowed with a very acute sense of smell, these insects will soon discover the presence of a dead mouse, mole, or small bird. Flying one by one to the carcase, they quickly settle down to their work, and commence to remove the soil from around the defunct creature. They then make their way beneath, and after an interval of a few hours undermine the body, which sinks by its own weight into the cavity that has been excavated, and is covered up by the earth falling from above. Carcases are sometimes buried in this manner a foot deep.

When the interment has been completed, the female beetles lay their eggs within the decaying flesh of the animal they have buried. These soon hatch, and the grubs that emerge at once commence to feed upon the food supply amidst which they were born, gradually consuming it until none is left. The grubs eventually burrow into the soil, where they fashion small cells and change into the pupa stage. Fifteen days afterwards they emerge from the chrysalis as fully developed insects, which fly away and continue the sequence of life.

The scarab beetles are other well-known scavengers. They feed upon the dung of horses and sheep, rolling up the substance into a ball about the size of a walnut and trundling it along with the aid of their feet to their underground home, where it is consumed at leisure. But special pellets are also made wherein the females lay their eggs; the grubs, when hatched, feeding upon the material thus provided by their mother.

Of the many different kinds of scarab beetles, the Egyptian species is of special interest. Not only was it regarded as sacred by the ancient Egyptians, but its likeness was often represented upon their tombs, as well as upon their rings and amulets. The curious, notched protuberances upon the front of the beetles' heads, as well as the tooth-like projections on the outer part of their fore-feet, were considered to be symbolical of the rays of the sun, and the spherical pellets the insects made as symbols of the earth ; while the creatures' association with the moon rested upon the belief that the beetles did not commence to feed upon their hidden treasure until 28 days (a lunar month) after being buried.

The common mealworm, as well as the beetle into which it transforms, will feed upon dead and decaying matter, but although it thus carries out very useful scavenging work, should it become established in flour and grain stores, it proves a perfect pest.

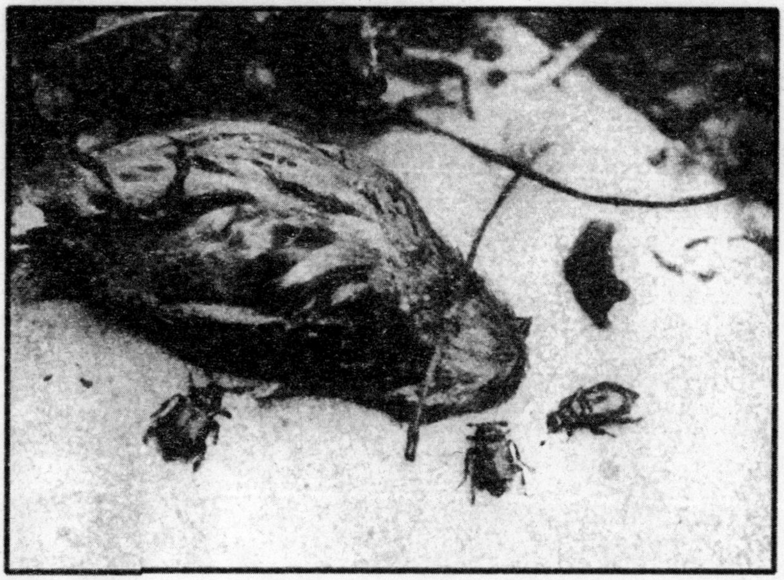

W. S. Berridge

CARRION BEETLES OF EGYPT AND EUROPE

Scarab beetles lay their eggs and feed upon the dung of sheep, rolling the substance into pellets (bottom). The sexton beetles (top) undermine any small corpse they find until it falls into the cavity. They then feed on, and lay their eggs in, it.

In a similar manner house flies are both benefactors and a menace to mankind. Feeding upon all manner of refuse, they settle upon food intended for human consumption, leaving behind bacilli they have collected and carried upon the pads of their feet and other parts of their bodies. In regard to the common house fly, the late Professor Lefroy, the great authority on insect pests, states that "its hairy, sticky feet, and the habit of regurgitating the contents of its crop and depositing its excreta at frequent intervals, constitute it an excellent inoculating agent for any bacteria it may pick up in the satisfaction of its unsavoury tastes."

Cholera, consumption, anthrax, typhoid and enteric fever may all be spread by flies, and in military camps they are the chief disseminators of the two latter diseases, many severe epidemics among troops having been definitely traced in the past to them Still, although flies are such a source of danger as distributers of disease, in their larval form they accomplish an immense amount of good work. The maggots of the common house fly and the lesser house fly feed upon decaying vegetable substances ; while those of the blow-fly, the blue-bottle and the green-bottle subsist upon fresh and putrid meat, as well as upon the carcases of dead animals. So great are the numbers of eggs laid by a female fly, and so voracious are the appetites of the maggots, that enormous quantities of food are consumed in a very short time. For this reason the grubs are to be numbered among the most efficient of animal scavengers, and the benefit they render in that stage counteracts to a great extent the harm they do as flies.

The larvae of some of the hover-flies will feed upon decaying animal and vegetable matter, as also will the small, worm-like grubs of fleas ; while to conclude our survey of "Animal Scavengers and Undertakers" mention must be made of the ants which will rapidly devour the body of a dead mouse, bird, or some other small creature, leaving behind nothing but a cleanly-picked skeleton.

The large, black ants, known as driver ants, and found in the African jungle, not only feed upon dead creatures but also on the living. When on the march they form up in files that have been known to extend for nearly a mile, and woe betide any animal that dares to dispute their path. A swarm of these tiny insects has even been seen attacking a venomous horned-viper.

For more than a quarter of an hour the reptile writhed about upon the ground with its body covered with ants tearing away at its flesh with their powerful jaws. Gradually the struggles of the snake grew weaker and weaker, until at last it lay lifeless upon the ground. The carcase was soon completely hidden by a mass of ants, two inches in depth, all intent upon obtaining a meal, and in a very short time only the victim's bones remained.

LUMP-SUCKER OF THE NORTH SEA THAT MAKES A VERY PRIMITIVE FORM OF NEST

As soon as the female lump-sucker has deposited her eggs the male proceeds to make a depression in the slimy, weedy surface of the rocks and presses the mass of eggs into it. The eggs are held together by a slimy substance which hardens in the water and enables them to adhere to the rocks. The process of making this very primitive nest takes the fish from five to fifteen minutes, and during this time the eggs are fertilised. After this the male fish loses the bright red tints on its skin. Lump-suckers are found along all the coasts of the North Sea and Baltic, although nowhere in great numbers. Their name arises from the fact that the ventral fins are united into a round disk, which exerts suction and enables the fish to cling to rocks and seaweeds.

The photographs by F. Schensky in this page and page 625 are reproduced by permission of Dr. Werner Klinkhardt, Leipzig, from Animal and Plant Life in the North Sea, published by the Biological Station, Heligoland

Chapter LX

Nests Under Water

By Wilfred Mark Webb

Secretary, The Selborne Society

THOSE useful sportsmen whose choice falls upon a camera instead of a gun have of recent years made widely known the domestic life of British birds. Mention, therefore, of the word nest conjures up in the minds of many people one of those delightful nurseries upon which even common kinds like the chaffinch and the long-tailed tit lavish a wealth of skill and labour.

These have their rivals, however, among four-footed animals, for the squirrel builds its drey in a convenient tree and the tiny harvest mouse supports its nest upon the stalks of ripening corn. In both of these homes the young are housed, but the dormouse also builds one for itself in which to sleep away the unfruitful months of winter.

At times no elaborate work is done and a nest may be merely a specially chosen place. Such is the hollow in the ground in which the night-jar lays her pair of eggs or the ledge of rock on which the guillemot sits upon her single one.

Nature too in some cases saves her creatures from being tied, even temporarily, to one spot while their children are helpless, by giving them a natural pocket, or pouch as we call it, so that they can carry their little ones about wherever they go.

Nests underground are not so familiar to the sight as they are by name. The rabbit makes a special burrow for its progeny and lines the end with wool from its breast, but insects with highly developed social instincts such as certain wasps and humble bees, construct a series of single-berth nurseries in a common dwelling inhabited by the queen-mother, the nurses and their charges. The less highly developed earwig is worthy of note, for the mother does not go away and leave her eggs as do most solitary insects, but watches over them until after they are hatched.

More out of the way still are nests under water and for that reason it may be interesting to consider what they are. True, we shall find no birds or bees, but examples will not be lacking of craftsmanship and parental care among other creatures which are lowlier in structure or in intelligence, such as frogs and fishes, spiders and various insects.

Practically speaking all the eggs which are laid under water have to develop in that liquid and are those of forms which live in water and breathe by means of gills during the early part of their actual existence, if not the whole of it, but we shall find one exception, at least, in Great Britain of another kind of animal of which the eggs are hatched below the surface of a pond or stream.

Except in rare cases among the nest-builders which live on land, when the work of looking after the eggs and young falls to the lot of one parent, it is the mother. We shall see, however, when we come to the water that among amphibia and fishes, at least, when a nurse is provided, it is the father who usually takes on these important duties. The British frogs and toads, which belong to the first-mentioned class and have a free-swimming tadpole stage, do not seem to trouble much where they lay their eggs when once they have got back to the water, and therefore in common with most creatures which do not look after their young they have an offspring so numerous that the chances are that some, at least, will survive.

Frog's spawn floats in masses on the surface but that of the common toad may be likened to transparent necklaces in which many small black beads have been embedded at intervals, and these remain under water attached to submerged plants.

The eggs of a Continental form known as the midwife toad are laid on land and being larger and less numerous have been likened to rosaries. The male in this case is very solicitous for his children's welfare. He wraps the chains round his hind legs and from time to time moistens them with dew at night or dips them into water. Ultimately when they are ready to hatch he takes them into the water. The male of the curious Surinam toad, which spends its whole life in water, also looks after the eggs as they are being laid. He does not, however, carry them about himself but presses them on to the back of the mother where each sinks into a little pouch which forms beneath it, and there development takes place.

The hiding-places which some toads prepare for their eggs are not at first under water, being made during the dry season, but spots are chosen which, when the water rises after the rains, will be certain to be submerged.

In the case of a Brazilian tree frog called the

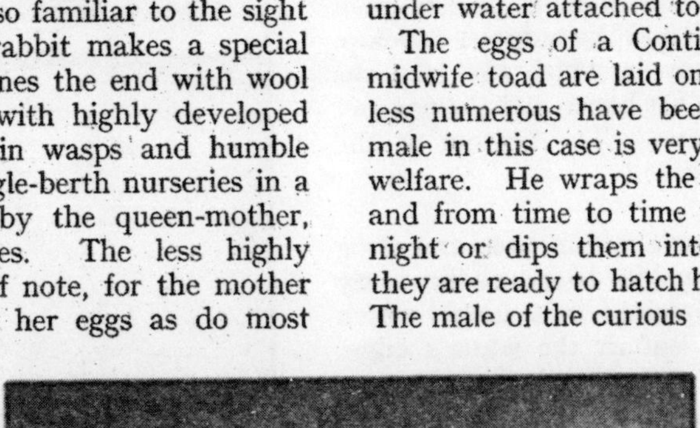

W. S. Berridge

BITTERLING THAT USES A LIVING NEST

A strange form of nest is used by the female bitterling, a small fresh-water fish of the carp family. The eggs are laid by means of a long ovipositor inside the shell of a fresh-water mussel, which thus involuntarily acts as a foster-mother and nest in one.

W. S. Berridge

and green he sets to work to gather bits of waterweed and other vegetable filaments and builds quite a fine nest. He does not trust entirely to his skill in weaving to keep the component parts in place but sticks them together with a glutinous secretion. It might be thought that this comes directly from the fish's mouth, with which he seizes and carries his material, but it has been shown to be a special secretion from the creature's kidneys.

The species under consideration builds its nest on the bottom, and when it has been put together, if its maker is not satisfied with the appearance, he tidies it up by pulling out any piece which makes it appear ragged, and tucks it in

" smith "—because the noise which it makes sounds like the beating of metal—the female is a wonderful nest maker. Unaided by the male or even hindered by his attentions, she builds up from the bottom of the pond at a place where it is not too deep, a circular wall of mud so as to enclose a little private pool in which her eggs can hatch and the tadpoles develop. Very remarkable is the way in which she smooths the inside of the walls with her hands and the parapet which rises above the water. The bottom of the pool is also carefully levelled.

Both the male and female of another tree frog found in Paraguay combine to secure the safety of their eggs, which are deposited in a funnel which they together make of a leaf at the water's edge. The jelly with which the eggs are, as usual, surrounded serves to stick the edges of the leaf together and prevent it from unrolling when the frogs release their hold, so that the eggs remain hidden.

When we come to fishes, we meet with some excellent examples of nests which, from the materials used and the way in which they are fashioned, approach most nearly to those made by birds. Here again the male looks after the babies and his, too, is the task of making the nest if it is at all of an elaborate nature.

First of all the sticklebacks may be considered, and the best known are the three-spined " tiddler " of ponds and streams, the ten-spined form, also common in the same situations, and the fifteen-spined species of the sea. In passing, however, we may mention that the last-mentioned fish is very remarkable, owing to the fact that it is equally at home in salt and in fresh water. In the case of the three-spined stickleback, the male in spring becomes gloriously coloured and when he shines with scarlet

PARADISE FISH AND ITS BUBBLE NEST

The Chinese paradise fishes hatch their eggs in a nest of bubbles. The male inhales some air at the surface, then by exhaling below water bubbles are produced in a mass. When the female lays her eggs the male puts them in the nest.

W. S. Berridge

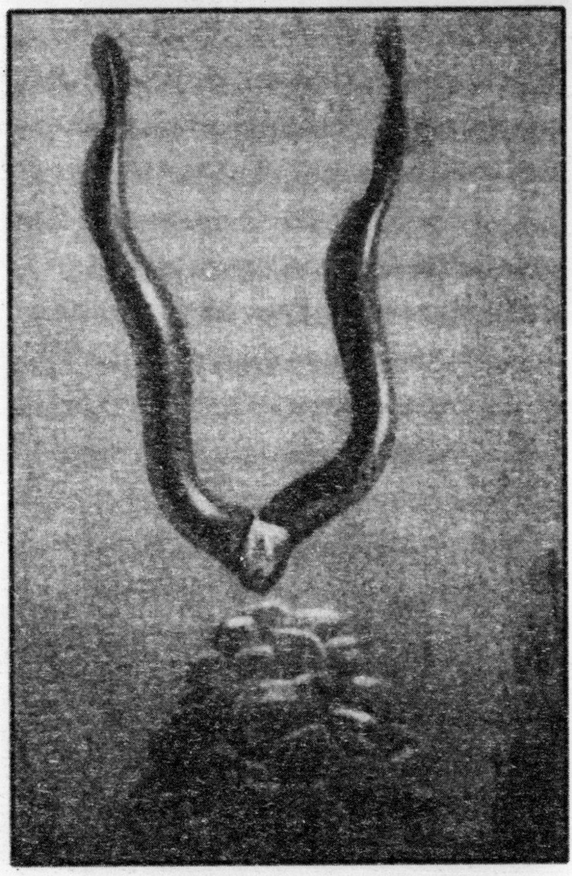

FISH NEST-MAKERS: BOWFIN AND LAMPREY
At breeding time the parent lampreys clear a space at the bottom of the stream and there deposit the eggs as in this drawing. Then they remove stones up-stream, and the removal disturbs the sand, which gets washed over the eggs. Above is a bowfin.

somewhere else in a very workman-like manner. The ten-spined stickleback, on the other hand, sets up a home for its young ones amongst the weeds and grasses near the bank, and the fifteen-spined form chooses a spot in a rock pool between tide marks and the elegantly constructed nest six or ten inches long usually hangs from a frond of seaweed

In all cases when the nest is completed it has but one opening in the side but later on after the female fish, by dint of much coaxing and caressing, has been inveigled into the nursery and has laid her eggs, she does not return by the original entrance through which she came in, but makes a new opening in the opposite side of the nest and so departs. The two orifices thus formed afterwards enable the male parent to fan a flow of water with his fins on to the developing eggs so as to keep them well aerated.

Before, however, growth can begin, the eggs have to be fertilised, and this is done by the milt (which in the case of the herring we call the soft roe), placed in the nest by the male fish.

Apparently the eggs may be deposited in instalments and sometimes more than one female fish may be induced to use the same nest.

It is not difficult for anyone to breed sticklebacks who can set up an aquarium (a glass battery jar makes a good one) with the right complement of weed to aerate the water and obviate any necessity of changing it. The great thing is to have only a very few fish in a small space and in the case of the sticklebacks after the eggs are laid it may be well, if one wishes to make certain of their safety, to leave only the male fish in the tank until they are hatched, for the females are very apt to devour them.

The small bowfin of North American rivers and lakes is as good a parent as the stickleback and has quite as interesting habits. Although the result of his labours certainly comes well within any general definition of a nest that one could frame, it savours, perhaps, of the castle as much as of the nursery pure and simple. This fish makes a clearing among the closely growing weeds by beating them down and actually biting them off, leaving a narrow entrance unblocked through which he can bring his bride and in which he takes up his position to keep away any intruders while she is depositing her eggs. Afterwards he remains on guard in the passage until these are hatched, when he still continues his parental duties, and shepherds them by swimming round them

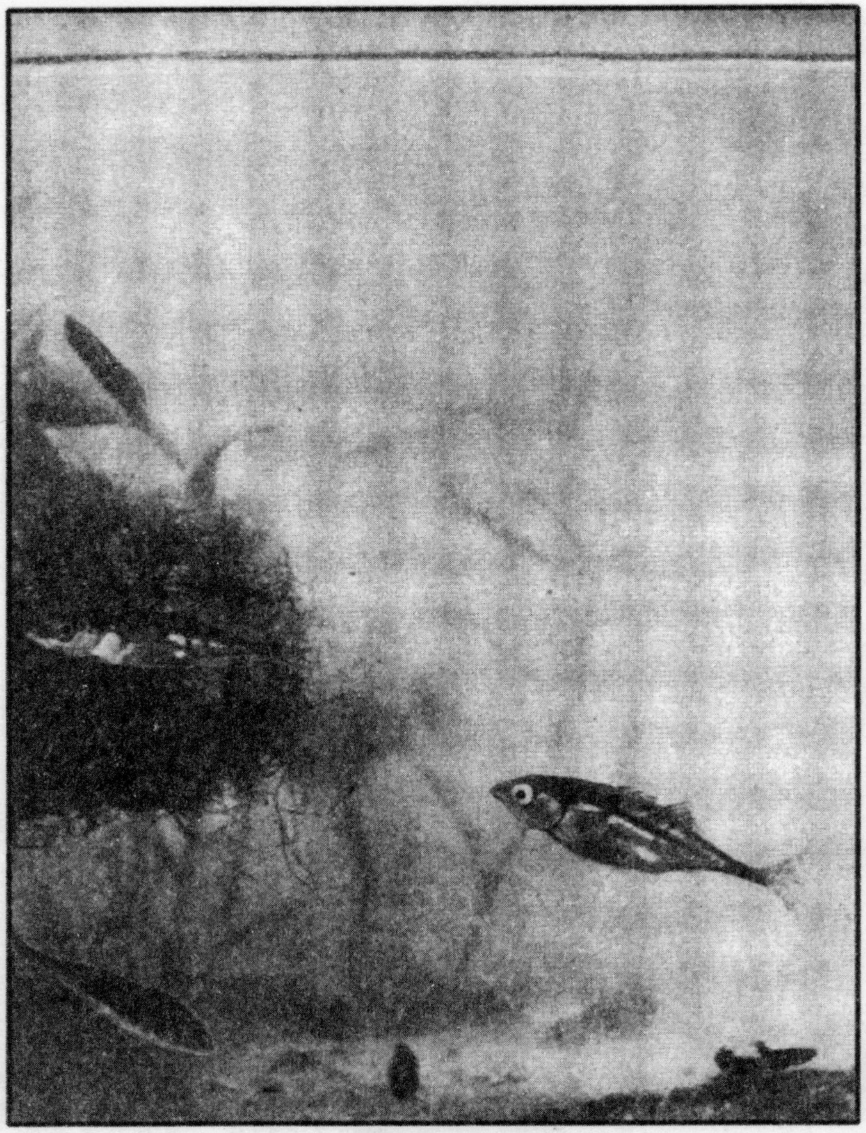

J. J. Ward

UNDER-WATER NEST OF THE STICKLEBACK AND THE DRAMA PLAYED ABOUT IT

Springtime finds the male three-spined stickleback turning the colour of its skin bright scarlet and green. In this lover's livery he sets about collecting filaments of waterweed with which to construct anest. The lengths of weed are woven together and fastened more firmly with a sticky substance secreted in the kidneys. The finishing touches are put in with a most admirable industry. The male then seeks a mate and endeavours to persuade her to enter the newly-built home. Here (left) we see the female below the nest making up her mind, while on the right is a deadly rival trying to lure her away to his own nest. The owner of the nest then drives him up above the nest (right), and is seen swimming out of the photograph to the left to renew his persuasions.

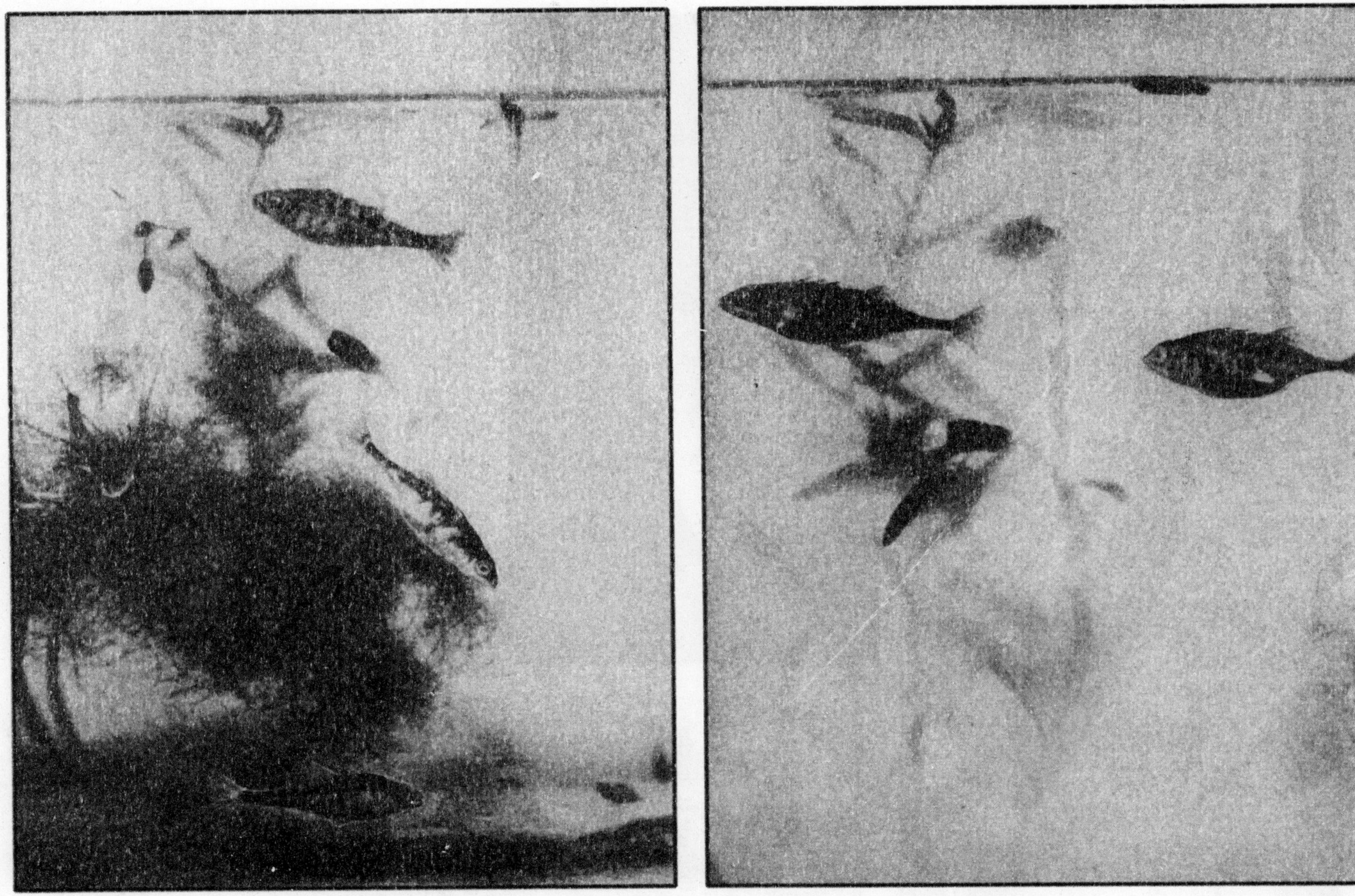

J. J. Ward

THE ETERNAL TRIANGLE: MALE STICKLEBACK, HIS MATE AND A DEADLY RIVAL

We have seen the first stages in the under-water drama of the stickleback's wooing in the opposite page. Now a later scene is before us where (left) the owner of the nest has just wounded and charged his insidious and persistent rival, who is seen drifting disconsolately above the nest. The female is still hovering undecided below the nest. In the right-hand photograph the rival still hovers near, despite his wounds, while the owner, his spines bristling, goes back on guard. When the female has entered the nest and laid her eggs she does not return by the same entrance, but bites a way through the other end. By means of the two holes in it a constant current of water can be driven through the nest by the male's fins while the eggs are hatching.

to make a nest, but the Chinese paradise fish uses them, and the male, by taking air into his mouth on the surface of the water and expelling it again, produces these himself. The small froth-blower having busied himself in this way for some time goes in search of a wife, and when she has been found he brings her to the strange nest. As she lays her eggs they sink to the bottom one by one, and the careful husband catches them as they drop, afterwards depositing them in the nest, to which they stick. The female of the paradise fish, like that of the stickleback, is only too prone to become an unnatural mother, and is one of the enemies from which her mate has to protect the eggs and young.

W. S. Berridge

THREE- AND TEN-SPINED STICKLEBACKS

While the three-spined stickleback builds its nest at the bottom, the ten-spined variety (top) also a fresh-water species, makes a home for its eggs and young near the bank among water-weeds and grasses. Sometimes eggs are deposited by the female several times, and it may even happen that more than one female will be induced to enter the same nest.

The wrasses or rock-fishes are worthy of mention on account of the mass of material which they gather together. The seaweed from a single nest at times would fill a peck measure and corals, broken shells and other things are also used.

More than one of the class of animals which we are considering make use of shells as nurseries. On the one hand, the female bitterling, which is a tiny fish found in Central Europe and often kept in captivity in England, has a very long ovipositor with which she introduces her eggs into the shell of a fresh-water mussel during the lifetime of the owner by inserting it between the valves while they are gaping open. In this way the mussel is made to act as a foster-mother. On the other hand, the gobies of the sea-borders use a single empty valve or a limpet shell or a crab-cart. They are interesting creatures to keep in the marine aquarium, and have the habit of coming out of the water from time to time, though not quite to the same extent as the tropical walking-fish.

WHEN the shell has been sought for by the male and found satisfactory, it is put by him into the position required, that is, with the convex side uppermost, to form a roof. Then the fish scoops out with its tail a depression in the sand beneath the shell and makes a small opening through which he and his mate can go in and out. Finally the house is covered with sand so that it is no longer noticeable and the grains are actually gummed to it with mucus by the male. Bubbles seem to be a curious material out of which

Another kind of foam, which floats and supports the young in the water after they are hatched, is the secretion of the male of a species of fish inhabiting swamps in tropical Africa. The fry hang on to the nest by a special sucker-like organ which is developed on the front of their head.

The lamprey is a primitive animal sometimes called "nine-eyes" from its numerous gill openings, and in its case, as in that of some other fishes, both parents clear a space at the bottom of the river in which the eggs are laid. The lampreys do more than this—they remove even quite large stones by means of their sucker-like mouths for some little distance above the nesting-place, as we should call it in the case of birds. During the process a considerable amount of sand is washed down by the current.

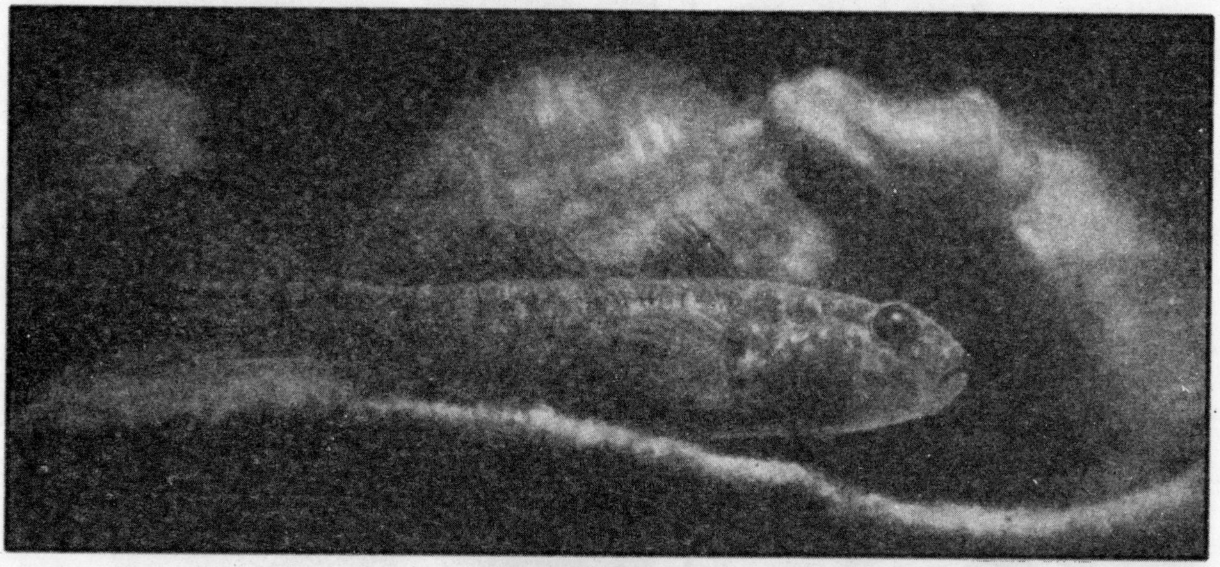

W. S. Berridge

which effectively covers up the eggs so that they are put quite out of sight. A finned inhabitant of a Queensland river makes matters more sure by piling large stones over its eggs. Others in South America make holes in the banks and line them with grass.

THE nesting-place of the Californian smelt is only under water when its period of usefulness is coming to an end. The parents in the nesting season take advantage of a high tide to get up on to the beach, and are left there high and dry. Their nest is a hole in the sand which they dig for the purpose, and when the eggs are deposited and covered up, the old fishes wriggle back into the water again. In a fortnight's time hatching takes place and at the next spring-tide the waves reach the nest, uncover it, and carry the young smelts back with them into the sea.

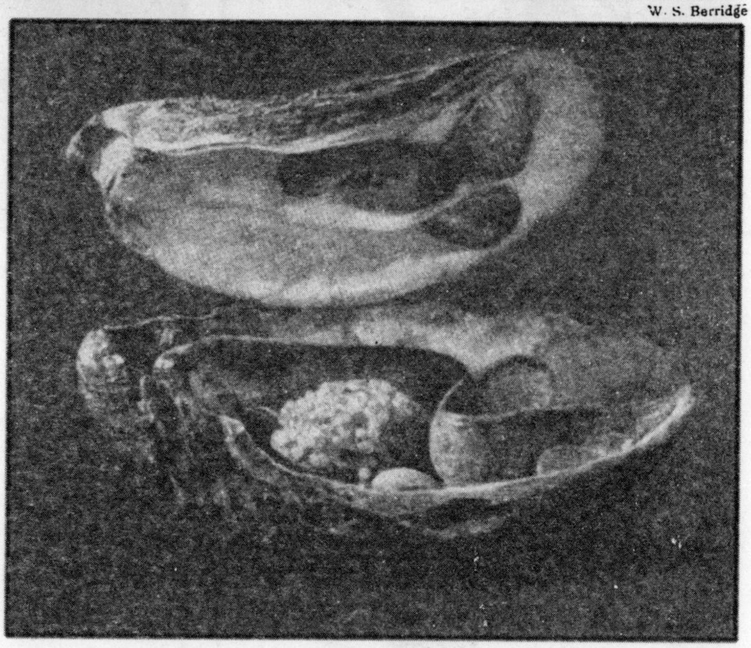

Natural History, N.Y.

FISH THAT USE SHELLS FOR NURSERIES

Butterfish are found in North American waters and lay their eggs in an oyster-shell, the female coiling herself round the mass of eggs and keeping guard (bottom). Notice that some limpets have also taken the advantage and are clinging to the inside of the upper valve or shell. Above is a sand goby using an empty shell as a nest.

Other fishes, though they do not make a special nest, put their eggs into crevices or holes bored in rocks by molluscs, and others again do little more than guard their eggs and keep the water moving over them. The curious looking lump-sucker, with grotesque and swollen body, is a case in point and the young for some time after they are born, cling to their father by means of their sucker-like underside.

The male of the pipe fish, which is a common inhabitant of the waters round the British coast, shares with the even more striking and rarer sea-horse (occasionally found in the same seas and shown from time to time in aquaria), the distinction of having a pouch in its underside. Into this he most carefully gathers up the eggs and pockets them, so to speak, until such time as the young emerge.

The egg-cases of some marine shells are striking to look at and those of our common whelk have the appearance of a closed nest, though each egg is really in a separate compartment. The young of the fresh-water whelk are hatched inside their mother's shell which, like that of her sea cousin, is provided with a lid or door to keep out intruders.

The beautiful purple shell called the Gulf Stream snail constructs a very serviceable raft which floats on the surface of the water, and to this the eggs are attached so that they hang down into the water. The young of many bivalves spend their early days clinging to the gills of their parent within the shell.

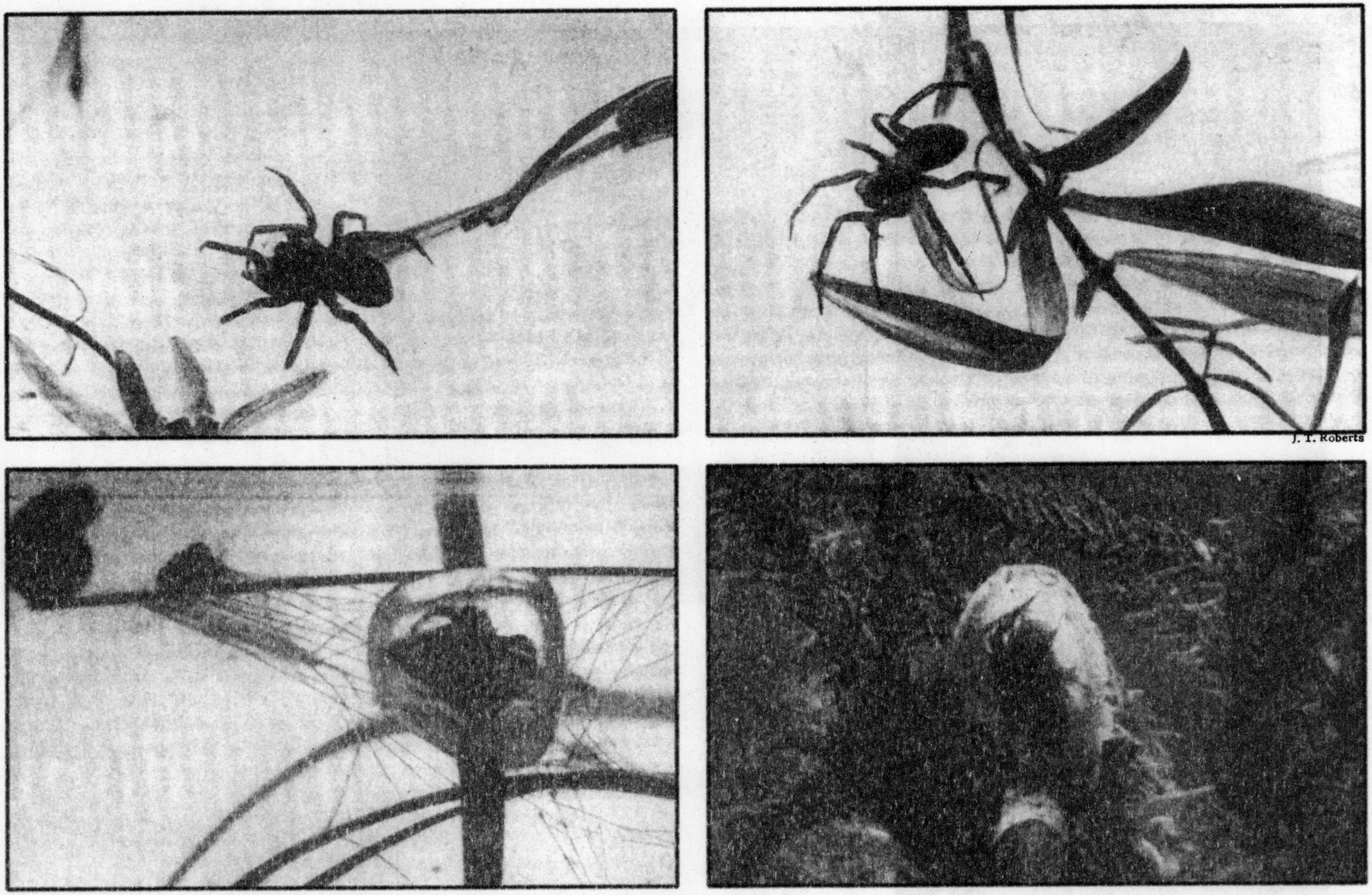

J. T. Roberts

F. W. Bond

HOW THE WATER-SPIDER SPINS ITS DIVING BELL NEST TO HOLD AIR

Some way below the surface the water-spider selects a suitable spot among the weeds as the site for its nest. It makes the nest out of silk, just as the ordinary garden spider makes its web. But in the case of the water-spider the silk is used to make a nest only, not a snare for catching food. The little creature begins operations by spinning threads from one branch of the water plant to another (top left). It may then have occasion to turn over the edge of a leaf (top right). When the construction is finished the result (bottom photographs) is thimble-shaped, and not unlike a diving bell alike in design and purpose. Troubles, however, are not over when the nest is finished, for another water-spider may try to gain possession.

Spider leaving nest

Capturing an air bubble at the surface

Diving with the bubble

Nearly home

Running down the side after releasing bubble

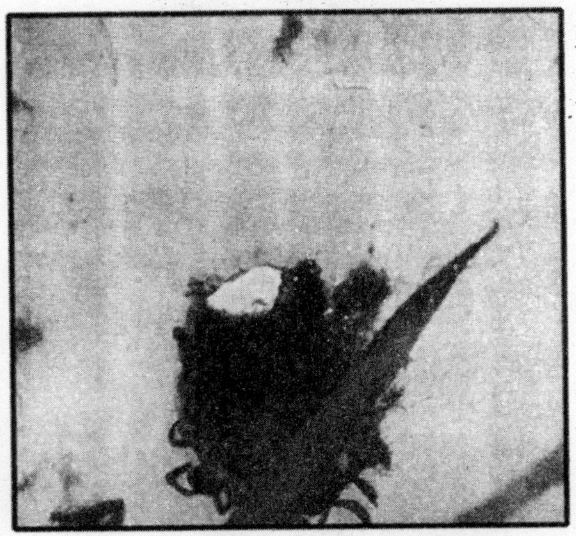

Entering the nest

PROCESS BY WHICH THE WATER-SPIDER CONTRIVES A NEST BELOW THE SURFACE

The water-spider breathes air and its young are also air-breathing from the very beginning of their lives. The problem of providing a nest for them under the water has been solved in a way as extraordinary for its ingenuity as for its simplicity. The spider, having constructed the nest (see page 652), ascends to the surface. There its hairy body is in contact with the air which clings to the hairs, when the spider goes down again, in a covering of small silver bubbles. These bubbles are released from time to time within the nest and, of course, rise to the top of it. Gradually they accumulate until the nest is full of imprisoned air where the young may develop. The above photographs by J. J. Ward show the spider's journey from nest to surface and back again.

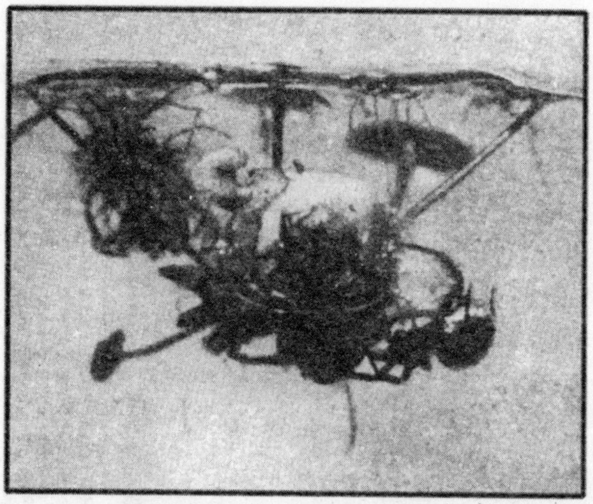

Male makes love to female inside nest

Female refuses to admit male to nest

Maie pulls nest to drive out female

Female approaching nest to drive out another female

She attacks the other female spider in nest

She is driven away by her rival

ROMANTIC ADVENTURES OF A FEMALE WATER-SPIDER IN HER NEST

First of all, in this panorama of a day in the life of a female watei-spider, we have the courtship (left photographs). The male (top) tries to enter the nest, but the inmate is coy and repulses him. Then he tries to entice her by pulling the nest on one side and by being generally active (centre and bottom). After his departure there arrives another female who takes a fancy to the nest and tries to drive the owner away. In the right-hand column of photographs we see her try and fail. The photographs are by J. J. Ward.

Nests Under Water

It is possible that at times they may be a nuisance and one pretty little species has a wonderful arrangement by which its children are kept in a nursery out of sight. When the female is building her shell she produces as part of each valve a little cup lined with pearly matter, and as the two cups are arranged so that the mouth of each coincides with that of its fellow, when the valves of the shell are closed the young ones are shut up completely in their shelly nursery. Some of the male shells have no sign of this, but others show a vestige of the cradle recalling the small teats in a male mammal.

One of the most interesting inhabitants of the ponds and for that matter, of aquaria, is the water-spider, which, when it is taken out of its element, resembles some land forms found under the bark of dead trees, but in water its body is studded with silver balls of the air which it carries down with it attached to the many hairs with which it is clothed. It does not make a web, but constructs a regular diving-bell some distance below the surface among the weeds, using the silk, with which it is supplied, for domestic purposes and not for producing a snare. In the diving-bell, which, of course, has the mouth downwards, the spider stores away from time to time some of the air which clings to its body, and when the eggs are laid in this remarkable arrangement the imprisoned air enables the young creatures to come to perfection without the necessity of developing even temporary gills.

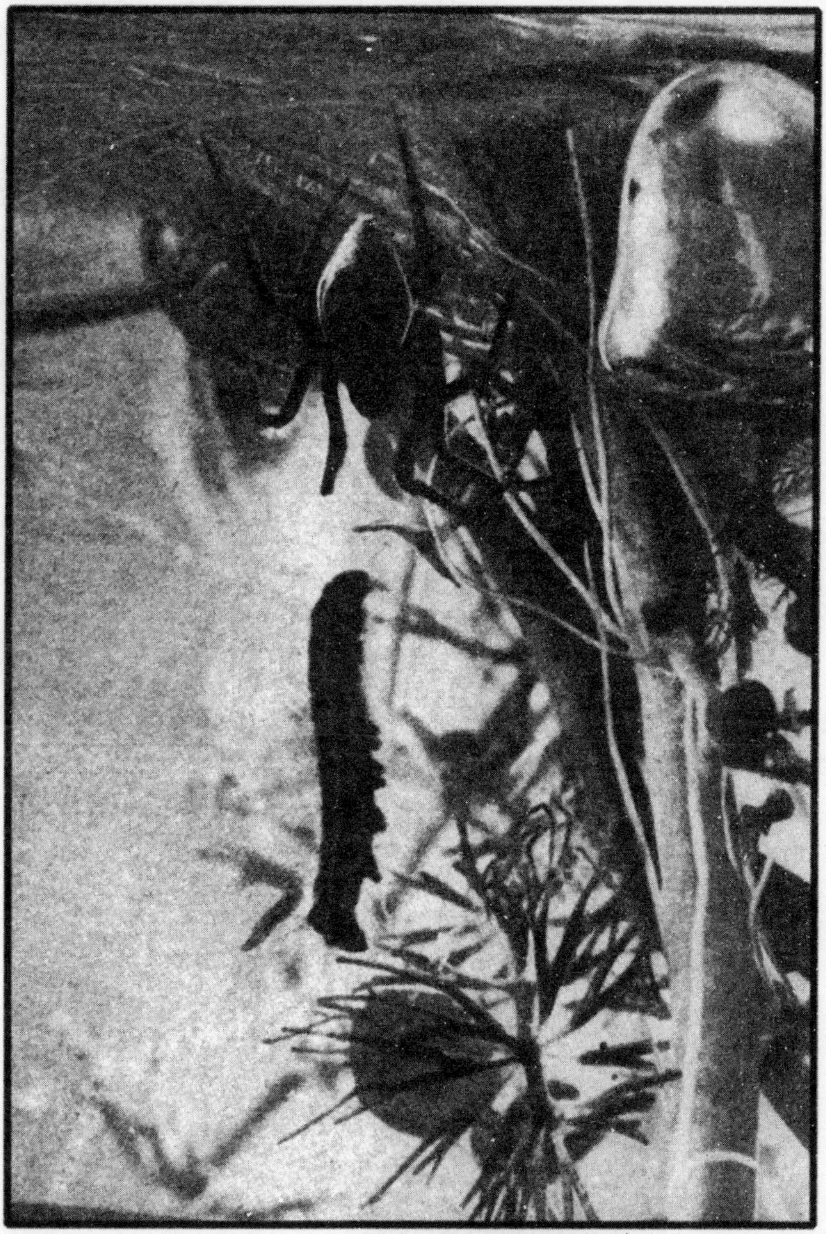

J. T. Roberts

WATER-SPIDER TAKING DOWN AIR TO ITS NEST

In this close view of a water-spider's nest we can see the bell-like form in which it is made. The spider descends, crawls down the side of the nest and then stores the bubbles, that are adhering to its body, inside. Notice the caterpillar that has had the misfortune to fall off some overhanging branch into the water and has been caught in some of the strands of the nest.

Among the insects, the great water beetle and its allies may be picked out as builders of nests under water The species named is the largest found in Britain with the exception of the stag beetle. Her nursery is made of silk like those of some spiders, and her spinning organs are at the end of her body, being in the form of conical tubes. When she is about to start work, she lies on her back with her last two pairs of legs amongst the weeds, and with the front ones she brings the filaments over her body. She then covers the weed on the underside with white silk, and shapes the nest as she weaves it, making it arched by pressing it with her fore-legs against the curve of her body. Having finished the top half she turns over and constructs the lower half in the same way, producing what may be described as a cocoon. In this she places her eggs in regular order and closes the mouth. Then she finishes her work by making a little mast, as it were, tubular in structure, which sticks up like a periscope from a submarine, and, it is believed, helps to admit a supply of air to the eggs The so-called water-scorpion is a weird-looking

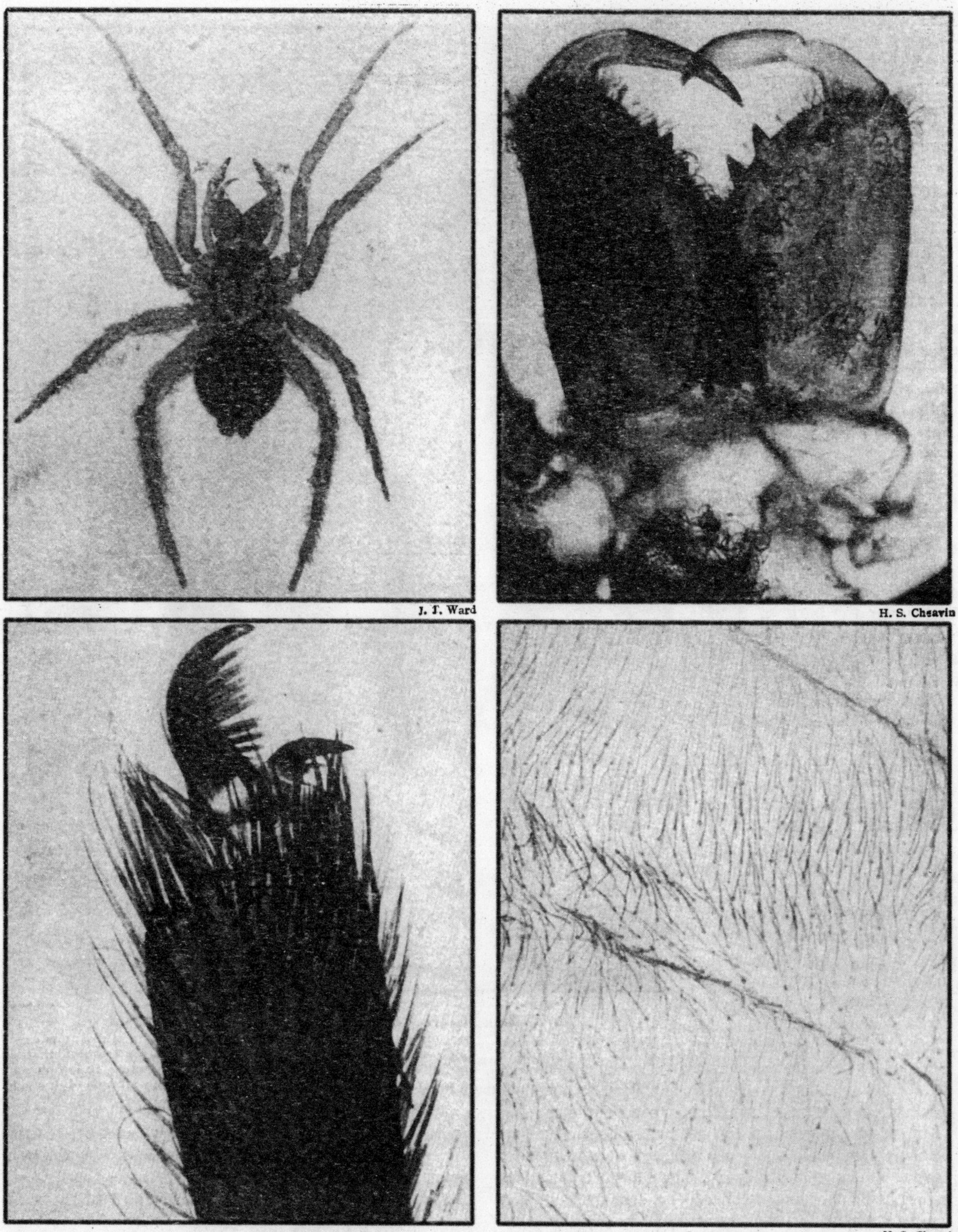

J. T. Ward

H. S. Cheavin

H. S. Cheavin

WATER SPIDER, ITS JAWS, FOOT AND SKIN

Highly magnified, the male of the water spider looks like this (top left). The top right-hand photograph shows the complicated mouth parts. Below we see the leg and foot (left), and in the right a section of the spider's skin. This is covered with long, strong hairs, and these catch the air and hold the bubbles while the spider is moving about below the surface. Only the microscope can show the intricate construction which enables this small being to live as it does—breathing air but under water.

insect common in fresh water. Technically it is a big bug with a piercing blood-sucking snout. It has also a long ovipositor which enables it to put its eggs right inside the stems of water plants out of harm's way.

It seems strange, but some insects use the eggs of other larger species, not only as nurseries but as larders as well, the contents serving to nourish the young one of the raider during its growth. There is a delicate water insect allied to the ichneumon flies and fairy-flies—one of two species discovered by the late Lord Avebury in England—which may be given as an example. It has four wings, with which it swims through the water and it deposits its eggs in those of dragon-flies.

The familiar woodlice, which have been called garden shrimps from their habitat, have a relative which lives in water, and is not quite so well armoured. When the eggs are laid by the female they are retained behind plates which stand away from the underside and form a most effective brood-pouch in which the large eggs develop.

Lastly, we may mention another lowly creature, the opossum shrimp, which carries its young about with it in a special receptacle like the marsupial from which it gets its first name, or the kangaroo. In the case of the shrimp the pouch is formed by expansions of some of its numerous limbs.

The desire to make a nest is really a manifestation of one of the strongest instincts in the animal world —the instinct to provide for the next generation and the continuance of the race. The nest is a fortress for the new life, growing up to replace the old—a pledge of the will to live.

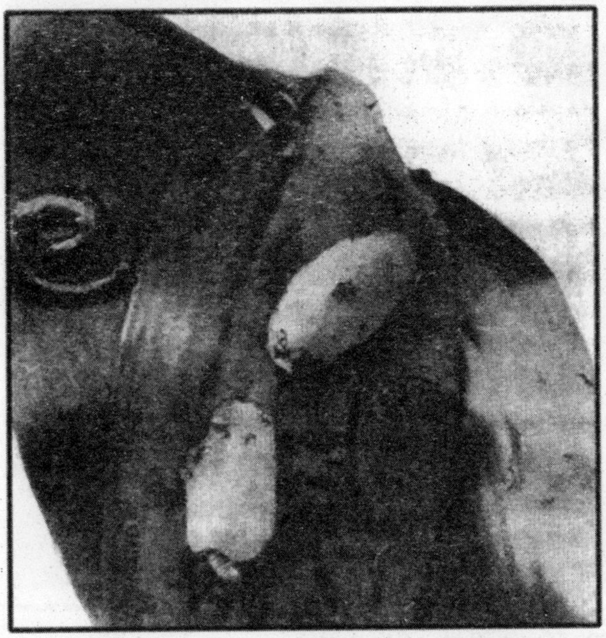

J. J. Ward

BROWN CHINA MARK MOTH AND ITS AQUATIC LARVAE

The brown china mark moth (top) spends the first part of its life below water. The larvae (bottom left), as soon as they have hatched, make for themselves coverings of pieces of pond weed, and while within them can breathe air. In the bottom left photograph two of these coverings are seen with one end of a larva protruding from the lower. The dark coiled body above is that of a leech. The right-hand photograph shows the pupa cases whence the developed creatures will emerge attached to some pond weed.

J. E. Saunders

Neville Kingston

GETTING WILD ANIMALS USED TO HUMAN HANDLING

To be able to handle a leopard it is necessary to catch the animal very young and accustom it to the scent and sight and touch of men before it has tasted the freedom of the wild. This young leopard (bottom), reposing quietly in its keeper's arms, has become accustomed to wearing a collar and chain like any dog. But it is never possible to be quite sure of even a young leopard's temper, individuals differing tremendously. What a feat it is, then, to take a bone from the very jaws of a full-grown leopard (top). Both animals here are African.

Chapter LXI

The Taming of the Wild

By G. M. Vevers

Superintendent of the London Zoological Society's Gardens

ALTHOUGH a zoological garden is primarily intended as a place where wild animals may be seen and studied in captivity and is not an institution for the training or taming of the exhibits, experience has shown that individual creatures which by association with human beings have become tame and are accustomed to being handled every day have a much longer expectation of life than others which resent the advances of man and do little but eat and brood upon their captivity. The latter readily fall a prey to one of the most distressing of all the maladies which may attack an animal in captivity. This, for want of a better name, may be called "cage ennui," and is the precursor of a multitude of mental and physical infirmities.

The solitary animal, above all, is most subject to this disease, and whenever possible it is the custom of zoos all over the world to try to exhibit pairs or groups of animals and not single specimens. In some cases, of course, this is found to be impossible, as when an animal has been for many years the sole occupant of a cage he is apt to regard any intrusion upon his privacy with active resentment. Tigers, as a rule, come under this category, and unless paired up in extreme youth seem to prefer solitary confinement. Lions, on the other hand, are much more friendly in disposition towards one another, and provided that a partner of the opposite sex is chosen the age or period of captivity seems to matter very little.

Taken as a whole, the anthropoid apes in confinement need the companionship of man or their own kind more than any other creature. Indeed, it is almost impossible for anyone to bring up a young gorilla unless it is treated more or less like a human child. These creatures become so deeply attached and dependent upon their keepers that even separation of a temporary nature causes them extreme mental anguish, and a change of ownership is almost invariably followed by the animal's death. The classical example of gorilla attachment was that of the famous John Daniel I to his owner, Miss Alyse Cunningham, who brought him home from Africa herself and took him into her flat in Sloane Street, where he was treated as one of the family. For many months John at the window was a familiar figure to passers-by in Sloane Street, but a tempting offer came from America, and John crossed the Atlantic, only to die of a broken heart a few days after his arrival in New York.

J. E. Saunders

WEARING A CUBAN BOA

Snakes are not so hard to tame as might be supposed, and even so large a one as this will enjoy being handled by someone to whom it is used. But it should be remembered that the snake has only to contract its coils to strangle its friend.

Animals vary very much in intelligence, and it naturally follows that the more intelligent the animal, the more readily it is tamed and comes to look for human sympathy and companionship.

The state of mind of a wild animal when brought into captivity depends to a great extent upon its age and the manner of its capture. If taken young, before it has started a life of independence, or if it is still under the protection of its parent, an animal will usually take readily to human beings, and will easily adapt itself to the conditions of captivity. If, on the other hand, an animal is taken in maturity or old age, after living a life of freedom, it starts its new existence with an instinctive hatred of its captors, and many months of patient training and

J. E. Saunders

FEEDING THE SHY GIRAFFE AT NECK'S AND ARM'S LENGTH

One advantage of the giraffe's long neck is that it can accept food from the human hand and, at the same time, keep the greater part of itself a comfortable distance away. Notice that the animal stands so high at the shoulder that even with the neck horizontal the end of its nose only just reaches the morsel held at the full stretch of the arm above the donor's head. In a wild state, the animal feeds largely on leaves and has to spread its forelegs wide if it wishes to graze.

persuasion are sometimes necessary before it can be approached without arousing panic in its mind or the desire to harm its keeper in its anxiety to escape or defend itself. Apart, therefore, from the risks run in their upbringing—for immature creatures are more delicate and susceptible to disease than older ones—it would seem that young animals are, on the whole, more suitable to bring into captivity than older ones which have experienced freedom in the wilds, and to which captivity must be far more of an ordeal than it is to a younger animal. Young animals, moreover, are more receptive to sympathy, whereas fully-grown creatures, unless they are in pain or suffering from some disease, are usually indifferent to human blandishment.

In dealing with wild animals it is not merely necessary to have a knowledge of their habits and modes of life as a whole, but it is very necessary to study each individual creature separately in order to have a complete understanding of its psychology and the inner processes of its mind. No two apes, for instance, are alike in their intelligence or in the amount of reasoning power of which they are capable, and again there is a complete difference in the attitude of mind of the two sexes. In relation to this, it is of the highest importance to know and to recognize when the age of puberty takes place, especially in male animals, for in most cases there is a distinct change of outlook at this time, and the animal which has been handled with impunity by all and sundry may, in an instant, under the subtle influence of sex, turn upon those whom it has previously regarded with affection. Bears, with very few exceptions, come under this heading, and, surprisingly enough, so do the manlike apes, and it is the exception rather than the rule for any chimpanzee to be regarded as safe after the age of seven or eight, at which time they attain sexual maturity.

In recent years a great change has taken place in the attitude of mankind to animals of all descriptions, and in this and most other countries dumb creatures are treated in a much more humane manner than they used to be. In the old days man tried to subjugate animals more by fear and cruelty than by patience and kindly treatment. These old methods, apart from being cruel and therefore to be deprecated, sooner or later almost invariably reacted upon the trainer with disastrous results. Nowadays, the first endeavour of every successful animal trainer is to establish by friendly methods a complete understanding between himself and his pupils.

The Taming of the Wild

The pioneer of the modern method of training and exhibiting animals was the late Carl Hagenbeck, of Hamburg. His work is to-day being carried on by his two sons, who not only control the gardens at Stellingen, but also are responsible for several large travelling circuses and menageries. In order to demonstrate that the animals are trained in a humane manner the Hagenbecks admit the public daily to their animal training school on payment of a very small entrance fee. By this means they not only provide an interesting and instructive entertainment, but they also place themselves beyond criticism.

In his book entitled "Beasts and Men" Carl Hagenbeck vividly describes the horror with which he viewed the old methods of training animals and the barbarous shows which were the outcome of ignorance and cruelty. Training in those days, if it can be so called, he states, "consisted in terrifying the animals with whips and red-hot irons, so that at the very sight of these implements they would fly through the cage and, in doing so, would leap over whatever obstacle was placed in their path." It was a common sight to see "trained" lions whose whiskers had been scorched off and who were frightfully burned about their mouths, and it was no unusual thing for the trainers to be attacked and torn to pieces. Nor could one blame the animals, for their lives were rendered insupportable and they merely acted in self-defence. By instituting the practice of studying the character of each individual animal, Hagenbeck succeeded in achieving by humane and intelligent methods incalculably better results than the old trainers had obtained by means of their implements of torture.

For the circus ring animals have to be chosen with great discrimination, for not every lion or tiger can be taught to perform tricks, however patient his trainer. But it is a mistake to suppose that all carnivora are naturally savage; nearly all are amenable to kind treatment and after a short while learn the lesson of obedience. It must not be thought, however, that the modern trainer, with his knowledge of animal psychology and his humane methods of dealing with his pupils, does not run the risk of being mauled. It is true that the risk he takes is very much less than in the case of the so-called trainers of the last century, but there is always a chance of a sudden outburst of temper due to an inborn natural ferocity; and, knowing this, one cannot but admire the man who, for his livelihood and, in most cases, for the love of animals, takes his life in his hands twice daily and enters into a den of lions armed only with a whip and a wallet containing a few pieces of meat. The former is used mainly to indicate the position which the animal is to take up and the exercises which it is to go through, and the meat a reward for obedience.

Neville Kingston

INTRODUCING THE LION CUB TO THE TIGER CUB

One of the most difficult tasks connected with the taming and keeping of wild animals is getting two different species of the large carnivora to dwell together. Unless the introduction is effected in extreme youth, satisfactory results are almost impossible. Here we see a keeper presenting a very young lion to a very young tiger. The latter, probably because it feels at a disadvantage in the basket and, anyhow, resents confinement, is furious when the lid is raised. The lion, however, is only filled with curiosity as to the contents of this hamper.

J. E. Saunders

WHEN HUMAN SENSE AND KINDNESS WIN CONFIDENCE AND TRUST

No child could rest more confidently or comfortably in its nurse's arms than this young fox which reclines, yawning, upon its friend's arm. Every detail of its pose—up-curled tongue, the forepaws resting contentedly on the lady's arm while the hind legs stand on one of her hands—shows ease. This animal, like the leopard in page 658, has a collar and chain in case of need. That bears are treacherous is notorious among those who have to do with them, and, while the young ones can be taught with patience, yet there comes a time when the animal is adult, and can be no more trusted. But, all the same, a bear can be pleasant enough, as our right-hand photograph shows.

Neville Kingston

TAME CLOUDED LEOPARD: BABY ALLIGATOR IN THE DENTIST'S HANDS

Lying peaceably in the keeper's arms, you would hardly know the so-called clouded leopard for the fierce creature it is in its life among the trees of the Sumatran forests. This is the most arboreal of all the large cat tribe, and its name is misleading, for it is not a true leopard, but an isolated species. It is also sometimes, and as erroneously, called the clouded tiger, though it is no more tiger than leopard. Notice the strong steel-handled chain attached to a stout collar, giving quite a domesticated air to the animal. The right-hand photograph shows a little crocodile which was suffering with the toothache. Its jaws, carefully propped open, are being examined to see if any teeth need extraction.

J. E. Saunders

ZOO BIRDS INTIMATE WITH THOSE WHO FEED THEM

While birds are not easy to train most birds learn to tolerate those who feed them. A king vulture at the London Zoo was used to being led by a certain lady. It formed the strange habit of nibbling at her stocking and trying to pull it off. This, too, was a bird which had previously been thought to be virtually untameable. In the lower photograph is a young hornbill on its first day at the Zoo. It became used to human society on its journey from the East and was quite ready, after a little coaxing, to feed from the lips of a bird lover.

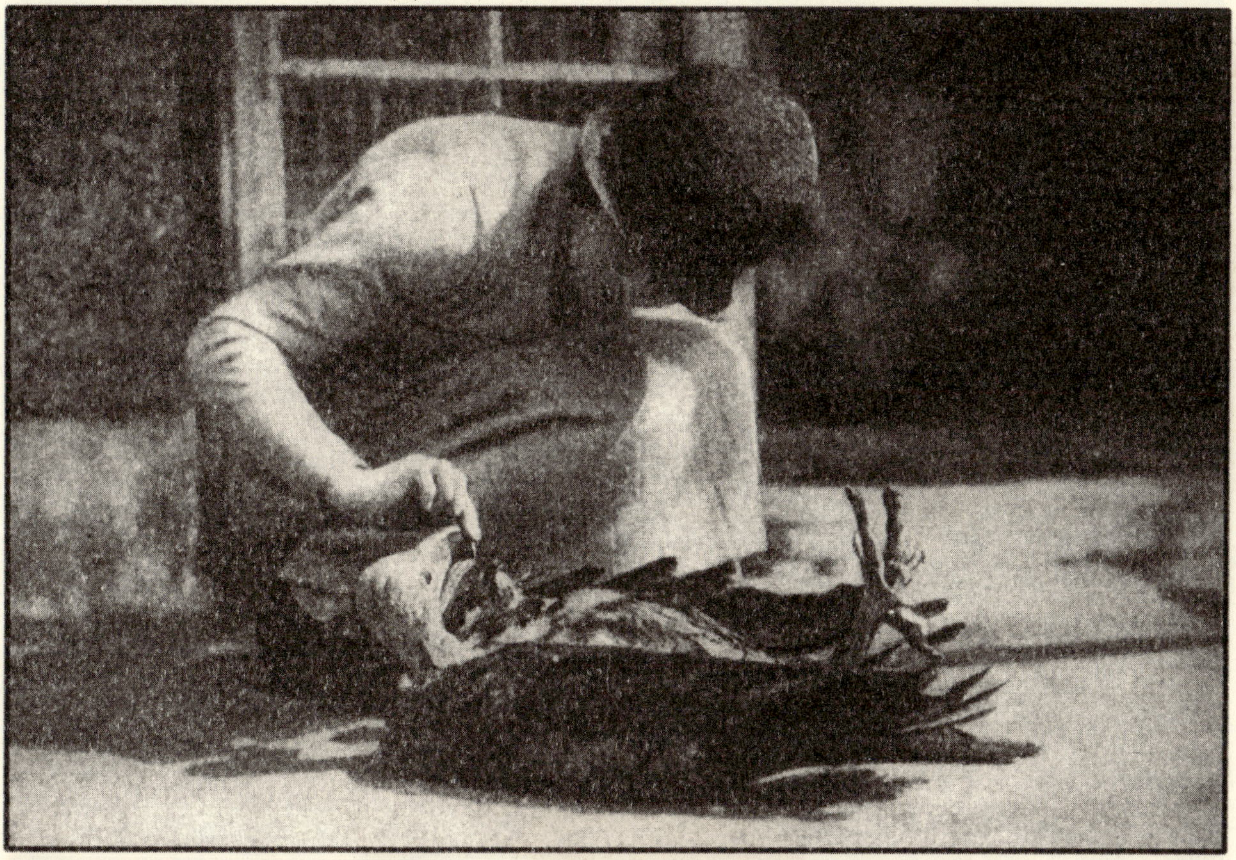

J. E. Saunders

CRUEL TALONS AND DANGEROUS BEAKS TAMED BY KINDNESS AND PATIENCE

One Fellow of the Royal Zoological Society, a lady, has been successful in her efforts to tame the fiercest eagles and also some vultures which had been considered to be quite unapproachable. Thus do the ideas of animals slowly change under the influence of time and experience. Wild creatures are no longer so glibly labelled tame or fierce as formerly. Below is a Chilean sea-eagle feeding quietly from the hand which it could, if it wished, tear open with a stroke of beak or claw; while above is a Pondicherry vulture lying contentedly on its back to be fed.

recently that Polar bears were introduced into the circus. This was achieved by Carl Hagenbeck's brother, Wilhelm, after a great deal of care and patience. Before this it was considered that Polar bears were untrainable, but he succeeded in training a troupe of seven to go through quite an exacting performance.

Carl Hagenbeck was a great adept at introducing numbers of different species of savage animals together in the same cage. This, when accomplished, forms a very attractive exhibit, but it requires weeks, sometimes months, of patient preparation for the animals have to see each other through bars before they

To indicate how rarely serious accidents occur in dealing with performing animals, Hagenbeck, in his memoirs, recalls only two cases of men being mauled during the whole of his experience as an animal trainer. One of these was an outsider from the audience who managed to make his way into a den of lions and tigers, and who barely escaped with his life, and the other was his brother-in-law, who received a severe mauling at the hands of a black bear against whom he had repeatedly been warned.

BEARS are notoriously treacherous animals, and although they have been trained as performing animals from time immemorial, the time comes when they can no longer be trusted, and they have been undoubtedly responsible for more accidents in zoos, circuses, and elsewhere than any other animal. This uncertain trait in the character of the bear is traditional in the countries in which these creatures flourish and become associated with human beings. Everyone who is familiar with the writings of Kipling and who has read "The Truce of the Bear" in his "Songs of the Five Nations" will realize the horrible treachery of which this beast is capable.

The performing bear referred to above is, of course, the common brown bear which inhabits Northern Europe and Asia. It was not until

J. E. Saunders

LARGE AND SMALL RELATIVES OF THE CAT

All cats like being scratched between the ears, and even so large a one as the cheetah is quite agreeable so long as the scratcher is familiar to it. The animal is thrusting up its head against the pressure of the hand with evident enjoyment. Above, we see a genet, a creature closely allied to the civet cats. Genets are smaller than domestic cats.

DIAMOND PYTHON SHOWS AFFECTION FOR ITS KEEPER

Since modern conditions prevailed in the reptile house at the London Zoological Gardens, the lot of the snakes has been far happier and the mortality has substantially decreased. Artificial sunlight and electric heating combine with tropical plants to make conditions as ideal as possible. Snakes like heat and become sluggish and refuse food when cold. They are not difficult to tame and will soon learn to recognize the call to food. This diamond python is treating its keeper to a snake "kiss."

are allowed to be introduced together into the same cage; and they have to be watched very carefully for some time after, and separation at feeding-time is very often a necessity. Hagenbeck, however, succeeded in bringing together many different kinds of animals, and it was no uncommon sight in pre-war days at Stellingen to see a group of lions, tigers, bears and hyenas all together in the same enclosure, apparently taking no exception to or even notice of each other.

A PLEASANT sight which is sometimes seen in zoos is a group of lion cubs, or even a full-grown lion, playing together with a small fox-terrier bitch which has acted as the foster-mother. This is sometimes regarded as cruel, but one has never heard of a foster bitch being hurt by her charges.

Carl Hagenbeck will also go down to posterity as the first man to show animals on the panorama or terrace system which not only reproduces, as far as possible, the natural surroundings of various groups, but also gives the onlooker a comprehensive view of the fauna of the different continents more or less at a glance. The Mappin Terraces and Monkey Hill at the London Zoo are both constructed on the Hagenbeck principle, and the results obtained, both from the point of view of the health and fecundity of the animals, as well as from the visitors' standpoint, have proved eminently satisfactory.

More recently further improvements have been made in the housing of delicate animals from tropical and sub-tropical countries. For example, in the old days, in practically every zoo, monkeys used to be kept under hot-house conditions; that is to say, their cages were housed in a glass building which was heated at a constant high temperature throughout the year. The result of this was that from time to time epidemics of tubercle and enteritis used to decimate the population of this type of house, and those animals which were fortunate enough to escape infection sooner or later were stricken with rickets and cage paralysis, and ended their days in misery on the floors of their cages.

The modern monkey house is the exact antithesis to this old type of building. Lofty and well ventilated, with every interior cage communicating with an open-air one by means of a door which can be easily worked by the inmates of the house, with artificially-warmed floors and ultra-violet ray lamps for winter use and the roof constructed of "vitaglass" to catch every ray of sunlight possible, the modern monkey house from the hygienic standpoint is as up to date as the most recently constructed of our hospital wards.

Perhaps the most wonderful house in any zoo in the world is the new reptile house at the London Zoo. It cost over £60,000 to construct and is heated and lighted entirely by electricity. Everything possible

cannot be tamed. Snakes, as a rule, of a size that can be carried, enjoy being handled by man and can be trained to recognize a call to food. Even alligators can be trained and exhibited, and there is an enormous lizard now living in the reptile house at the London Zoo which answers to the name of "Sumbawa" and follows its keeper about like a dog (see pages 32 to 44).

Birds, with the exception perhaps of parrots, are not easy to train to do tricks, but there are certain species of hornbills which exhibit unusual intelligence and very soon become friendly with those looking after them, and can be trained to do a series of amusing tricks provided food of some description is at the end of each performance. There are several examples of these birds at present living in the new bird house at the London Zoo, and each has a different set of tricks which it goes through with its keeper every afternoon at feeding time. Occasionally, individual birds of other species show themselves adaptable to training and many, of course, enjoy being handled and perch on the

has been done to reproduce the conditions under which all kinds of reptiles live in nature. The warmth of each den is controlled thermostatically and the heat can be increased or decreased according to the individual creature which, for the time being, may occupy any particular enclosure or den. Similarly, every compartment is fitted with an artificial sun which can be turned on when the weather is dull or whenever any of the reptiles are sluggish and refuse to feed, for most snakes and lizards will not feed unless they are thoroughly warmed up beforehand. Painted backgrounds and tropical plants all help to make the captives in this wonderful house feel more at home and, during the past twelve months in which it was opened there was an apparent decrease in the mortality of the inhabitants as compared with that of previous years, and, furthermore that their general condition had very plainly improved to an enormous extent. It is a mistake to suppose that reptiles

Saunders

FRIENDLY ANTEATER AND HORNBILL

After becoming accustomed to its friend a captive anteater (bottom) consents to be lifted up. Above is an Indian hornbill. The lady feeding it is careful to steady with her foot the camp stool on which the bird is perched. Attention to detail and avoidance of shock to the animal are essentials in taming the wild.

person feeding them; but it may be taken as a rule that bird intelligence is not of a high order, although some birds, such as parrots, ravens, mynahs, and jackdaws have the imitative faculty very well developed.

Of recent years some strange friendships with birds have been made at the Zoo, and one lady Fellow of the Society has succeeded in taming not only some of the fiercest eagles but also several vultures which have hitherto been regarded as quite unapproachable.

THE treatment of a sick animal is not an easy matter, as it presents the same difficulties of diagnosis which confront the physician when dealing with a young child—for, like a child, the animal cannot tell you what is wrong with it or where the pain is, unless there is an obvious injury. Furthermore, most animals resent any form of physical examination, and it is generally wiser to make a guess at the diagnosis from the more obvious symptoms than to distress and perhaps accentuate the disease or disability from which the animal is suffering by attempting manual examination.

This is most certainly the case with such animals as small antelope, deer and other such timid creatures, for any physical interference on the part of

Professor Bastian Schmid

A FROG HYPNOTISED

Man's power to hypnotise animals is most remarkable. It has been found that purely mechanical influence will produce the hypnosis. This frog, for instance, was held vertically and then laid down. Its limbs could then be placed in all sorts of attitudes.

W. S. Berridge

A HOODED GOSHAWK

Training birds of prey to hunt for man is an ancient art. Here is a goshawk hooded and ready to be taken out upon the falconer's wrist. When suitable quarry is espied the hood is removed and the hawk, quickly noting its prey, flies off in pursuit.

the animal doctor generally results in these cases in one or more broken leg bones. In such cases it is usual to keep the animal without water for some hours until it is thirsty and then put a dose of medicine in its drinking trough.

There are certain routine operations which are carried out at all zoos from time to time. These include cutting the claws of the large carnivora which, in captivity, are liable to grow into the pads and cause pain and lameness, filing or cutting the beaver's teeth, which also become overgrown owing to lack of use, and the reduction of the hoofs of certain ungulates, such as zebras, which from time to time get unavoidably overgrown through lack of exercise upon a suitable soil.

W. S. Berridge

The ultimate health and happiness of an animal in captivity depend very largely on the care exercised by those employed to effect its capture and look after it during the time which it spends on the journey to the zoo. Early impressions of human treatment and association are very much liable to influence the animal's behaviour during its first years of captivity. These points are dealt with in the chapter entitled "How Wild Animals are Caught" in this work, pages 587 to 601.

In former days it was the practice in cutting the claws of lions, tigers and leopards to cast a noose round the victim's leg and draw it to the bars, when the offending claw could be clipped with a large pair of cutting pliers. Now a much more humane and scientific method is adopted. The patient is enticed into a specially constructed anaesthetic box which is to all intents and purposes airtight. Into this a mixture of warm chloroform and ether vapour is pumped out of a large Shipway apparatus. The stages of anaesthesia in the animal are observed through protected windows in the sides and top of the box. When anaesthesia is complete the slides at each end of the box are opened and the creature's toe-nails are clipped in turn. It usually takes a little less than half an hour from the commencement of anaesthesia until the animal is thoroughly awake once more.

In running a zoological collection, the watchword should be "Prevention is better than cure." This axiom not only applies to the health of the animals but also to their management, for many ugly accidents can be prevented by foresight and common sense.

All of which goes to prove that the accumulated experience of man, together with an ever-increasing knowledge of the nature and habits of living creatures, has resulted in a scientific attitude of mind being brought to bear upon the many problems which are presented by animals living in captivity. The present results are good, but if the same attitude is maintained in the future a still happier existence for all captive creatures is certainly going to be ensured.

J. E. Saunders

PLACID OSTRICH AND WILDLY KICKING ZEBRA

While an ostrich (bottom) can be accustomed to human beings without much fuss, the breaking in of a zebra (top) is a very different affair. It takes several men to rope the wildly struggling animal, and a long and carefully conducted training has to be carried out before anything like tameness is achieved.